# Introduction to
# ANALYTIC FUNCTIONS

WILFRED KAPLAN, *University of Michigan*

 **ADDISON-WESLEY PUBLISHING COMPANY**

READING, MASSACHUSETTS · PALO ALTO · LONDON · DON MILLS, ONTARIO

This book is in the **Addison-Wesley Series in Mathematics**

# Introduction

The present volume can be considered as a revised and considerably enlarged version of the author's *A First Course in Functions of a Complex Variable*, which was essentially a reprint of Chapter 9 of the author's *Advanced Calculus*. The material of that chapter has now been broken up into eight separate chapters, many of the references to other chapters of *Advanced Calculus* have been avoided by rewriting, and a large new chapter has been added on analytic functions of several complex variables. This book is therefore a self-contained introduction to the theory of analytic functions of one or more complex variables.

In one's study of mathematics, complex numbers are usually first encountered in algebra in the solution of quadratic equations. The imaginary numbers $a + b\sqrt{-1}$, thus introduced, may at first appear to be merely a curiosity of no great import. Further study, especially in trigonometry and calculus, shows that complex numbers are somehow in the background in the treatment of all the major functions: the trigonometric functions, the exponential function, the logarithm, the functions of algebra. The more one probes into all branches of mathematics, the more one encounters complex numbers and the basic functions constructed from them, the analytic functions.

The "imaginary" nature of complex numbers is further dispelled by their importance in applications: in physics, in engineering, in all the sciences. We illustrate the way complex numbers appear in these applications by the problem of finding harmonic functions of two real variables; that is, functions $u(x, y)$ such that $u$ satisfies the Laplace equation:

$$\frac{\partial^2 u}{\partial x^2} + \frac{\partial^2 u}{\partial y^2} = 0$$

in a given region in the $xy$-plane. This equation is a major one in physics and engineering, since it describes the behavior of electrostatic potentials, of equilibrium temperatures, and many other basic phenomena. Now complex numbers happen to produce harmonic functions by the following process. With $z = x + iy$, $i$ denoting $\sqrt{-1}$, we form $z^2 = (x + iy)^2$, $z^3 = (x + iy)^3$, and so on. Upon expanding, we find that $z^2 = x^2 - y^2 + 2ixy$, so that $z^2$ has *real part* $u = x^2 - y^2$ and *imaginary part* $v = 2xy$. We verify easily that both functions $x^2 - y^2$ and $2xy$ satisfy the Laplace equation for all $(x, y)$, so that both are harmonic. Similarly, we verify that $z^3 = x^3 - 3xy^2 + i(3x^2y - y^3)$ and the real and imaginary parts $x^3 - 3xy^2$, $3x^2y - y^3$ are harmonic for all $(x, y)$. In fact we can show that for every positive integer $n$, $z^n = (x + iy)^n$ has real and imaginary parts which are harmonic. Furthermore, because the Laplace equation is linear, the same statement applies to the real and imaginary parts of every polynomial $a_0z^n + a_1z^{n-1} + \cdots + a_n$, with real or complex coefficients. The statement applies even to the limiting case of a power series $\sum_{n=0}^{\infty} {}_ncz^n$ or, more generally, $\sum_{n=0}^{\infty} c_n(z - z_0)^n$, under appropriate conditions of convergence. In fact, we have now exhausted the field, for *every* harmonic function is obtainable in this way: for example, as the real part of a power series.

## SUMMARY

Chapter 1 introduces the complex number system, and Chapter 2 develops the concepts of the calculus for complex functions. Chapter 3 considers the central concept of analytic function; many examples are given in this chapter and the following one. Chapter 5 is devoted to power series expansions and the relation between analytic functions and harmonic functions.    Chapter 6 considers Laurent expansions, singularities and residues, and their applications.    Chapter 7 is a long one, devoted to conformal mapping and its applications in physics and engineering.    Chapter 8 provides a brief introduction to analytic continuation and Riemann surfaces.

The final chapter, the longest chapter in the book, is a systematic development of the elementary properties of analytic functions of several complex variables.    Until recently this topic has been reserved for very advanced treatises and research literature.    Its inclusion in the present volume is motivated by the rapidly growing interest in the subject, and by the new applications, for example, in quantum mechanics and in the theory of nonlinear differential equations.

The volume closes with a bibliography, separated into two sections: one for functions of one variable, one for functions of several variables.

The text assumes a knowledge of the basic concepts of advanced calculus. References are given where appropriate, the author's text being referred to simply as *Advanced Calculus*.

The equations in Section 1–1 are numbered $(1-10)$, $(1-11)$, . . . , those in Section 3–2 as $(3-20)$, $(3-21)$, . . .    Thus the equation number also indicates the number of the section in which the equation appears.

*Ann Arbor, Michigan*                                                    W.K.
*August 1966*

# Contents

# 1 □ *Complex Numbers*

## 1–1 □ THE COMPLEX NUMBER SYSTEM

Complex numbers are numbers of form

$$x + iy,$$

where $x$ and $y$ are real. We write

$$z = x + iy$$

and plot complex numbers in the $xy$ plane, also termed the $z$ plane
(Fig. 1–1).

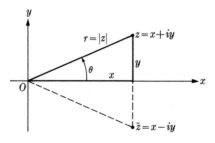

FIG. 1–1. Complex number plane.

Two complex numbers are regarded as distinct unless they have the
same $x$ and $y$. Hence, by definition,

$$x_1 + iy_1 = x_2 + iy_2 \quad \text{if and only if} \quad x_1 = x_2, \, y_1 = y_2. \quad (1\text{--}10)$$

When $z = x + iy$, we write

$$x = \text{Re}(z) = \text{real part of } z,$$
$$y = \text{Im}(z) = \text{imaginary part of } z,$$
$$\theta = \arg z = \text{argument of } z \text{ (amplitude of } z), \qquad (1\text{--}11)$$
$$r = |z| = \text{absolute value of } z \text{ (modulus of } z),$$
$$x - iy = \bar{z} = \text{conjugate of } z.$$

These quantities are shown in Fig. 1–1. The angle $\theta$ is measured in radians and determined only up to multiples of $2\pi$; it is undefined for $x = y = 0$.
The operations of addition and multiplication are defined as follows:

$$(x_1 + iy_1) + (x_2 + iy_2) = x_1 + x_2 + i(y_1 + y_2),$$
$$(x_1 + iy_1) \cdot (x_2 + iy_2) = x_1 x_2 - y_1 y_2 + i(x_1 y_2 + x_2 y_1). \qquad (1\text{--}12)$$

One then verifies the rules of algebra:

$$z_1 + z_2 = z_2 + z_1, \qquad z_1 \cdot z_2 = z_2 \cdot z_1,$$
$$z_1 + (z_2 + z_3) = (z_1 + z_2) + z_3, \qquad z_1 \cdot (z_2 z_3) = (z_1 z_2) \cdot z_3, \qquad (1\text{--}13)$$
$$z_1 \cdot (z_2 + z_3) = z_1 \cdot z_2 + z_1 \cdot z_3.$$

The numbers of form $x + i \cdot 0$ behave exactly like real numbers and we write

$$x + i0 = x.$$

We call $z = x + i0$ a *real* complex number. In particular, $0 + i0 = 0$, $1 + i0 = 1$ and these have the usual properties:

$$1 \cdot z = z, \qquad z + 0 = z, \qquad z \cdot 0 = 0. \qquad (1\text{--}14)$$

The number $0 + i \cdot 1$ is written as $i$; by (1–12) it has the property:

$$i^2 = -1.$$

The complex number $z = x + iy$ can be obtained by addition of the real number $x$ (i.e., $x + i0$) to the product of $i$ by the real number $y$. Hence the notation $x + iy$ is justified. Numbers of the form $iy$ are termed *pure imaginary*.
The equations

$$z_1 + z = z_2, \qquad z_1 \cdot z = z_2$$

have unique solutions for $z$:

$$z = z_2 - z_1, \qquad z = \frac{z_2}{z_1},$$

provided there is no division by 0. Subtraction of $z_1$ is the same as addition of the negative of $z_1$:

$$z_2 - z_1 = z_2 + (-z_1), \qquad -z_1 = (-1) \cdot z_1.$$

Other algebraic properties are deducible from those listed; in general, algebraic operations with complex numbers proceed as for real numbers, with $i$ treated as a variable satisfying the equation $i^2 = -1$.

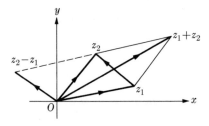

FIG. 1–2.   Addition and subtraction of complex numbers.

With each complex number $z$ one can associate the vector $Oz$, whose components are $x$ and $y$. The rule of addition (1–12) is then the same as for vectors; this is illustrated graphically in Fig. 1–2. Subtraction of $z_1$ from $z_2$ can also be carried out as for vectors; one obtains the vector from $z_1$ to $z_2$, which must then be replaced by an equal vector of form $Oz$. This is also illustrated in Fig. 1–2. From this we deduce the important rule that

$$|z_2 - z_1| = \text{distance from } z_1 \text{ to } z_2.$$

From the same figure we deduce the two inequalities:

$$\begin{aligned} |z_1 + z_2| &\leq |z_1| + |z_2|, \\ |z_2 - z_1| &\geq |\,|z_2| - |z_1|\,|. \end{aligned} \qquad (1\text{–}15)$$

The first states that each side of a triangle is less than or equal to the sum of the other two sides; the second states the (logically equivalent) property that the difference of two sides is less than or equal to the third side.
    The rules

$$\begin{aligned} \text{Re}(z_1 \pm z_2) &= \text{Re}(z_1) \pm \text{Re}(z_2), \\ \text{Im}(z_1 \pm z_2) &= \text{Im}(z_1) \pm \text{Im}(z_2), \\ \bar{z} &= \text{Re}(z) - i\,\text{Im}(z), \end{aligned} \qquad (1\text{–}16)$$

are essentially restatements of the definitions of addition and conjugate.

From these we at once conclude:

$$\overline{z_1 + z_2} = \bar{z}_1 + \bar{z}_2. \tag{1–17}$$

We also note the properties:

$$z + \bar{z} = 2x = 2\,\mathrm{Re}(z), \qquad z - \bar{z} = 2iy = 2i\,\mathrm{Im}(z) \tag{1–18}$$

and

$$z \cdot \bar{z} = x^2 + y^2 = |z|^2. \tag{1–19}$$

## 1–2 □ POLAR FORM OF COMPLEX NUMBERS

From the properties of polar coordinates one obtains the relation

$$z = x + iy = r\cos\theta + ir\sin\theta = r(\cos\theta + i\sin\theta). \tag{1–20}$$

We term $r(\cos\theta + i\sin\theta)$ the *polar form* of $z$. This is of considerable aid in analyzing multiplication and division, for

$$
\begin{aligned}
z_1 \cdot z_2 &= r_1(\cos\theta_1 + i\sin\theta_1) \cdot r_2(\cos\theta_2 + i\sin\theta_2) \\
&= r_1 r_2[(\cos\theta_1\cos\theta_2 - \sin\theta_1\sin\theta_2) + i(\sin\theta_1\cos\theta_2 + \cos\theta_1\sin\theta_2)] \\
&= r_1 r_2[\cos(\theta_1 + \theta_2) + i\sin(\theta_1 + \theta_2)]. \tag{1–21}
\end{aligned}
$$

One has thus the rules

$$
\begin{aligned}
|z_1 \cdot z_2| &= |z_1| \cdot |z_2|, \\
\arg(z_1 \cdot z_2) &= \arg z_1 + \arg z_2 \quad \text{(up to multiples of } 2\pi\text{).}
\end{aligned}
\tag{1–22}
$$

This can be used as the basis for a graphical construction of the product $z_1 \cdot z_2$, as shown in Fig. 1–3. The triangle with vertices $O$, $1$, $z_1$ must be similar to the triangle with vertices $O$, $z_2$, $z_1z_2$.

From the definition of division we deduce the properties paralleling (1–22):

$$\left|\frac{z_1}{z_2}\right| = \frac{|z_1|}{|z_2|},$$

$$\arg\left(\frac{z_1}{z_2}\right) = \arg z_1 - \arg z_2 \tag{1–23}$$

(up to multiples of $2\pi$).

If this is combined with the operation of subtraction, we conclude that

$$\arg\frac{z_3 - z_1}{z_2 - z_1}$$

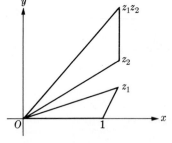

FIG. 1–3.   Multiplication of complex numbers.

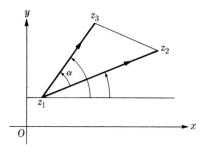

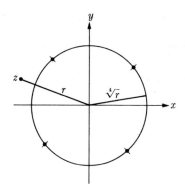

FIG. 1-4.   $\alpha = \arg \dfrac{z_3 - z_1}{z_2 - z_1}$.          FIG. 1-5.   Fourth roots of $z$.

represents the angle at vertex $z_1$ of the triangle $z_1z_2z_3$, as shown in Fig. 1-4. We also note the rule

$$|\bar{z}| = |z|, \qquad \arg \bar{z} = -\arg z \quad \text{(up to multiples of } 2\pi), \qquad (1\text{--}24)$$

from which we conclude, on the basis of (1-22) and (1-23), that

$$\overline{z_1 \cdot z_2} = \bar{z}_1 \cdot \bar{z}_2,$$
$$\overline{\left(\frac{z_1}{z_2}\right)} = \frac{\bar{z}_1}{\bar{z}_2}. \qquad (1\text{--}25)$$

By repeated application of (1-21) one deduces the formula for the $n$th power of $z$:

$$z^n = [r(\cos \theta + i \sin \theta)]^n = r^n(\cos n\theta + i \sin n\theta) \quad (n = 1, 2, \ldots).$$
$$(1\text{--}26)$$

For $r = 1$, this is the *de Moivre theorem:*

$$(\cos \theta + i \sin \theta)^n = \cos n\theta + i \sin n\theta \quad (n = 1, 2, \ldots). \qquad (1\text{--}27)$$

This in turn leads to a rule for the $n$th roots of $z$.   For if

$$z_1^n = z, \qquad z_1 = r_1(\cos \theta_1 + i \sin \theta_1),$$

then

$$r_1^n(\cos n\theta_1 + i \sin n\theta_1) = r(\cos \theta + i \sin \theta).$$

Hence

$$r_1 = \sqrt[n]{r} \qquad \text{(the real positive } n\text{th root),}$$
$$n\theta_1 = \theta + 2k\pi \qquad (k = 0, \pm 1, \pm 2, \ldots).$$

One obtains only $n$ different complex numbers here: namely, the numbers

$$\sqrt[n]{z} = z^{1/n} = \sqrt[n]{r}\left[\cos\left(\frac{\theta}{n} + \frac{2k\pi}{n}\right) + i\sin\left(\frac{\theta}{n} + \frac{2k\pi}{n}\right)\right]$$

$$(k = 0, 1, \ldots, n-1). \quad (1\text{--}28)$$

This is illustrated in Fig. 1–5, with $n = 4$.

The rule (1–19), $z \cdot \bar{z} = |z|^2$, will be found exceedingly useful. For example, it aids in the carrying out of division:

$$\frac{3-i}{5+2i} = \frac{3-i}{5+2i} \cdot \frac{5-2i}{5-2i} = \frac{13-11i}{29}.$$

To get rid of imaginaries in the denominator, one simply multiplies and divides by the conjugate of the denominator.

## 1–3 □ THE EXPONENTIAL FUNCTION

We write

$$e^{x+iy} = e^x(\cos y + i\sin y) \quad (1\text{--}30)$$

as the definition of $e^z$ for complex $z$. When $y = 0$, $e^z$ reduces to the familiar function $e^x$. This function will be studied and used extensively in the later sections. We introduce it here because of the *Euler formula:*

$$e^{i\theta} = \cos\theta + i\sin\theta, \quad (1\text{--}31)$$

which is a special case of (1–30). This is a very convenient abbreviation. We can now write:

$$z = r(\cos\theta + i\sin\theta) = re^{i\theta}$$

and obtain a more concise way of writing $z$ in polar form. From (1–22) and (1–23) we conclude that

$$e^{i\theta_1} \cdot e^{i\theta_2} = e^{i(\theta_1+\theta_2)},$$

$$\frac{e^{i\theta_2}}{e^{i\theta_1}} = e^{i(\theta_2-\theta_1)}. \quad (1\text{--}32)$$

These are familiar properties of the real exponential function. The operation of multiplication is now as follows:

$$z_1 \cdot z_2 = r_1 e^{i\theta_1} \cdot r_2 e^{i\theta_2} = r_1 r_2 e^{i(\theta_1+\theta_2)}. \quad (1\text{--}33)$$

Similarly

$$z^n = (re^{i\theta})^n = r^n e^{in\theta} \quad (n = 1, 2, \ldots). \quad (1\text{--}34)$$

The formula (1–28) for $z^{1/n}$ can also be written concisely:

$$z^{1/n} = (re^{i\theta})^{1/n} = r^{1/n}e^{i(\theta+2k\pi)/n} \quad (k = 0, 1, \ldots, n-1). \quad (1\text{–}35)$$

**PROBLEMS**

1. Graph the complex numbers: $1, i, -1, -i, 1+i, -1+i, \sqrt{3}-\sqrt{2}i$.
2. Reduce to the form $x + iy$:

   (a) $(2 + 3i) + (5 - 2i)$          (b) $(1 - i) \cdot (2 + i)$

   (c) $\dfrac{1 - i}{3 + i}$          (d) $\dfrac{i}{1+i} + \dfrac{1+i}{i}$

   (e) $(1 + i)^{10}$          (f) $i^{17}$.

3. Prove that $|1 - z| = |1 - \bar{z}|$. Interpret geometrically.
4. Prove that, if $|a| = 1$ and $|b| \neq 1$, then

$$\left|\frac{a - b}{1 - \bar{b}a}\right| = 1.$$

[*Hint: let* $z = (a - b)/(1 - \bar{b}a)$. *Show that* $\bar{z} \cdot z = 1$ *and use the rule:* $\bar{z} \cdot z = |z|^2$.]

5. Evaluate the following roots:

   (a) $\sqrt{i}$,  (b) $\sqrt[3]{1}$,  (c) $\sqrt[3]{-1+i}$,  (d) $\sqrt[4]{-1}$,  (e) $\sqrt[5]{-32}$.
6. Solve the equations:

   (a) $z^2 + 3 = 0$          (b) $z^4 + 16 = 0$

   (c) $z^8 - 2z^4 + 1 = 0$          (d) $z^3 + z^2 + z + 1 = 0$.

   [*Hint: multiply by* $z - 1$.]
7. Prove the identities

$$\cos 3\theta = \cos^3 \theta - 3 \cos \theta \sin^2 \theta, \qquad \sin 3\theta = 3 \cos^2 \theta \sin \theta - \sin^3 \theta.$$

[*Hint: use* (1–27).]

8. Graph the following loci:

   (a) $|z| = 1$          (b) $\arg z = \pi/4$
   (c) $\text{Re}(z) = 1$          (d) $\text{Im}(z) = -1$
   (e) $|z| < 1$          (f) $|z| \leq 1$
   (g) $|z - 1| = 1$          (h) $|z - 1| < 2$
   (i) $|z - 1| \leq 1$          (j) $|z - 1| \geq 1$
   (k) $|z - 2| = |z - 2i|$          (l) $|z - 2| = 2|z - 2i|$

(m) $|z - 1| + |z + 1| = 3$     (n) $|z - 1| - |z + 1| = 1$
(o) $\mathrm{Re}(z - 1) = |z|$     (p) $z \cdot \bar{z} + (1 + i)z + (1 - i)\bar{z} + 1 = 0$
(q) $\mathrm{Re}(z) > 0$     (r) $0 < \mathrm{Im}(z) < 2\pi.$

9. (a) Prove the rules (1–13).
   (b) Prove that the rule

$$(re^{i\theta})^n = r^n e^{in\theta}$$

   remains correct for $n = -1, -2, \ldots,$ if $z^{-n}$ is defined as $1/z^n$
   $(z \neq 0).$

## ANSWERS

2. (a) $7 + i,$   (b) $3 - i,$   (c) $\frac{1}{5} - \frac{2}{5}i,$   (d) $\frac{3}{2} - \frac{1}{2}i,$   (e) $32i,$   (f) $i.$

5. (a) $\pm\dfrac{\sqrt{2}}{2}(1 + i),$                    (b) $1, \quad -\dfrac{1}{2} \pm \dfrac{\sqrt{3}}{2}i,$

   (c) $\sqrt[6]{2}\left(\cos\dfrac{k\pi}{12} + i\sin\dfrac{k\pi}{12}\right),$   $k = 3, 11, 19,$

   (d) $\pm\dfrac{\sqrt{2}}{2}(1 + i), \quad \pm\dfrac{\sqrt{2}}{2}(1 - i),$

   (e) $2\left(\cos\dfrac{k\pi}{5} + i\sin\dfrac{k\pi}{5}\right),$   $k = 1, 3, 5, 7, 9.$

6. (a) $\pm\sqrt{3}\,i,$                    (b) $\pm\sqrt{2}\,(1 + i), \quad \pm\sqrt{2}\,(1 - i),$
   (c) $1, 1, i, i, -1, -1, -i, -i,$     (d) $-1, \pm i.$

## 1–4 □ SEQUENCES AND SERIES OF COMPLEX NUMBERS

If to each integer $n = 1, 2, \ldots$ a complex number $z_n$ is assigned, then a sequence of complex numbers: $z_n$ is defined.   The sequence is said to *converge* to the *limit* $z_0$:

$$\lim_{n \to \infty} z_n = z_0$$

if, for each positive $\epsilon,$ an $N$ can be chosen such that $|z_n - z_0| < \epsilon$ for $n > N.$   If the sequence fails to converge, it is said to *diverge*.

A convergent sequence is suggested in Fig. 1–6.

The following theorem reduces the theory of convergence of complex sequences to that for real sequences.

**Theorem 1.**  *The sequence $z_n$ converges to $z_0$ if and only if* $\mathrm{Re}(z_n)$ *converges to* $\mathrm{Re}(z_0)$ *and* $\mathrm{Im}(z_n)$ *converges to* $\mathrm{Im}(z_0).$

To prove the theorem, we remark that, if $|z_n - z_0| < \epsilon$, then $(x_n, y_n)$ is within the circle of radius $\epsilon$ about $(x_0, y_0)$, so that necessarily

$$|x_n - x_0| < \epsilon, \qquad |y_n - y_0| < \epsilon.$$

Thus convergence of $z_n = x_n + iy_n$ to $z_0 = x_0 + iy_0$ implies convergence of $x_n$ to $x_0$ and $y_n$ to $y_0$. Conversely, if $x_n$ converges to $x_0$ and $y_n$ converges to $y_0$, then for given $\epsilon$, $N$ can be chosen so large that

$$|x_n - x_0| < \tfrac{1}{2}\epsilon,$$

$$|y_n - y_0| < \tfrac{1}{2}\epsilon \quad \text{for } n > N.$$

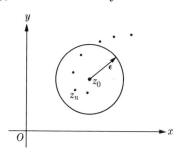

Fig. 1–6. Sequence converging to $z_0$.

These inequalities force $(x_n, y_n)$ to lie within a *square* with center $(x_0, y_0)$ and side $\epsilon$; hence $(x_n, y_n)$ must lie within the *circle* of radius $\epsilon$ about $(x_0, y_0)$, so that $|z_n - z_0| < \epsilon$ for $n > N$. Accordingly, $z_n$ must converge to $z_0$.

**Theorem 2** (Cauchy criterion). *The sequence $z_n$ converges, if and only if for each positive $\epsilon$ an $N$ can be found such that*

$$|z_m - z_n| < \epsilon \quad \text{for} \quad n > N \quad \text{and} \quad m > N.$$

This is proved by applying Theorem 1 to refer the convergence of $z_n$ back to the two real sequences $x_n$, $y_n$ and then applying the Cauchy criterion for real sequences.

**Theorem 3.** *If $\lim z_n = z_0$ and $\lim w_n = w_0$, then*

$$\lim (z_n \pm w_n) = z_0 \pm w_0, \qquad \lim (z_n \cdot w_n) = z_0 \cdot w_0,$$

$$\lim \frac{z_n}{w_n} = \frac{z_0}{w_0} \qquad (w_0 \neq 0).$$

This is also proved by application of Theorem 1 (see Problem 4 below). One writes

$$\lim_{n \to \infty} z_n = \infty$$

and says, "the sequence $z_n$ diverges to infinity," if, for the real sequence $|z_n|$,

$$\lim_{n \to \infty} |z_n| = \infty.$$

Hence, for each real number $K$ it must be possible to find an $N$ such that

$$|z_n| > K \quad \text{for} \quad n > N;$$

given any circle with center $z = 0$ and radius $K$, all members $z_n$ of the sequence lie outside the circle for $n$ sufficiently large. It should be remarked that there is no distinction, for complex numbers, between $+\infty$ and $-\infty$; there is just one complex number $\infty$. This special number will be discussed further in Section 6–3.

An infinite series of complex numbers is an indicated sum of the members of a sequence:

$$z_1 + z_2 + \cdots + z_n + \cdots = \sum_{n=1}^{\infty} z_n.$$

This is said to *converge* and have the *sum S* if

$$\lim_{n \to \infty} S_n = S,$$

where $S_n$ is the $n$th partial sum:

$$S_n = z_1 + \cdots + z_n.$$

If the sequence $S_n$ diverges, the series is said to *diverge*. The series is said to be *absolutely convergent* if the series

$$|z_1| + \cdots + |z_n| + \cdots = \sum_{n=1}^{\infty} |z_n|$$

converges.

**Theorem 4.** $\displaystyle\sum_{n=1}^{\infty} z_n = S$ *if and only if*

$$\sum_{n=1}^{\infty} \operatorname{Re}(z_n) = \operatorname{Re}(S) \quad \text{and} \quad \sum_{n=1}^{\infty} \operatorname{Im}(z_n) = \operatorname{Im}(S).$$

This is an immediate consequence of Theorem 1.

**Theorem 5.** *If $\sum z_n$ is absolutely convergent, then $\sum z_n$ converges.*

We prove this by applying the Cauchy criterion. Let $S_n$ be the $n$th partial sum for the series $\sum z_n$; let $T_n$ be the $n$th partial sum for the series $\sum |z_n|$. Since $\sum |z_n|$ converges, the sequence $T_n$ converges. Hence, by Theorem 2, for given $\epsilon > 0$, $N$ can be found so that

$$|T_m - T_n| < \epsilon \quad \text{for} \quad m > N, n > N.$$

Now for $m > n$,

$$|S_m - S_n| = |z_{n+1} + \cdots + z_m|$$
$$\leq |z_{n+1}| + \cdots + |z_m| = T_m - T_n = |T_m - T_n|.$$

Thus $|S_m - S_n| \leq |T_m - T_n|$ for $m > n$. In the same way we show that the inequality holds for $m < n$ (for $m = n$ both sides are 0). Accordingly, for $m > N$, $n > N$,

$$|S_m - S_n| \leq |T_m - T_n| < \epsilon.$$

Therefore by the Cauchy criterion, the sequence $S_n$ converges and the series $\sum z_n$ is convergent.

**Theorem 6.** *If the nth term of the series $\sum z_n$ fails to converge to 0, then $\sum z_n$ diverges.*

The proof is left as an exercise (Problem 5 below).

**Theorem 7** (Comparison test for convergence). *If $|z_n| \leq a_n$, where $\sum a_n$ converges, then $\sum z_n$ is absolutely convergent.*

*Proof.* By the comparison test for real series, $\sum |z_n|$ converges, so that, by Theorem 5, $\sum z_n$ also converges.

**Theorem 8** (Ratio test). *If the ratio*

$$\left| \frac{z_{n+1}}{z_n} \right|$$

*converges to $L$, then the series $\sum z_n$ is absolutely convergent if $L < 1$, and is divergent if $L > 1$. More generally, the series is absolutely convergent if the ratio remains less than a number $r$ which is less than 1 for $n$ sufficiently large; the series diverges if the ratio is greater than or equal to 1 for $n$ sufficiently large.*

**Theorem 9** (Root test). *If the sequence*

$$\sqrt[n]{|z_n|}$$

*converges to $L$, then the series $\sum z_n$ converges if $L < 1$ and diverges if $L > 1$. More generally, the series converges absolutely if*

$$\overline{\lim_{n \to \infty}} \sqrt[n]{|z_n|} < 1$$

*and diverges if*

$$\overline{\lim_{n \to \infty}} \sqrt[n]{|z_n|} > 1.$$

**Theorem 10.** *If*

$$\sum_{n=0}^{\infty} z_n = z^* \quad and \quad \sum_{n=0}^{\infty} w_n = w^*,$$

*then*

$$\sum_{n=0}^{\infty} (z_n \pm w_n) = z^* \pm w^*.$$

*If both series are absolutely convergent, then*

$$z_0 w_0 + (z_0 w_1 + z_1 w_0) + \cdots + (z_0 w_n + z_1 w_{n-1} + \cdots + z_n w_0)$$
$$+ \cdots = z^* \cdot w^*;$$

*the series on the left is absolutely convergent and the parentheses can be removed without affecting absolute convergence or the sum.*

These theorems are proved as for real series (see *Advanced Calculus,*\* pp. 316–318 and pp. 332–336).

## PROBLEMS

1. For each of the following sequences graph the first five numbers and find the limit of the sequence if it exists:

   (a) $z_n = \dfrac{in}{n^2 + i}$ (b) $z_n = e^{\pi in/8}$ (c) $z_n = \left(\dfrac{1+i}{4}\right)^n$.

2. Determine which of the following statements is true:

   (a) if the sequence $z_n$ converges, then so does $|z_n|$
   (b) if the sequence $z_n$ converges, then so does $\arg z_n$
   (c) if $\arg z_n$ and $|z_n|$ converge, then $z_n$ converges.

3. Test for absolute convergence and for convergence:

   (a) $\displaystyle\sum_{n=1}^{\infty} \frac{i^n}{n^2}$ (b) $\displaystyle\sum_{n=2}^{\infty} \frac{i^n}{\log n}$ (c) $\displaystyle\sum_{n=1}^{\infty} \frac{(1+i)^n}{n}$

   (d) $\displaystyle\sum_{n=1}^{\infty} \frac{|1+i|^n}{i^n}$ (e) $\displaystyle\sum_{n=1}^{\infty} \frac{e^{2in}}{n^2}$.

4. Prove: if $\lim z_n = z_0$ and $\lim w_n = w_0$, then $\lim z_n w_n = z_0 w_0$.

[*Hint: write* $z_n = x_n + iy_n$, $z_0 = x_0 + iy_0$, $w_n = u_n + iv_n$, $w_0 = u_0 + iv_0$ *and apply Theorem 1.*]

---

\* The author's text of this title (Reading: Addison-Wesley Publishing Co., Inc., 1952) will be referred to simply as *Advanced Calculus.*

5. Prove Theorem 6:

    (a) by applying Theorem 4,

    (b) by applying the Cauchy criterion,

    (c) by writing $z_n = S_n - S_{n-1}$ and taking limits on both sides.

## ANSWERS

1. (a) limit is 0,     (b) no limit,     (c) limit is 0.     2. (a) and (c) are true.

3. (a) absolute convergence,     (b) convergence, not absolute,
   (c) divergence,     (d) divergence,
   (e) absolute convergence.

# 2 □ *Functions of a Complex Variable*

## 2-1 □ CONCEPT OF COMPLEX FUNCTION

If to each $z = x + iy$ of a certain set a complex number $w = u + iv$ is assigned, then we say that $w$ is a function of $z$ over the given set: $w = f(z)$. The values of $w$ may happen to be real or pure imaginary. The following are functions of $z$ in the set indicated:

$$w = z^3 \text{ (all } z), \qquad w = (1/z^2) + 1 \text{ (all } z \text{ except } \pm i),$$
$$w = |z| \text{ (all } z),$$
$$w = \theta = \arg z, \text{ where } 0 \leq \theta < 2\pi \text{ (all } z \text{ except 0)},$$
$$w = \bar{z} \text{ (all } z).$$

For almost all the functions considered in this book, the independent variable $z$ will vary over some domain (open region) in the $z$ plane.*

---

* We use the following terminology for *sets of points* in the plane. By a *neighborhood* of radius $\epsilon$ of point $z_0$ we mean the set of all $z$ such that $|z - z_0| < \epsilon$. By an *open* set we mean a set $E$ such that every point $z_0$ in $E$ has a neighborhood lying wholly in $E$. By a *domain* or *open region* we mean a nonempty open connected set; that is, a nonempty open set any two points of which can be joined by a broken line lying in the set. From this definition it follows that a domain cannot be formed of two nonempty open sets without common point. By a *boundary* point of a set $E$ we mean a point, every neighborhood of which contains at least one point in $E$ and one point not in $E$. By a *region* we mean a domain plus, perhaps, some or all of its boundary points. By a *closed region* we mean a domain plus all its boundary points. By a *closed* set $E$ we mean a set $E$ such that the points not in $E$ form an open set; every closed region is a closed set. A set $E$ is *bounded* if there is a constant $K$ such that $|z| \leq K$ for all $z$ in $E$.

14

Let $D$ be a domain in the $z$ plane and let $w = f(z)$ be defined in $D$. To each $z = x + iy$ in $D$ is then assigned a value of $w = u + iv$. Thus $u = \text{Re}(w)$ depends on $x$ and $y$, as does $v = \text{Im}(w)$. For example, if $w = z^2$, then

$$u + iv = (x + iy)^2 = x^2 - y^2 + i \cdot 2xy;$$

hence

$$u = x^2 - y^2, \qquad v = 2xy.$$

*The complex function $w = f(z)$ is equivalent to two real functions $u(x, y)$, $v(x, y)$.*

Such a pair of functions of two variables can be interpreted as a *transformation* from the $xy$ plane to the $uv$ plane. Thus, if $w = z^2$ and $D$ is chosen as the circular region: $|z - 1| < 1$, then to each point of $D$ corresponds a point of the domain $D_1$ (interior of a cardioid) shown in Fig. 2–1.

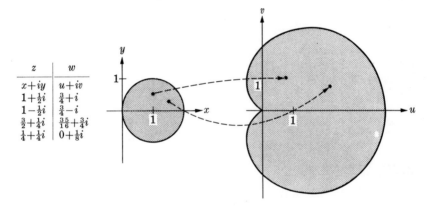

| $z$ | $w$ |
|---|---|
| $x+iy$ | $u+iv$ |
| $1+\frac{1}{2}i$ | $\frac{3}{4}+i$ |
| $1-\frac{1}{2}i$ | $\frac{3}{4}-i$ |
| $\frac{3}{2}+\frac{1}{4}i$ | $\frac{35}{16}+\frac{3}{4}i$ |
| $\frac{1}{4}+\frac{1}{4}i$ | $0+\frac{1}{8}i$ |

FIG. 2–1.   The function $w = z^2$.

For $z = 1$, $w = z^2 = 1$ and other paired points are shown in the table of Fig. 2–1. The assignment of $w$ values to the points $z$ is also indicated by curved arrows joining the $z$ to the corresponding $w$. This method of graphing the function is clearly a clumsy one; it will be improved on in Section 7–2.

Another interpretation of the pair of functions $u(x, y)$, $v(x, y)$ is that of a vector field in the plane. This will be studied further in Section 7–5.

The function $w = f(z)$ may be defined, not in terms of familiar operations on $z$, as in the examples above, but by operations on $x$ and $y$. Thus

$$w = x^2 y + y^3 + i(x^3 - xy)$$

defines $w = u + iv$ as a function of $z = x + iy$ for all $z$; for, given $z$, we find $x$, $y$, and then $w$. The corresponding real functions $u(x, y)$, $v(x, y)$ are as follows:

$$u = x^2y + y^3, \qquad v = x^3 - xy.$$

The point to be emphasized is that the two methods are completely equivalent. Each function $w = f(z)$ is the same as two real functions: $u = g(x, y)$, $v = h(x, y)$ and each pair of real functions in $D$ defines one function $w = f(z)$ in $D$.

A complex number $z_0$ is termed a *zero* (or *root*) of a function $f(z)$ if $f(z_0) = 0$. For example, $z_0 = i$ is a zero of $f(z) = z^2 + 1$.

## 2-2 □ LIMITS AND CONTINUITY

Let $w = f(z)$ be defined in the domain $D$ except perhaps at the point $z_0$ of $D$. Then one writes

$$\lim_{z \to z_0} f(z) = c$$

if, for each positive $\epsilon$, a positive $\delta$ can be chosen so that $|f(z) - c| < \epsilon$ for $0 < |z - z_0| < \delta$. In words: $f(z)$ is as close as desired to $c$, as long as $z$ is sufficiently close to $z_0$; this is illustrated in Fig. 2–2.

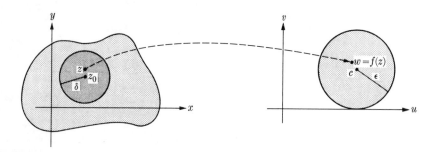

Fig. 2–2.   Limits for complex functions.

The function $w = f(z)$ is said to be continuous at $z_0$ if $f(z_0)$ is defined and

$$\lim_{z \to z_0} f(z) = f(z_0).$$

**Theorem 11.** *Let $w = f(z)$ be defined in the domain $D$ except perhaps at the point $z_0 = x_0 + iy_0$ of $D$. Let*

$$u = g(x, y), \qquad v = h(x, y)$$

*be the corresponding real functions of x and y.   Then*

$$\lim_{z \to z_0} f(z) = c = a + ib$$

*if and only if*

$$\lim_{\substack{x \to x_0 \\ y \to y_0}} g(x, y) = a, \qquad \lim_{\substack{x \to x_0 \\ y \to y_0}} h(x, y) = b.$$

*If $f(z_0)$ is defined, then $f(z)$ is continuous at $z_0$ if and only if $g(x, y)$ and $h(z, y)$ are continuous at $(x_0, y_0)$.*

The proof is the same as the proof of the corresponding principle for sequences, Theorem 1 of Section 1–4.

EXAMPLE.  The function

$$w = \log (x^2 + y^2) + i(x^2 - y^2)$$

is defined and continuous except for $z = 0$, since this holds for the real functions

$$u = \log (x^2 + y^2), \qquad v = x^2 - y^2.$$

**Theorem 12.**  *If $\lim_{z \to z_0} f(z) = c$ and $\lim_{z \to z_0} g(z) = d$, then*

$$\lim_{z \to z_0} [f(z) + g(z)] = c + d, \qquad \lim_{z \to z_0} [f(z) \cdot g(z)] = c \cdot d,$$

$$\lim_{z \to z_0} \frac{f(z)}{g(z)} = \frac{c}{d} \quad (d \neq 0).$$

*The sum, product, and quotient (except for division by zero) of continuous functions is continuous.   A continuous function of a continuous function is continuous.*

This theorem states in concise form the analogues for complex functions of the familiar limit and continuity theorems.  They can be proved as for real variables or as an application of Theorem 11.  Thus let $f(z) = u_1 + iv_1$, $g(z) = u_2 + iv_2$.  Then

$$f(z) \cdot g(z) = (u_1 + iv_1)(u_2 + iv_2) = u_1 u_2 - v_1 v_2 + i(u_1 v_2 + u_2 v_1).$$

If $f$ and $g$ are continuous at $z_0 = x_0 + iy_0$, then $u_1$, $u_2$, $v_1$, $v_2$ are continuous at $(x_0, y_0)$, so that $u_1 u_2 - v_1 v_2$ and $u_1 v_2 + u_2 v_1$ are continuous at $(x_0, y_0)$ by theorems for real variables.  Hence $f(z) \cdot g(z)$ is continuous at $z_0$.  The other principles are proved in the same way.

By repeated application of Theorem 12, one verifies that each *polynomial*

$$w = a_0 + a_1 z + \cdots + a_n z^n$$

is continuous for all $z$, as is each *rational function:*

$$w = \frac{P(z)}{Q(z)} \quad (P, Q \text{ polynomials})$$

in each domain containing no zero of the denominator.

**Theorem 13.**  *Let $f(z)$ be defined in a domain $D$ and let $f(z)$ be continuous at the point $z_0$ of $D$.  Then*

$$\lim_{n \to \infty} f(z_n) = f(z_0)$$

*for every sequence $z_n$ converging to $z_0$.*

The proof is left as an exercise (Prob. 6, following Section 2–3.).

Let $f(z)$ be defined in $D$ except perhaps at the point $z_0$ of $D$.  One writes

$$\lim_{z \to z_0} f(z) = \infty$$

if

$$\lim_{z \to z_0} |f(z)| = \infty \; ;$$

i.e., if, for each real number $K$, there is a positive $\delta$ such that

$$|f(z)| > K \quad \text{for} \quad 0 < |z - z_0| < \delta.$$

Similarly, if $f(z)$ is defined for $|z| > R$ for some $R$, then

$$\lim_{z \to \infty} f(z) = c,$$

if for each $\epsilon > 0$ one can find a number $R_0$ such that

$$|f(z) - c| < \epsilon \quad \text{for} \quad |z| > R_0;$$

on the other hand,

$$\lim_{z \to \infty} f(z) = \infty,$$

if for each real number $K$ there is a number $R_0$ such that

$$|f(z)| > K \quad \text{for} \quad |z| > R_0.$$

All these definitions emphasize that there is just one complex number $\infty$ and that "approaching $\infty$" is equivalent to receding from the origin.  A further discussion is given in Section 6–3.

The notions of limits and continuity can be extended to functions defined on an arbitrary set of points $E$ in the $z$ plane and the above results continue to hold. For most applications here, the functions will be defined in a domain. Occasionally we shall consider functions defined in a closed region or on a curve.

## 2-3 □ SEQUENCES AND SERIES OF FUNCTIONS

If the functions $f_1(z), \ldots, f_n(z), \ldots$ are all defined in the same domain $D$, they form a sequence of functions in $D$. Thus to each $z_0$ in $D$ is assigned a sequence of complex numbers $f_1(z_0), \ldots, f_n(z_0), \ldots$. The sequence $f_n(z)$ is said to *converge* in $D$ to the *limit* $f(z)$:

$$\lim_{n \to \infty} f_n(z) = f(z)$$

if

$$\lim_{n \to \infty} f_n(z_0) = f(z_0)$$

for each $z_0$ in $D$.

If the terms of an infinite series are the functions $f_n(z)$, all defined in $D$, then one has a series:

$$f_1(z) + \cdots + f_n(z) + \cdots = \sum_{n=1}^{\infty} f_n(z)$$

of functions in $D$. This series converges in $D$ to the sum $S(z)$ if

$$\lim_{n \to \infty} S_n(z) = S(z),$$

where $S_n(z)$ is the $n$th partial sum:

$$S_n(z) = f_1(z) + \cdots + f_n(z).$$

The series is said to be *uniformly convergent* in $D$ (or in a set of points $E$ in $D$), if to each $\epsilon > 0$ an $N$ can be assigned—the same for all points of $D$ (or $E$)—such that for all $z$ in $D$ (or $E$) one has

$$|S_n(z) - S(z)| < \epsilon \quad \text{for} \quad n > N.$$

EXAMPLE 1. The complex geometric series:

$$1 + z + z^2 + \cdots + z^n + \cdots = \sum_{n=0}^{\infty} z^n$$

is convergent for $|z| < 1$ to the sum $1/(1 - z)$. For

$$S_n(z) = 1 + \cdots + z^{n-1} = \frac{1 - z^n}{1 - z} = \frac{1}{1 - z} - z^n \frac{1}{1 - z}.$$

Hence

$$\left| S_n(z) - \frac{1}{1 - z} \right| = \left| z^n \cdot \frac{1}{1 - z} \right| = |z|^n \frac{1}{|1 - z|}.$$

If $z$ is a fixed point of the domain $|z| < 1$, then $|1 - z|$ is a fixed positive number, as in Fig. 2–3. As $n$ increases, $|z|^n$ converges to 0, since $|z| < 1$. Hence $S_n(z)$ converges to $1/(1 - z)$. However, the "absolute error"

$$\frac{|z|^n}{|1 - z|}$$

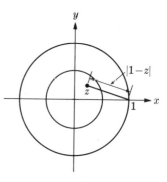

for each *fixed* $n$ depends on the distance $|1 - z|$ between 1 and $z$. As $z$ approaches 1, this error becomes infinite; however, if $z$ remains within a circle $|z| \leq \frac{1}{2}$, for example, the error is largest for $z = \frac{1}{2}$. Hence the convergence of the series is uniform for $|z| \leq \frac{1}{2}$. For when $|z| \leq \frac{1}{2}$,

$$\left| S_n(z) - \frac{1}{1 - z} \right| \leq \left( \frac{1}{2} \right)^n \cdot 2 = \frac{1}{2^{n-1}} ;$$

FIGURE 2–3

if $n$ is chosen sufficiently large, the error is less than a preassigned $\epsilon$ for all $z$ of the circle $|z| \leq \frac{1}{2}$.

**Theorem 14** (M-test). *Let*

$$M_1 + \cdots + M_n + \cdots = \sum_{n=1}^{\infty} M_n$$

*be a convergent series of positive real numbers. Let $\sum f_n(z)$ be a series of complex functions $f_n(z)$, all defined in a region $R$. If*

$$|f_n(z)| \leq M_n \quad \text{for all } z \text{ in } R,$$

*then the series $\sum f_n(z)$ is uniformly convergent in $R$ and is absolutely convergent for each $z$ in $R$.*

**Theorem 15.** *Let the series $\sum f_n(z)$ be uniformly convergent to the sum $f(z)$ in a region $R$ and let all the functions $f_1(z), f_2(z), \ldots$ be continuous in $R$. Then the sum $f(z)$ is also continuous in $R$.*

These theorems are proved as for real functions (*Advanced Calculus*, pp. 342–346), or can be reduced to theorems on real functions by Theorems 4 and 11 (Sections 1–4 and 2–2). The region $R$ can be replaced by a general set $E$ in both theorems.

EXAMPLE 2. We consider again the geometric series $\sum_{n=0}^{\infty} z^n$. We can prove uniform convergence without knowing the sum of the series. Let $k$

be a positive real number less than 1; then

$$|z|^n \leq M_n = k^n$$

for all $z$ of the region: $|z| \leq k$. Since $\sum M_n = \sum k^n$ converges for $k < 1$, we conclude by Theorem 14 that $\sum z^n$ converges uniformly and absolutely for $|z| \leq k$. Hence, by Theorem 15 the sum of the series is continuous in each region $|z| \leq k$; therefore, the sum must be continuous for $|z| < 1$.

*Remark.* If a series $\sum f_n(z)$ is uniformly convergent to $f(z)$ on a set $E$, and $g(z)$ is defined and *bounded* on $E$, $|g(z)| < K$, then the series $\sum g(z)f_n(z)$ converges uniformly to $g(z)f(z)$ on $E$. For

$$|g(z)f_1(z) + \cdots + g(z)f_n(z) - g(z)f(z)|$$
$$= |g(z)| \, |f_1(z) + \cdots + f_n(z) - f(z)| < K\epsilon$$

for $n$ sufficiently large. We note that $g(z)$ is bounded on $E$ if $g(z)$ is continuous on $E$ and $E$ is a bounded closed set, as follows from standard theorems on real functions.

## PROBLEMS

1. For each of the following functions of $z$ tabulate the function for 5 different values of $z$ and indicate graphically the correspondence between $z$ values and $w$ values:

(a) $w = z^4$        (b) $w = 2z$        (c) $w = z + 3 + 2i$

(d) $w = \dfrac{1}{z}$        (e) $w = e^{i(\pi/3)}z$        (f) $w = \dfrac{2z - 1}{z - 2}$.

2. Determine, for each of the functions (a), (b), (c), (d), (e) of Problem 1, the range of $w$ as $z$ varies over the circle $|z| \leq 1$.

3. Write as two real functions of $x$ and $y$:

(a) $w = z^3$        (b) $w = \dfrac{1}{z}$        (c) $w = \dfrac{z}{1 + z}$

(d) $w = z + \dfrac{1}{z}$        (e) $w = e^z$        (f) $w = ze^z$.

4. Determine the values of $z$ for which the following functions of $z$ are continuous:

(a) $w = z^2 - z$        (b) $w = xy + i(x^3 + y^3)$

(c) $w = \dfrac{2 - iz^2}{z^2 + 1}$        (d) $w = e^z$

(e) $w = \text{Re}(z)$

(f) $w = \bar{z}$

(g) $w = |z|$

(h) $w = \log |z| + i \arg z$, where $-\pi < \arg z \leqq \pi$.

5. Show that each of the following series is uniformly and absolutely convergent for $|z| \leqq 1$:

(a) $\sum\limits_{n=1}^{\infty} \dfrac{z^n}{n!}$

(b) $\sum\limits_{n=1}^{\infty} \dfrac{z^n}{n2^n}$

(c) $\sum\limits_{n=1}^{\infty} \dfrac{(z-1)^n}{3^n}$

(d) $\sum\limits_{n=1}^{\infty} \dfrac{\sin nx + i \cos ny}{n^2}$.

6. Prove Theorem 13.

## ANSWERS

2. (a) $|w| \leqq 1$,     (b) $|w| \leqq 2$,     (c) $|w - 3 - 2i| \leqq 1$,
   (d) $|w| \geqq 1$,     (e) $|w| \leqq 1$.

3. (a) $u = x^3 - 3xy^2$,     $v = 3x^2y - y^3$;

   (b) $u = \dfrac{x}{x^2 + y^2}$,     $v = \dfrac{-y}{x^2 + y^2}$;

   (c) $u = \dfrac{x^2 + y^2 + x}{(x+1)^2 + y^2}$,     $v = \dfrac{y}{(x+1)^2 + y^2}$;

   (d) $u = x + \dfrac{x}{x^2 + y^2}$,     $v = y - \dfrac{y}{x^2 + y^2}$;

   (e) $u = e^x \cos y$,     $v = e^x \sin y$,

   (f) $u = xe^x \cos y - ye^x \sin y$,     $v = xe^x \sin y + ye^x \cos y$.

4. (a) all $z$,     (b) all $z$,     (c) $z \neq \pm i$,     (d) all $z$,     (e) all $z$,     (f) all $z$,
   (g) all $z$,     (h) all $z$ except for $z$ real and negative or zero.

## 2-4 □ DERIVATIVES AND DIFFERENTIALS

Let $w = f(z)$ be given in $D$ and let $z_0$ be a point of $D$. Then $w$ is said to have a derivative at $z_0$ if

$$\lim_{\Delta z \to 0} \frac{f(z_0 + \Delta z) - f(z_0)}{\Delta z}$$

exists; the value of the limit is then denoted by $f'(z_0)$. This definition is in appearance the same as that for functions of a real variable and it will be seen that the derivative does have the usual properties. However, it will also be shown that, if $w = f(z)$ has a continuous derivative in a domain $D$, then $f(z)$ has a number of additional properties; in particular, the corresponding real functions $u$ and $v$ must be *harmonic*; that is, $u$ and $v$

satisfy the Laplace equation:

$$\frac{\partial^2 u}{\partial x^2} + \frac{\partial^2 u}{\partial y^2} = 0, \qquad \frac{\partial^2 v}{\partial x^2} + \frac{\partial^2 v}{\partial y^2} = 0,$$

or in polar coordinates (for $r \neq 0$)

$$\frac{\partial^2 u}{\partial r^2} + \frac{1}{r^2}\frac{\partial^2 u}{\partial \theta^2} + \frac{1}{r}\frac{\partial u}{\partial r} = 0, \qquad \frac{\partial^2 v}{\partial r^2} + \frac{1}{r^2}\frac{\partial^2 v}{\partial \theta^2} + \frac{1}{r}\frac{\partial v}{\partial r} = 0.$$

The reason for the remarkable consequences of possession of a derivative lies in the fact that the increment $\Delta z$ is allowed to approach 0 in any manner. If one restricted $\Delta z$ so that $z_0 + \Delta z$ approached $z_0$ along a particular line, then one would obtain a "directional derivative." But here the limit obtained is required to be the *same for all directions*, so that the "directional derivative" has the same value in all directions. Moreover, $z_0 + \Delta z$ may approach $z_0$ in a quite arbitrary manner, for example, along a spiral path. The limit of the ratio $\Delta w/\Delta z$ must be the same for all manners of approach.

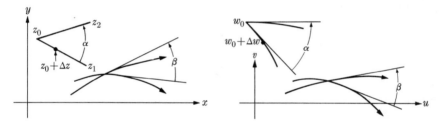

FIG. 2–4.    Derivative and conformal mapping.

If, as in Fig. 2–4, $z_0 + \Delta z$ approaches $z_0$ along a line $z_0 z_1$, then in general $w_0 + \Delta w = f(z_0 + \Delta z)$ will approach $w_0$ along a curve through $w_0$. The existence of the derivative implies that $\Delta w$ is approximately a constant $c$ ($c = a + bi$) times $\Delta z$:

$$\Delta w \sim c\,\Delta z \quad [c = f'(z_0)].$$

Thus

$$|\Delta w| \sim |c| \cdot |\Delta z|$$

and

$$\arg \Delta w \sim \arg c + \arg \Delta z;$$

that is, $\Delta w$ has (approximately) a modulus $|\Delta w|$ which is in a fixed ratio to $|\Delta z|$ and a direction $\arg \Delta w$ which differs by a fixed angle from that of $\Delta z$. Accordingly, if the line $z_0 z_1$ is replaced by a line $z_0 z_2$ forming an angle $\alpha$ with the first line, then the corresponding curve in the $w$ plane will also rotate through angle $\alpha$ in the same direction. If $z_0 + \Delta z$ varies on a small circle about $z_0$, then $w_0 + \Delta w$ varies (approximately) on a small circle about $w_0$; if $z_0 + \Delta z$ rotates through an angle $\alpha$ about $z_0$, $w_0 + \Delta w$ does (approximately) the same about $w_0$. [It has been assumed here that $f'(z_0) = c \neq 0$; the case $f'(z_0) = 0$ requires special discussion.]

A transformation from the $xy$ plane to the $uv$ plane is said to be *conformal* and *sense-preserving* if to each pair of curves forming angle $\beta$ in the $xy$ plane there corresponds a pair of curves forming the same angle $\beta$ (in the same sense) in the $uv$ plane (cf. Fig. 2–4). It follows from the discussion just given that, if $w = f(z)$ has a derivative in $D$, then the corresponding transformation from the $xy$ plane to the $uv$ plane is conformal and sense-preserving except where $f'(z) = 0$. This will be studied in detail in Section 7–1.

Now let $w = f(z)$ be given in $D$ and let $f'(z_0)$ exist and have value $c$. For $\Delta z \neq 0$ let

$$\epsilon = \frac{\Delta w}{\Delta z} - c = \frac{f(z_0 + \Delta z) - f(z_0)}{\Delta z} - c$$

and let $\epsilon = 0$ for $\Delta z = 0$. Then by definition of the derivative,

$$\lim_{\Delta z \to 0} \epsilon = 0. \tag{2–40}$$

Thus $\epsilon(\Delta z)$ is continuous at $\Delta z = 0$. We can write

$$\Delta w = c\,\Delta z + \epsilon\,\Delta z. \tag{2–41}$$

This equation shows that $\Delta w$ must approach 0 as $\Delta z$ approaches 0; *hence, if $f'(z_0)$ exists, $f(z)$ must be continuous at $z_0$.* In general, we say that a function $w = f(z)$ has a differential

$$dw = c\,\Delta z$$

at $z_0$, if at $z_0$

$$\Delta w = c\,\Delta z + \epsilon\,\Delta z,$$

where $c$ is independent of $\Delta z$ and

$$\lim_{\Delta z \to 0} \epsilon = 0 = \epsilon(0).$$

Thus Eqs. (2–40) and (2–41) state that, if $w$ has a derivative at $z_0$, then $w$ has a differential at $z_0$. Conversely, if $w$ has a differential at $z_0$, then

$$\frac{\Delta w}{\Delta z} = c + \epsilon, \qquad \lim_{\Delta z \to 0} \epsilon = 0,$$

so that

$$\lim_{\Delta z \to 0} \frac{\Delta w}{\Delta z} = c$$

and $w$ has a derivative $f'(z_0) = c$.

**Theorem 16.** *If $w = f(z)$ has a differential*

$$dw = c\,\Delta z$$

*at $z_0$, then $w$ has a derivative $f'(z_0) = c$. Conversely, if $w$ has a derivative at $z_0$, then $w$ has a differential at $z_0$:*

$$dw = f'(z_0)\,\Delta z.$$

Thus "differentiability" and possession of a derivative are the same. Just as for real functions, the differential defines a linear approximation to the given function:

$$w - w_0 = f'(z_0)(z - z_0).$$

One can now prove that the basic functions:

$$w = z^n \quad (n = 1, 2, \ldots) \tag{2-42}$$

have derivatives:

$$\frac{dw}{dz} = nz^{n-1}. \tag{2-43}$$

One can also write

$$dw = nz^{n-1}\,dz$$

(with $dz$ replacing $\Delta z$ for the same reason as in ordinary calculus).

The usual rules of calculus continue to hold: if $w_1$ and $w_2$ are differentiable in $D$, then

$$d(w_1 + w_2) = dw_1 + dw_2, \qquad d(w_1 w_2) = w_1\,dw_2 + w_2\,dw_1,$$

$$d\left(\frac{w_1}{w_2}\right) = \frac{w_2\,dw_1 - w_1\,dw_2}{w_2^2} \qquad (w_2 \neq 0). \tag{2-44}$$

These are proved exactly as for real variables. There is also a function-of-function rule: if $w_2$ is a differentiable function of $w_1$ and $w_1$ is a differentiable function of $z$, then, wherever $w_2[w_1(z)]$ is defined,

$$\frac{dw_2}{dz} = \frac{dw_2}{dw_1} \cdot \frac{dw_1}{dz}. \tag{2-45}$$

The proof is like that of the chain rules in real calculus.

## PROBLEMS

1. Let the function $w = 2iz + 1$ be given. Compute

$$\frac{\Delta w}{\Delta z} = \frac{f(z_0 + \Delta z) - f(z_0)}{\Delta z}$$

for $z_0 = i$ and the following choices of $\Delta z$:

(a) $\Delta z = 1$,      (b) $\Delta z = i$,      (c) $\Delta z = -1$,      (d) $\Delta z = -i$.

Show the results graphically, plotting the points $z_0$, $z_0 + \Delta z$, $w_0$, $w_0 + \Delta w$.

2. Proceed as in Problem 1, using $w = f(z) = z^2$. Compare the results, noting that $dw = 2i\,dz$ at $z = i$, so that $w = 2i(z - i) - 1 = 2iz + 1$ is the best linear approximation to $w = z^2$ at $z = i$.

3. Differentiate the complex functions:

(a) $w = z^5 - 3z^2 - 1$          (b) $w = \dfrac{z}{1 - z}$

(c) $w = (1 - z)^4(z^2 + 1)^3$      (d) $w = \left(\dfrac{z - 1}{z + 1}\right)^4.$

4. Prove that $dz^n = nz^{n-1}\,dz \quad (n = 1, 2, \ldots)$.

5. Prove the rules (2–44).

6. Prove the rule (2–45).

[*Hint: write* $\Delta w_2 = c_2\,\Delta w_1 + \epsilon_2\,\Delta w_1$; *divide both sides by* $\Delta z$ *and let* $\Delta z$ *approach* 0.]

7. Let a curve $C$ be given by differentiable functions

$$x = x(t), \qquad y = y(t), \qquad t_1 \le t \le t_2.$$

(a) Show that the complex number

$$\frac{dx}{dt} + i\frac{dy}{dt} = \frac{dz}{dt} = \lim_{\Delta t \to 0} \frac{\Delta x + i\,\Delta y}{\Delta t}$$

represents a vector tangent to the curve. Note that this is a derivative of a complex function of a *real variable* $t$ and not the derivative of a complex function of a complex variable, as in the preceding analysis.

(b) Let $w = u + iv$ be a differentiable function of $z$ in a domain containing $C$. Show that

$$\frac{dw}{dt} = f'(z)\frac{dz}{dt}.$$

[*Hint: proceed as in Prob. 6.*]

The equation $w = f[z(t)]$ defines a curve $C': u = u(t), v = v(t)$ in the $w$ plane which is the image of $C$; thus, by (a), $dw/dt$ defines a tangent vector to the image curve; cf. also Prob. 14 following Section 7–2.

8. Let two lines forming angle $\alpha$ at $(x_0, y_0)$ be given in parametric form:

$$x = x_0 + a_1 t, \qquad y = y_0 + b_1 t;$$
$$x = x_0 + a_2 t, \qquad y = y_0 + b_2 t.$$

(a) Show that, unless $x_0 = y_0 = 0$, the images of these lines under the transformation $w = z^2$ are two curves intersecting at angle $\alpha$.

[*Hint: find the tangent vectors to the curves as complex numbers as in Prob. 7. Note that* arg $(z_2/z_1)$ *defines the angle between two vectors represented by* $z_1$ *and* $z_2$.]

(b) Show that for $x_0 = y_0 = 0$ the image curves are two straight lines intersecting at angle $2\alpha$.

9. Let $w = f(z)$ have a derivative at $z_0$.

(a) Let $z_0 + \Delta z$ approach $z_0$ along a parallel to the $x$ axis: $\Delta z = \Delta x$, to conclude that

$$f'(z_0) = \frac{\partial u}{\partial x} + i \frac{\partial v}{\partial x}.$$

(b) Let $z_0 + \Delta z$ approach $z_0$ along a parallel to the $y$ axis: $\Delta z = i \Delta y$ to conclude that

$$f'(z_0) = \frac{\partial v}{\partial y} - i \frac{\partial u}{\partial y}.$$

(c) Equate the results of (a) and (b) to conclude that

$$\frac{\partial u}{\partial x} = \frac{\partial v}{\partial y}, \qquad \frac{\partial u}{\partial y} = -\frac{\partial v}{\partial x}.$$

These are the Cauchy-Riemann equations.

10. Let $w = f(z)$ have a derivative at $z_0$.

(a) Let $z_0 + \Delta z$ approach $z_0$ along a line making angle $\alpha$ with the $x$ axis: $\Delta z = \Delta s (\cos \alpha + i \sin \alpha) = \Delta s \cdot e^{i\alpha}$ to conclude that

$$f'(z_0) = e^{-i\alpha} \left( \frac{du}{ds} + i \frac{dv}{ds} \right),$$

where

$$\frac{du}{ds} = \nabla_\alpha u, \qquad \frac{dv}{ds} = \nabla_\alpha v$$

are the directional derivatives of $u$ and $v$ in the direction chosen.

(b) Let $z_0 + \Delta z$ approach $z_0$ as in part (a), with $\alpha$ replaced by $\alpha + (\pi/2)$. Show that

$$f'(z_0) = e^{-i\alpha} \left( \nabla_{\alpha+(\pi/2)} v - i \nabla_{\alpha+(\pi/2)} u \right).$$

(c) Equate the results of (a) and (b) to conclude that

$$\nabla_\alpha u = \nabla_{\alpha+(\pi/2)} v;$$

that is, the directional derivative of $u$ in direction $\alpha$ equals the directional derivative of $v$ in direction $\alpha + (\pi/2)$.

(d) Obtain the Cauchy-Riemann equations of Prob. 9(c) as special cases of (c) ($\alpha = 0$ and $\alpha = \pi/2$).

(e) Show from (c) that, if $u$ and $v$ are expressed in polar coordinates, then

$$\frac{\partial u}{\partial r} = \frac{1}{r}\frac{\partial v}{\partial \theta}, \qquad \frac{1}{r}\frac{\partial u}{\partial \theta} = -\frac{\partial v}{\partial r} \quad (r \neq 0).$$

[*Hint: take $\alpha = \theta$ and $\alpha = \frac{1}{2}\pi + \theta$.*]

## ANSWERS

1. all parts: $2i$.

2. (a) $1 + 2i$,      (b) $3i$,          (c) $-1 + 2i$,      (d) $i$.

3. (a) $5z^4 - 6z$,   (b) $(1 - z)^{-2}$,   (c) $(1 - z)^3(z^2 + 1)^2(-4 + 6z - 10z^2)$,
   (d) $8(z - 1)^3(z + 1)^{-5}$.

## 2–5 □ INTEGRALS

By a *path* in the complex plane we mean a curve $C$ defined by parametric equations

$$x = x(t), \qquad y = y(t), \qquad a \leq t \leq b, \tag{2–50}$$

where $x(t)$ and $y(t)$ are continuous. If the path starts and ends at the same point,

$$x(a) = x(b), \qquad y(a) = y(b),$$

we call it a *closed path*. If the path passes through each point $(x, y)$ for at most one value of $t$, except possibly for the values $t = a$ and $b$, the path is called *simple*. Thus the equations $x = \cos t, y = \sin t, 0 \leq t \leq 2\pi$, represent a circle as a simple closed path. The path $C$ is called *smooth* if $x(t)$ and $y(t)$ have continuous derivatives for $a \leq t \leq b$. The path is called *piecewise smooth* if the interval $a \leq t \leq b$ can be divided into several intervals, for each of which the corresponding path is smooth; thus a broken line, traced at constant speed, is a piecewise smooth path.

Wherever $x'(t)$ and $y'(t)$ exist, the vector with $x$-component $x'(t)$ and $y$-component $y'(t)$ is tangent to the path at the point $(x(t), y(t))$. We can write Eqs. (2–50) concisely as

$$z = z(t), \qquad a \leqq t \leqq b, \tag{2–51}$$

where $z = x + iy$. Thus a path is described by a complex function of a *real* variable. We define $z'(t)$ in the usual fashion and verify that $z'(t) = x'(t) + iy'(t)$ (see Prob. 7, following Section 2–4), so that the complex number $z'(t)$ represents a vector tangent to the path.

We can also integrate a function $z(t) = x(t) + iy(t)$:

$$\int_a^b z(t)\,dt = \int_a^b [x(t) + iy(t)]\,dt = \int_a^b x(t)\,dt + i\int_a^b y(t)\,dt.$$

The usual properties of integrals continue to hold. In particular,

$$\int_a^b \frac{dz}{dt}\,dt = z(b) - z(a).$$

Let $w = f(z)$ be defined in a domain $D$ and let $C$ be a piecewise smooth path in $D$:

$$x = x(t), \qquad y = y(t), \qquad a \leqq t \leqq b.$$

The complex integral is defined as a line integral:

$$\int_C f(z)\,dz = \lim \sum_{i=1}^n f(z_j^*)\,\Delta_j z. \tag{2–52}$$

The path $C$ is assumed to have a definite direction, usually that of increasing $t$. The interval $a \leqq t \leqq b$ is subdivided into $n$ parts by $t_0 = a, \ldots, t_n = b$; $z_j = x(t_j) + iy(t_j)$, and $\Delta z_j = z_j - z_{j-1}$; $t_j^*$ is a point of the $j$th subinterval and $z_j^* = x(t_j^*) + iy(t_j^*)$. This is suggested in Fig. 2–5. The limit is taken as $n$ becomes infinite, while the maximum of $\Delta_1 t, \ldots, \Delta_n t$ approaches 0.

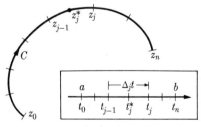

Fɪɢ. 2–5.   Complex line integral.

If one takes real and imaginary parts in the definition (2–52), one finds

$$\int_C f(z)\,dz = \lim \sum (u + iv)(\Delta x + i\,\Delta y)$$

$$= \lim \left\{ \sum (u\,\Delta x - v\,\Delta y) + i \sum (v\,\Delta x + u\,\Delta y) \right\};$$

that is,

$$\int_C f(z)\,dz = \int_C (u + iv)(dx + i\,dy)$$

$$= \int_C (u\,dx - v\,dy) + i \int_C (v\,dx + u\,dy). \qquad (2\text{–}53)$$

The complex line integral is thus simply a combination of two real line integrals. One can now apply all of the theory of such line integrals. In particular, we can assert at once:

**Theorem 17.** *If $f(z)$ is continuous in $D$ and $C$ is piecewise smooth, then the integral (2–52) exists and*

$$\int_C f(z)\,dz = \int_a^b \left( u\frac{dx}{dt} - v\frac{dy}{dt} \right) dt + i \int_a^b \left( v\frac{dx}{dt} + u\frac{dy}{dt} \right) dt. \qquad (2\text{–}54)$$

If we represent $C$ as $z = z(t)$ as in (2–51), then one can write the formula (2–54) more concisely:

$$\int_C f(z)\,dz = \int_a^b f[z(t)]\frac{dz}{dt}\,dt. \qquad (2\text{–}54')$$

EXAMPLE 1.   Let $C$ be the path: $x = 2t$, $y = 3t$, $1 \leq t \leq 2$.   Let $f(z) = z^2$. Then

$$\int_C z^2\,dz = \int_1^2 (2t + 3it)^2(2 + 3i)\,dt$$

$$= (2 + 3i)^3 \int_1^2 t^2\,dt = \frac{7}{3}(2 + 3i)^3 = -107\tfrac{1}{3} + 21i.$$

EXAMPLE 2.  Let $C$ be the circular path: $x = \cos t$, $y = \sin t$, $0 \leq t \leq 2\pi$. This can be written more concisely thus: $z = e^{it}$, $0 \leq t \leq 2\pi$.  Also, $dz/dt = -\sin t + i\cos t = ie^{it}$.  Hence

$$\int_C \frac{1}{z}\,dz = \int_0^{2\pi} e^{-it}(ie^{it})\,dt = i \int_0^{2\pi} dt = 2\pi i.$$

Further properties of complex integrals follow from those of real integrals:

**Theorem 18.** *Let $f(z)$ and $g(z)$ be continuous in a domain $D$. Let $C$ be a piecewise smooth path in $D$. Then*

$$\int_C [f(z) + g(z)]\, dz = \int_C f(z)\, dz + \int_C g(z)\, dz. \qquad (2\text{–}55)$$

*Further,*

$$\int_C kf(z)\, dz = k \int_C f(z)\, dz, \quad k = \text{const}, \qquad (2\text{–}56)$$

$$\int_C f(z)\, dz = \int_{C_1} f(z)\, dz + \int_{C_2} f(z)\, dz, \qquad (2\text{–}57)$$

*where $C$ is composed of a path $C_1$ from $z_0$ to $z_1$ and a path $C_2$ from $z_1$ to $z_2$, and*

$$\int_C f(z)\, dz = - \int_{C'} f(z)\, dz, \qquad (2\text{–}58)$$

*where $C'$ is obtained from $C$ by reversing direction on $C$.*

Upper estimates for the absolute value of a complex integral are obtained by the following theorem.

**Theorem 19.** *Let $f(z)$ be continuous on $C$ and let*

$$L = \int_C ds = \int_a^b \sqrt{\left(\frac{dx}{dt}\right)^2 + \left(\frac{dy}{dt}\right)^2}\, dt$$

*be the length of $C$. Then*

$$\left| \int_C f(z)\, dz \right| \leqq \int_C |f(z)|\, ds \leqq M \cdot L, \qquad (2\text{–}59)$$

*where $|f(z)| \leqq M$ on $C$.*

*Proof.* The line integral $\int |f(z)|\, ds$ is defined as a limit:

$$\int_C |f(z)|\, ds = \lim \sum_{j=1}^n |f(z_j^*)|\, \Delta_j s,$$

where $\Delta_j s$ is the length of the $j$th arc of $C$. Now

$$|f(z_j^*) \, \Delta_j z| = |f(z_j^*)| \cdot |\Delta_j z| \leq |f(z_j^*)| \cdot \Delta_j s,$$

for $|\Delta_j z|$ represents the *chord* of the arc $\Delta_j s$. Hence

$$\left| \sum f(z_j^*) \, \Delta_j z \right| \leq \sum |f(z_j^*) \, \Delta_j z| \leq \sum |f(z_j^*)| \, \Delta_j s,$$

by repeated application of inequality (1–15). Passing to the limit we conclude:

$$\left| \int_C f(z) \, dz \right| \leq \int_C |f(z)| \, ds.$$

This gives the first inequality. The second follows from the remark that

$$\sum |f(z_j^*)| \, \Delta_j s \leq M \sum \Delta_j s = ML.$$

The number $M$ can be chosen as the maximum of the continuous function $|f(z)|$ on $C$ or as any larger number.

**Theorem 20.** *A uniformly convergent series of continuous functions can be integrated term by term; i.e., if the functions $f_n(z)$ are all continuous on $C$ and $\sum_{n=1}^{\infty} f_n(z)$ converges uniformly to $f(z)$ on $C$, then*

$$\int_C f(z) \, dz = \sum_{n=1}^{\infty} \int_C f_n(z) \, dz.$$

This is proved as for real variables.

## PROBLEMS

1. Evaluate the following integrals:

(a) $\displaystyle\int_1^i (x^2 + iy^3) \, dz$ on the straight line from 1 to $i$

(b) $\displaystyle\int_0^{1+i} (z + 1) \, dz$ on the parabola $y = x^2$

(c) $\displaystyle\oint_C x \, dz$ on the circle $|z| = 1$

(d) $\displaystyle\oint \frac{z}{z^2 + 1} \, dz$ on the circle $|z| = 2$.

2. Write each of the following integrals $\int f(z)\,dz$ in the form (2–53), i.e., in terms of two real line integrals; then show that each of the real line integrals is independent of path in the $z$ plane:

(a) $\int z\,dz = \int(x\,dx - y\,dy) + i\int(y\,dx + x\,dy)$
(b) $\int iz^2\,dz$     (c) $\int z^3\,dz$     (d) $\int(1+i)(z+i)\,dz$     (e) $\int z^4\,dz$.

3. Using (2–53), show that $\int f(z)\,dz$ is independent of path in a simply connected domain in which $u$ and $v$ have continuous first partial derivatives, provided

$$\frac{\partial u}{\partial x} = \frac{\partial v}{\partial y}, \qquad \frac{\partial u}{\partial y} = -\frac{\partial v}{\partial x}.$$

These are the Cauchy-Riemann equations.

4. Show that the Cauchy-Riemann equations of Prob. 3 hold if and only if, when $u$ and $v$ are expressed in polar coordinates $r$, $\theta$,

$$\frac{\partial u}{\partial r} = \frac{1}{r}\frac{\partial v}{\partial \theta}, \qquad \frac{1}{r}\frac{\partial u}{\partial \theta} = -\frac{\partial v}{\partial r} \quad (r \neq 0). \tag{a}$$

[*Hint: apply the chain rules to show that*

$$\frac{\partial u}{\partial r} = \frac{\partial u}{\partial x}\cos\theta + \frac{\partial u}{\partial y}\sin\theta, \qquad \frac{1}{r}\frac{\partial u}{\partial \theta} = \cdots,$$

*and similarly for* $v$. *From these four equations show that*

$$\left(\frac{\partial u}{\partial r} - \frac{1}{r}\frac{\partial v}{\partial \theta}\right)^2 + \left(\frac{1}{r}\frac{\partial u}{\partial \theta} + \frac{\partial v}{\partial r}\right)^2 = \left(\frac{\partial u}{\partial x} - \frac{\partial v}{\partial y}\right)^2 + \left(\frac{\partial u}{\partial y} + \frac{\partial v}{\partial x}\right)^2.$$

*The assertion follows at once from this identity.*]

5. Use the results of Probs. 3 and 4 to show that

$$\int z^n\,dz \quad (n = 1, 2, \ldots)$$

is independent of path in the $z$ plane.

[*Hint: use Eq. (1–26) to express* $z^n$ *in polar coordinates. Then verify that* (a) *holds. The origin must be treated separately by rectangular coordinates.*]

6. (a) Show that, if the Cauchy-Riemann equations (Prob. 3) hold and $u$ and $v$ have continuous second partial derivatives, then $u$ and $v$ are harmonic functions.

(b) Use the Laplace equation in polar coordinates (Section 2–4) to verify that $\mathrm{Re}(z^n)$ and $\mathrm{Im}(z^n)$ are harmonic for $n = 1, 2, \ldots$

[*Hint: use* (1–26). *The origin must again be treated separately in rectangular coordinates.*]

7. (a) Evaluate

$$\oint \frac{1}{z} \, dz$$

on the circle $|z| = R$.

(b) Show that the integral of part (a) is $0$ on every simple closed path not enclosing the origin or through the origin.

(c) Show that

$$\oint \frac{1}{z^2} \, dz = 0$$

on every simple closed path not through the origin.

**ANSWERS**

1. (a) $\frac{1}{12}(-7 + i)$,      (b) $1 + 2i$,      (c) $\pi i$,      (d) $2\pi i$.

7. (a) $2\pi i$.

# 3 □ *Analytic Functions*

## 3-1 □ ANALYTIC FUNCTIONS. CAUCHY-RIEMANN EQUATIONS

A function $w = f(z)$, defined in a domain $D$, is said to be an *analytic function* in $D$ if $w$ has a continuous derivative in $D$. Almost the entire theory of functions of a complex variable is confined to the study of such functions. Furthermore, almost all functions used in the applications of mathematics to physical problems are analytic functions or are derived from such. As was pointed out in the Introduction, the study of analytic functions is equivalent to the study of harmonic functions of $x$ and $y$; this connection will be studied further below.

It will be seen that possession of a continuous derivative implies possession of a continuous second derivative, third derivative, ..., and in fact convergence of the Taylor series

$$f(z_0) + f'(z_0) \frac{(z - z_0)}{1!} + f''(z_0) \frac{(z - z_0)^2}{2!} + \cdots$$

in a neighborhood of each $z_0$ of $D$. One could thus define an analytic function as one so representable by Taylor series, and this definition is often used. The two definitions are equivalent, for convergence of the Taylor series in a neighborhood of each $z_0$ implies continuity of the derivatives of all orders.

While it is possible to construct continuous functions of $z$ which are not analytic (examples will be given below), it is impossible to construct a function $f(z)$ possessing a derivative, but not a continuous one, in $D$. In other words, if $f(z)$ has a derivative in $D$, the derivative is necessarily continuous, so that $f(z)$ is analytic. One could therefore define an analytic

35

function as one merely possessing a derivative in domain $D$ and this definition is also often used. For a proof that existence of the derivative implies
its continuity, one is referred to L. V. Ahlfors* and Section 5–4 below.

**Theorem 21.** *If $w = u + iv = f(z)$ is analytic in $D$, then $u$ and $v$ have
continuous first partial derivatives in $D$ and satisfy the Cauchy-Riemann
equations:*

$$\frac{\partial u}{\partial x} = \frac{\partial v}{\partial y}, \qquad \frac{\partial u}{\partial y} = -\frac{\partial v}{\partial x} \qquad (3\text{–}10)$$

*in $D$. Furthermore,*

$$\frac{dw}{dz} = \frac{\partial u}{\partial x} + i\frac{\partial v}{\partial x} = \frac{\partial v}{\partial y} + i\frac{\partial v}{\partial x} = \frac{\partial u}{\partial x} - i\frac{\partial u}{\partial y} = \frac{\partial v}{\partial y} - i\frac{\partial u}{\partial y}. \qquad (3\text{–}11)$$

*Proof.* Let $z_0$ be a fixed point of $D$ and let $\Delta w = f(z_0 + \Delta z) - f(z_0)$.
Since $f$ is analytic, one has

$$\Delta w = c\,\Delta z + \epsilon \cdot \Delta z, \qquad c = f'(z_0),$$

in accordance with Theorem 16 (Section 2–4). If one writes (Fig. 3–1)

$$\Delta w = \Delta u + i\,\Delta v, \qquad c = a + ib, \qquad \epsilon = \epsilon_1 + i\epsilon_2, \qquad \Delta z = \Delta x + i\,\Delta y,$$

then this becomes

$$\Delta u + i\,\Delta v = (a + ib)(\Delta x + i\,\Delta y) + (\epsilon_1 + i\epsilon_2)(\Delta x + i\,\Delta y).$$

If one compares real and imaginary parts on
left and right, one concludes that

$$\Delta u = a\,\Delta x - b\,\Delta y + \epsilon_1\,\Delta x - \epsilon_2\,\Delta y,$$
$$\Delta v = b\,\Delta x + a\,\Delta y + \epsilon_2\,\Delta x + \epsilon_1\,\Delta y.$$

Since $\epsilon$ approaches $0$ as $\Delta z$ approaches $0$, one
has

$$\lim_{\substack{\Delta x \to 0 \\ \Delta y \to 0}} \epsilon_1 = 0, \qquad \lim_{\substack{\Delta x \to 0 \\ \Delta y \to 0}} \epsilon_2 = 0.$$

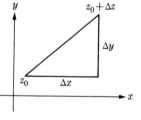

FIGURE 3–1

Thus $u$ and $v$ have differentials (see Section 2–6 of *Advanced Calculus*):

$$du = a\,dx - b\,dy, \qquad dv = b\,dx + a\,dy, \qquad (3\text{–}12)$$

and

$$\frac{\partial u}{\partial x} = a = \frac{\partial v}{\partial y}, \qquad \frac{\partial u}{\partial y} = -b = -\frac{\partial v}{\partial x}. \qquad (3\text{–}13)$$

---

* See Chapter 3 of *Complex Analysis*, New York: McGraw-Hill, 1953.

Thus (3–10) follows.  Further,

$$f'(z_0) = c = a + ib = \frac{\partial u}{\partial x} + i\frac{\partial v}{\partial x} = \frac{\partial v}{\partial y} + i\frac{\partial v}{\partial x} = \cdots$$

by (3–13).  Hence equations (3–11) are established.  Since $c = f'(z_0)$ varies continuously with $z_0$, we conclude that $a = \partial u/\partial x = \partial v/\partial y$ and $b = -(\partial u/\partial y) = \partial v/\partial x$ are continuous functions of $x$ and $y$ (Theorem 11 in Section 2–2).

**Theorem 22** (Converse of Theorem 21).  *If $w = u + iv = f(z)$ is defined in D, if u and v have continuous first partial derivatives in D and the Cauchy-Riemann equations,*

$$\frac{\partial u}{\partial x} = \frac{\partial v}{\partial y}, \qquad \frac{\partial u}{\partial y} = -\frac{\partial v}{\partial x},$$

*hold in D, then f(z) is analytic in D.*

*Proof.*  Let $z_0 = x_0 + iy_0$ be fixed as in the preceding proof.  By the continuity of their first partial derivatives, $u$ and $v$ have differentials at $(x_0, y_0)$ (see *Advanced Calculus*, pp. 83–84):

$$\Delta u = \frac{\partial u}{\partial x}\Delta x + \frac{\partial u}{\partial y}\Delta y + \epsilon_1 \Delta x + \epsilon_2 \Delta y,$$

$$\Delta v = \frac{\partial v}{\partial x}\Delta x + \frac{\partial v}{\partial y}\Delta y + \epsilon_3 \Delta x + \epsilon_4 \Delta y,$$

where $\epsilon_1, \ldots, \epsilon_4$ all approach 0 as $(x, y) \to (x_0, y_0)$.  If we write $a = \partial u/\partial x = \partial v/\partial y, b = -(\partial u/\partial y) = \partial v/\partial x$ and add these equations, we find

$$\Delta w = \Delta u + i\,\Delta v = (a + ib)(\Delta x + i\,\Delta y) + (\epsilon_1 + i\epsilon_3)\,\Delta x + (\epsilon_2 + i\epsilon_4)\,\Delta y.$$

Hence

$$\Delta w = (a + ib)(\Delta x + i\,\Delta y) + \epsilon\,\Delta z,$$

where

$$\epsilon = (\epsilon_1 + i\epsilon_3)\frac{\Delta x}{\Delta z} + (\epsilon_2 + i\epsilon_4)\frac{\Delta y}{\Delta z}.$$

If we show that $\epsilon \to 0$ as $\Delta z \to 0$, then it follows that $w$ is differentiable in $D$, hence by Theorem 16 (Section 2–4) that $w$ has a derivative:

$$\frac{dw}{dz} = a + ib = \frac{\partial u}{\partial x} + i\frac{\partial v}{\partial x} = \cdots.$$

Since $\partial u/\partial x$ and $\partial v/\partial x$ are continuous, the derivative is continuous, so that $w$ is analytic.

To show that $\epsilon \to 0$ as $\Delta z \to 0$, we remark that

$$|\epsilon| = \left|(\epsilon_1 + i\epsilon_3)\frac{\Delta x}{\Delta z} + (\epsilon_2 + i\epsilon_4)\frac{\Delta y}{\Delta z}\right| \leqq |\epsilon_1 + i\epsilon_3|\left|\frac{\Delta x}{\Delta z}\right| + |\epsilon_2 + i\epsilon_4|\left|\frac{\Delta y}{\Delta z}\right|$$

$$\leqq |\epsilon_1 + i\epsilon_3| + |\epsilon_2 + i\epsilon_4| \leqq |\epsilon_1| + |\epsilon_3| + |\epsilon_2| + |\epsilon_4|,$$

for, as Fig. 3–1 shows,

$$\left|\frac{\Delta x}{\Delta z}\right| \leqq 1, \qquad \left|\frac{\Delta y}{\Delta z}\right| \leqq 1.$$

Since $\epsilon_1$, $\epsilon_2$, $\epsilon_3$, $\epsilon_4$ all approach 0 as $(x, y) \to (x_0, y_0)$, it follows that

$$\lim_{z \to z_0} \epsilon = 0.$$

Thus the theorem is proved.

The two theorems provide a perfect test for analyticity: if $f(z)$ is analytic, then the Cauchy-Riemann equations hold; if the Cauchy-Riemann equations hold (and the derivatives concerned are continuous), then $f(z)$ is analytic.

*Remark.* The proofs of Theorems 21 and 22 show that these theorems can be restated as follows: $f(z)$ has a derivative at $z_0$ if and only if $u$ and $v$ have differentials at $z_0$ and the Cauchy-Riemann equations hold at $z_0$; if $f'(z)$ exists in $D$, then $f'(z)$ is continuous at $z_0$ if and only if $\partial u/\partial x$, $\partial u/\partial y$, $\partial v/\partial x$, $\partial v/\partial y$ are continuous at $z_0$. Another deduction of the Cauchy-Riemann equations from the existence of $f'(z_0)$ is given in Prob. 9 following Section 2–4.

EXAMPLE 1. $w = z^2 = x^2 - y^2 + i \cdot 2xy$. Here

$$u = x^2 - y^2, \qquad v = 2xy.$$

Thus

$$\frac{\partial u}{\partial x} = 2x = \frac{\partial v}{\partial y}, \qquad \frac{\partial u}{\partial y} = -2y = -\frac{\partial v}{\partial x}$$

and $w$ is analytic for all $z$.

EXAMPLE 2. $w = \dfrac{x}{x^2 + y^2} - \dfrac{iy}{x^2 + y^2}$. Here

$$\frac{\partial u}{\partial x} = \frac{y^2 - x^2}{(x^2 + y^2)^2} = \frac{\partial v}{\partial y}, \qquad \frac{\partial u}{\partial y} = \frac{-2xy}{(x^2 + y^2)^2} = -\frac{\partial v}{\partial x}.$$

Hence $w$ is analytic except for $x^2 + y^2 = 0$, i.e., for $z = 0$.

EXAMPLE 3. $w = x - iy = \bar{z}$. Here $u = x$, $v = -y$ and

$$\frac{\partial u}{\partial x} = 1, \qquad \frac{\partial v}{\partial y} = -1, \qquad \frac{\partial u}{\partial y} = 0 = \frac{\partial v}{\partial x}.$$

Thus $w$ is not analytic in any domain.

EXAMPLE 4. $w = x^2y^2 + 2x^2y^2i$. Here

$$\frac{\partial u}{\partial x} = 2xy^2, \qquad \frac{\partial v}{\partial y} = 4x^2y, \qquad \frac{\partial u}{\partial y} = 2x^2y, \qquad \frac{\partial v}{\partial x} = 4xy^2.$$

The Cauchy-Riemann equations give

$$2xy^2 = 4x^2y, \qquad 2x^2y = -4xy^2.$$

These equations are satisfied only along the lines $x = 0$, $y = 0$. There is *no domain* in which the Cauchy-Riemann equations hold, hence no domain in which $f(z)$ is analytic. One does not consider functions analytic only at certain points unless these points form a domain.

The terms "analytic at a point" or "analytic along a curve" are used, apparently in contradiction to the remark just made. However, we say that $f(z)$ is *analytic at the point $z_0$* only if there is a domain containing $z_0$ within which $f(z)$ is analytic. Similarly $f(z)$ is *analytic along a curve $C$* only if $f(z)$ is analytic in a domain containing $C$.

**Theorem 23.** *The sum, product, or quotient of analytic functions is analytic (provided, in the last case, the denominator is not equal to 0 at any point of the domain under consideration). All polynomials are analytic for all $z$. Every rational function is analytic in each domain containing no zero of the denominator. An analytic function of an analytic function is analytic.*

This follows from Theorem 12 (Section 2–2) and Eqs. (2–44) and (2–45).

**Theorem 24.** *If $w = u + iv$ is analytic in $D$, then the directional derivative of $u$ in direction $\alpha$ equals the directional derivative of $v$ in direction $\alpha + \frac{1}{2}\pi$:*

$$\nabla_\alpha u = \nabla_{\alpha+(\pi/2)}v. \tag{3–14}$$

*Proof.* The directional derivative of $u$ in direction $\alpha$ (Fig. 3–2) is given by

$$\nabla_\alpha u = \frac{\partial u}{\partial x}\cos\alpha + \frac{\partial u}{\partial y}\sin\alpha$$

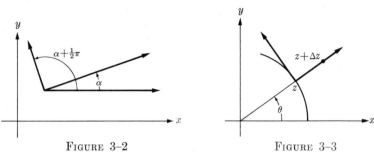

FIGURE 3–2                        FIGURE 3–3

(see *Advanced Calculus*, Section 2–10). By the Cauchy-Riemann equations, this reduces to

$$\frac{\partial v}{\partial y}\cos\alpha - \frac{\partial v}{\partial x}\sin\alpha = \frac{\partial v}{\partial x}\cos\left(\alpha + \frac{\pi}{2}\right) + \frac{\partial v}{\partial y}\sin\left(\alpha + \frac{\pi}{2}\right),$$

which is the directional derivative of $v$ in direction $\alpha + \frac{1}{2}\pi$.

It should be noted that the Cauchy-Riemann equations themselves correspond to the special cases $\alpha = 0$ and $\alpha = \pi/2$. Thus the truth of the condition (3–14) for two choices of $\alpha$ differing by $\pi/2$ implies the truth of this condition for all choices of $\alpha$. From this fact one deduces the following rule:

**Theorem 25.** *If $u$ and $v$ have continuous partial derivatives in a domain $D$ which does not include $z = 0$, then $w = f(z)$ is analytic in $D$, if and only if, when $u$ and $v$ are expressed in polar coordinates $r$, $\theta$,*

$$\frac{\partial u}{\partial r} = \frac{1}{r}\frac{\partial v}{\partial \theta}, \qquad \frac{1}{r}\frac{\partial u}{\partial \theta} = -\frac{\partial v}{\partial r} \qquad (3\text{--}15)$$

*and, when these equations hold,*

$$\frac{dw}{dz} = e^{-i\theta}\left(\frac{\partial u}{\partial r} + i\frac{\partial v}{\partial r}\right). \qquad (3\text{--}16)$$

*Proof.* Equations (3–15) express the conditions (3–14) for $\alpha = \theta$ and $\alpha = \theta + \frac{1}{2}\pi$ (Fig. 3–3); hence (3–15) implies that this condition holds for all directions, so that $w$ is analytic. Conversely, if $w$ is analytic, then (3–14) holds, so that (3–15) is obtained by choosing $\alpha = \theta$ and $\alpha = \theta + \frac{1}{2}\pi$. To prove (3–16) we let $z + \Delta z$ approach $z$ along the line $\theta = \text{const}$ through $z$, as in Fig. 3–3, so that

$$\Delta z = \Delta r e^{i\theta}, \qquad \frac{\Delta w}{\Delta z} = \frac{\Delta u + i\,\Delta v}{\Delta r e^{i\theta}}.$$

If we let $\Delta r$ approach 0, then (3–16) is obtained.

One can extend the conditions (3–15) to the point $z = 0$, for here (3–14) becomes

$$\left.\frac{\partial u}{\partial r}\right|_{\substack{r=0 \\ \theta=\alpha}} = \left.\frac{\partial v}{\partial r}\right|_{\substack{r=0 \\ \theta=\alpha+(\pi/2)}} \tag{3–17}$$

For example, if $w = z + z^2$, then

$$u = x + x^2 - y^2 = r \cos \theta + r^2(\cos^2 \theta - \sin^2 \theta),$$
$$v = y + 2xy = r \sin \theta + 2r^2 \sin \theta \cos \theta.$$

Hence

$$\frac{\partial u}{\partial r} = \cos \theta + 2r(\cos^2 \theta - \sin^2 \theta), \qquad \frac{\partial v}{\partial r} = \sin \theta + 4r \sin \theta \cos \theta,$$

and

$$\left.\frac{\partial u}{\partial r}\right|_{\substack{r=0 \\ \theta=\alpha}} = \cos \alpha = \left.\frac{\partial v}{\partial r}\right|_{\substack{r=0 \\ \theta=\alpha+(\pi/2)}} = \sin\left(\alpha + \frac{\pi}{2}\right).$$

## PROBLEMS

1. Verify that the following are analytic functions of $z$:
   (a) $w = x^2 - y^2 - 2xy + i(x^2 - y^2 + 2xy)$, all $z$
   (b) $w = \dfrac{x^3 + xy^2 + x + i(x^2 y + y^3 - y)}{x^2 + y^2}$, $\quad z \neq 0$
   (c) $w = e^z = e^x \cos y + ie^x \sin y$, all $z$
   (d) $w = \sin x \cosh y + i \cos x \sinh y$, all $z$ (this is $\sin z$)
   (e) $w = \log r + i\theta$, $r > 0$, $-\pi < \theta < \pi$ (this is one choice of $\log z$)
   (f) $w = \sqrt{z} = \sqrt{r} \cos \dfrac{\theta}{2} + i\sqrt{r} \sin \dfrac{\theta}{2}$, $\quad r > 0$, $\quad -\pi < \theta < \pi$.

2. Test for analyticity:
   (a) $w = x^2 + y^2 + 2ixy$
   (b) $w = 2x - 3y + i(3x + 2y)$
   (c) $w = \dfrac{x + iy}{x^2 + y^2} = \dfrac{\cos \theta}{r} + i\dfrac{\sin \theta}{r}$
   (d) $w = |x^2 - y^2| + 2i|xy|$.

3. Choose the real constants $a$, $b$, $c$, ... so that the following functions become analytic:
   (a) $w = x + ay + i(bx + cy)$
   (b) $w = x^2 + axy + by^2 + i(cx^2 + dxy + y^2)$
   (c) $w = \cos x \cosh y + a \cos x \sinh y + i(b \sin x \sinh y + \sin x \cosh y)$.

**ANSWERS**

2. (a) analytic nowhere,
   (b) analytic for all $z$,
   (c) analytic nowhere,
   (d) analytic in the 4 domains $(x^2 - y^2)xy > 0$.

3. (a) $c = 1$, $a = -b$;
   (b) $a = 2$, $b = -1$, $c = -1$, $d = 2$;
   (c) $a = -1$, $b = -1$.

## 3-2 □ INTEGRALS OF ANALYTIC FUNCTIONS. CAUCHY INTEGRAL THEOREM

The following theorem is fundamental for the theory of analytic functions:

**Theorem 26** (Cauchy integral theorem). *If $f(z)$ is analytic in a simply connected domain $D$, then*

$$\oint_C f(z)\, dz = 0$$

*on every simple closed path $C$ in $D$.*

*Proof.* One has, by (2–53) above (see Fig. 3–4):

$$\oint_C f(z)\, dz = \oint_C u\, dx - v\, dy + i \oint_C v\, dx + u\, dy.$$

The two real line integrals are equal to 0, provided $u$ and $v$ have continuous derivatives in $D$ and

$$\frac{\partial u}{\partial y} = -\frac{\partial v}{\partial x} \quad \text{and} \quad \frac{\partial v}{\partial y} = \frac{\partial u}{\partial x}.$$

These are just the Cauchy-Riemann equations. Hence

$$\oint_C f(z)\, dz = 0 + i \cdot 0 = 0.$$

This is stated in an equivalent form in Theorem 26a.

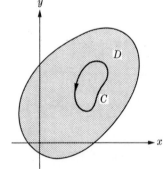

FIG. 3–4.   Cauchy integral theorem.

**Theorem 26a.**  *If $f(z)$ is analytic in the simply connected domain $D$, then*

$$\int f(z)\, dz$$

*is independent of the path in $D$.*

For the Cauchy-Riemann equations imply that the two real line integrals $\int u\, dx - v\, dy$ and $\int v\, dx + u\, dy$ are independent of path in the simply connected domain $D$. If $C$ is a path from $z_1$ to $z_2$, one can now write

$$\int_C f(z)\, dz = \int_{z_1}^{z_2} f(z)\, dz,$$

the integral being the same for all paths $C$ from $z_1$ to $z_2$.

There is a converse to the Cauchy integral theorem:

**Theorem 27.**  *Let $f(z) = u + iv$ be continuous in $D$ and let $u$ and $v$ have continuous partial derivatives in $D$. If*

$$\oint_C f(z)\, dz = 0 \qquad\qquad (3\text{–}20)$$

*on every simple closed path $C$ in $D$, then $f(z)$ is analytic in $D$.*

*Proof.*  The condition (3–20) implies that

$$\oint_C u\, dx - v\, dy = 0, \qquad \oint_C v\, dx + u\, dy = 0$$

on all simple closed paths $C$. Hence

$$u\, dx - v\, dy = dU, \qquad v\, dx + u\, dy = dV$$

for appropriate functions $U(x, y)$, $V(x, y)$ (see *Advanced Calculus*, pp. 244–245). Thus

$$\frac{\partial U}{\partial x} = u, \qquad \frac{\partial U}{\partial y} = -v, \qquad \frac{\partial V}{\partial x} = v, \qquad \frac{\partial V}{\partial y} = u$$

and

$$\frac{\partial u}{\partial x} = \frac{\partial^2 V}{\partial x\, \partial y} = \frac{\partial v}{\partial y}, \qquad \frac{\partial u}{\partial y} = \frac{\partial^2 U}{\partial x\, \partial y} = -\frac{\partial v}{\partial x}.$$

Thus the Cauchy-Riemann equations hold and $f(z)$ is analytic.

This theorem can be proved without the assumption that $u$ and $v$ have continuous derivatives in $D$; it is then known as *Morera's theorem*. For a proof, see p. 98 of *Complex Analysis* by L. V. Ahlfors.

**Theorem 28.** *If $f(z)$ is analytic in $D$, then*

$$\int_{z_1}^{z_2} f'(z)\,dz = f(z)\Big|_{z_1}^{z_2} = f(z_2) - f(z_1) \tag{3-21}$$

*on every path in $D$ from $z_1$ to $z_2$. In particular,*

$$\int_C f'(z)\,dz = 0$$

*on every closed path in $D$.*

*Proof.* By (3–11) above

$$
\begin{aligned}
\int_{z_1}^{z_2} f'(z)\,dz &= \int_{z_1}^{z_2} \left(\frac{\partial u}{\partial x} + i\frac{\partial v}{\partial x}\right)(dx + i\,dy) \\
&= \int_{z_1}^{z_2}\left(\frac{\partial u}{\partial x}\,dx + \frac{\partial u}{\partial y}\,dy\right) + i\int_{z_1}^{z_2}\left(\frac{\partial v}{\partial x}\,dx + \frac{\partial v}{\partial y}\,dy\right) \\
&= \int_{z_1}^{z_2} du + i\,dv = (u + iv)\Big|_{z_1}^{z_2} = f(z_2) - f(z_1).
\end{aligned}
$$

The second statement in the theorem is obtained by taking $z_1 = z_2$.

This rule is the basis for evaluation of simple integrals just as in elementary calculus. Thus one has

$$\int_i^{1+i} z^2\,dz = \frac{z^3}{3}\Big|_i^{1+i} = \frac{(1+i)^3 - i^3}{3} = -\frac{2}{3} + i,$$

$$\int_i^{-i} \frac{1}{z^2}\,dz = -\frac{1}{z}\Big|_i^{-i} = -i - i = -2i.$$

In the first of these any path can be used, in the second, any path not through the origin.

**Theorem 29.** *If $f(z)$ is analytic in $D$ and $D$ is simply connected, then*

$$F(z) = \int_{z_1}^{z} f(z)\,dz \quad (z_1 \text{ fixed in } D) \tag{3-22}$$

*is an indefinite integral of* $f(z)$; *i.e.,* $F'(z) = f(z)$. *Thus* $F(z)$ *is itself analytic.*

*Proof.* Since $f(z)$ is analytic in $D$ and $D$ is simply connected,

$$\int_{z_1}^{z} f(z)\, dz$$

is independent of the path and defines a function $F$ which depends only on the upper limit $z$. One has further

$$F = U + iV,$$

where

$$U = \int_{z_1}^{z} u\, dx - v\, dy, \qquad V = \int_{z_1}^{z} v\, dx + u\, dy,$$

and both integrals are independent of path. Therefore,

$$dU = u\, dx - v\, dy, \qquad dV = v\, dx + u\, dy,$$

as in the proof of Theorem 27 above. Hence $U$ and $V$ satisfy the Cauchy-Riemann equations, so that $F = U + iV$ is analytic and

$$F'(z) = \frac{\partial U}{\partial x} + i\frac{\partial V}{\partial x} = u + iv = f(z).$$

## 3–3 □ CHANGE OF VARIABLE IN COMPLEX INTEGRALS

**Theorem 30.** *Let $C_w$ be a path from $w_1$ to $w_2$ in the $w$ plane and let $f(w)$ be continuous on $C_w$. Let $w = g(z)$ be analytic in a domain $D$ of the $z$ plane and let $C_z$,*

$$z = z(t), \qquad t_1 \leqq t \leqq t_2,$$

*be a path from $z_1 = z(t_1)$ to $z_2 = z(t_2)$ in $D$. Let $g(z_1) = w_1, g(z_2) = w_2$. As $z$ traces $C_z$ once in the given direction, let $w = g(z)$ trace $C_w$ once in the given direction. Then*

$$\int_{C_w}^{w_2}{}_{w_1} f(w)\, dw = \int_{C_z}^{z_2}{}_{z_1} f[g(z)]\frac{dw}{dz}\, dz. \qquad (3\text{–}30)$$

*Proof.* The assumptions are illustrated in Fig. 3–5. The parameter $t$ can also be used as parameter for $C_w$, so that $C_w$ is given by the equation

$$w = g[z(t)], \qquad t_1 \leqq t \leqq t_2.$$

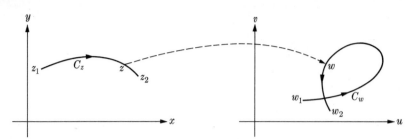

FIG. 3–5.   Change of variable in an integral.

Hence

$$\int_{C_w}^{w_2}_{w_1} f(w)\,dw = \int_{t_1}^{t_2} f\{g[z(t)]\}\,\frac{dw}{dt}\,dt.$$

However, by Theorem 16 in Section 2–4,

$$\frac{dw}{dt} = \lim_{\Delta t \to 0}\frac{\Delta w}{\Delta t} = \lim_{\Delta t \to 0}\left(\frac{dw}{dz}\frac{\Delta z}{\Delta t} + \epsilon\,\frac{\Delta z}{\Delta t}\right) = \frac{dw}{dz}\frac{dz}{dt}.$$

Hence

$$\int_{C_w} f(w)\,dw = \int_{t_1}^{t_2} f\{g[z(t)]\}\,\frac{dw}{dz}\frac{dz}{dt}\,dt = \int_{C_z} f[g(z)]\frac{dw}{dz}\,dz$$

by (2–54′).

EXAMPLE.   To evaluate the integral

$$\oint_{|w|=1}\frac{dw}{w},$$

we set $w = e^z$ and take as $C_z$ the line segment from 0 to $2\pi i$. On this line segment $w = e^{iy} = \cos y + i \sin y$; as $y$ varies from 0 to $2\pi$, $w$ traces the circle $|w| = 1$ once in the positive direction. Now $e^z$ is easily shown to be analytic [Prob. 1(c) following Section 3–1] and

$$\frac{d}{dz}e^z = \frac{\partial}{\partial x}(e^x \cos y) + i\frac{\partial}{\partial x}(e^x \sin y)$$

$$= e^x(\cos y + i \sin y) = e^z.$$

Hence by (3–30)

$$\oint_{|w|=1}\frac{dw}{w} = \int_0^{2\pi i}\frac{1}{e^z}e^z\,dz = \int_0^{2\pi i} dz = 2\pi i.$$

**PROBLEMS**

1. Evaluate the following integrals:

(a) $\oint z^2 \, dz$, where $C$ is the square with vertices $1, i, -1, -i$

(b) $\int_1^i \frac{1}{z} \, dz$ on the circular arc: $z = \cos t + i \sin t, \quad 0 \leq t \leq \frac{\pi}{2}$

(c) $\oint \frac{1}{z} \, dz$ on the ellipse: $x^2 + 2y^2 = 1$

(d) $\int_0^{2+i} (z^2 - iz + 2) \, dz$ on the line joining the points

(e) $\oint \frac{1}{z - 4} \, dz$ on the circle: $|z| = 1$

(f) $\int_{(1,\, 1)}^{(3,\, 2)} (x^2 - y^2) \, dx - 2xy \, dy$
on the straight line joining the points.

2. Evaluate with the aid of the indicated substitutions:

(a) $\oint_{|z|=2} \frac{2z \, dz}{z^2 + 1}, \; w = z^2 + 1.$

[*Hint: show that as $z$ traces the circle once in the positive direction, $w$ traces the circle $|w - 1| = 4$ twice in the positive direction*];

(b) $\oint_{|z|=2} \frac{z^3 \, dz}{z^4 - 1}, \; w = z^4 - 1.$

3. Evaluate these derivatives. The integrals are independent of path.

(a) $\dfrac{d}{dz_1} \int_1^{z_1} z^2 \, dz$     (b) $\dfrac{d}{dz_1} \int_0^{z_1} (z^3 - z + 1) \, dz$

(c) $\dfrac{d}{dz_1} \int_0^{z_1^2} z^3 \, dz$     (d) $\dfrac{d}{dz_1} \int_{z_1}^{z_1^2} (z^2 + 1) \, dz.$

4. Assuming Leibnitz's rule (Section 4–12 of *Advanced Calculus*) to be capable of generalization to the functions considered, evaluate the following derivatives:

(a) $\dfrac{d}{dz_1} \oint_{|z|=1} \dfrac{z^2 + 1}{z - z_1} \, dz \quad (|z_1| \neq 1)$

(b) $\dfrac{d}{dz_1} \oint_{|z|=1} \dfrac{e^z}{(z - z_1)^2} \, dz \quad (|z_1| \neq 1).$

5. Prove: If $f'(z) \equiv 0$ in domain $D$, then $f(z) \equiv$ const in $D$. Hence all indefinite integrals of $f(z)$ are given by $F(z) + C$, if $F(z)$ is one indefinite integral.

## ANSWERS

1. (a) 0,     (b) $\frac{1}{2}\pi i$,     (c) $2\pi i$,     (d) $\frac{1}{6}(40 + 25i)$,     (e) 0,     (f) $-\frac{7}{3}$.

2. (a) $4\pi i$,     (b) $2\pi i$.

3. (a) $z_1^2$,     (b) $z_1^3 - z_1 + 1$,     (c) $2z_1^7$,     (d) $2z_1^5 - z_1^2 + 2z_1 - 1$.

4. (a) $\displaystyle\oint_{|z|=1} \frac{z^2 + 1}{(z - z_1)^2}\, dz,$        (b) $\displaystyle\oint_{|z|=1} \frac{2e^z}{(z - z_1)^3}\, dz.$

## 3-4 □ ELEMENTARY ANALYTIC FUNCTIONS

It has been pointed out that the polynomials

$$w = a_0 + a_1 z + \cdots + a_n z^n$$

are analytic for all $z$, as are the rational functions

$$w = \frac{a_0 + a_1 z + \cdots + a_n z^n}{b_0 + b_1 z + \cdots + b_m z^m}$$

in any domain not containing a zero of the denominator. The function

$$w = e^z = e^x \cos y + i e^x \sin y$$

is also analytic for all $z$, since

$$\frac{\partial u}{\partial x} = e^x \cos y = \frac{\partial v}{\partial y}, \qquad \frac{\partial u}{\partial y} = -e^x \sin y = -\frac{\partial v}{\partial x}.$$

We now enlarge the list of elementary analytic functions by the following definitions:

$$\sin z = \frac{e^{iz} - e^{-iz}}{2i}; \qquad\qquad (3\text{-}40)$$

$$\cos z = \frac{e^{iz} + e^{-iz}}{2}; \qquad\qquad (3\text{-}41)$$

$$\sinh z = \frac{e^z - e^{-z}}{2}; \qquad\qquad (3\text{-}42)$$

$$\cosh z = \frac{e^z + e^{-z}}{2}. \qquad\qquad (3\text{-}43)$$

The other trigonometric and hyperbolic functions can be defined in terms of these by the familiar formulas.

Since $e^{iz}$, $e^{-iz}$, $e^{-z}$ are all analytic for all $z$ (analytic function of an analytic function), we conclude that $\sin z$, $\cos z$, $\sinh z$, $\cosh z$ are analytic for all $z$.

If $y = 0$, $e^z$ reduces to the usual function $e^x$ of the real variable $x$. When $x = 0$, one has

$$e^{iy} = \cos y + i \sin y.$$

If $y$ is replaced by $-y$, one finds

$$e^{-iy} = \cos y - i \sin y.$$

If these equations are added, one finds

$$e^{iy} + e^{-iy} = 2 \cos y, \tag{3-44}$$

and if they are subtracted, one finds

$$e^{iy} - e^{-iy} = 2i \sin y. \tag{3-45}$$

The equations (3–44) and (3–45) suggest the definitions (3–40) and (3–41) and show that they reduce to the familiar functions when $z$ is real. Equations (3–42) and (3–43) are precisely the usual definitions.

Two basic theorems of more advanced theory are useful at this point. For proofs the reader is referred to *A Course in Mathematical Analysis* by E. Goursat.* See also Section 8–1 and Prob. 1 following Section 8–2.

**Theorem A.** *Given a function $f(x)$ of the real variable $x$, $a \leqq x \leqq b$, there is at most one analytic function $F(z)$ which reduces to $f(x)$ when $z$ is real.*

**Theorem B.** *If $f(z)$, $g(z)$, ... are functions which are all analytic in a domain $D$ which includes part of the real axis, and $f(z)$, $g(z)$, ... satisfy an algebraic identity when $z$ is real, then these functions satisfy the same identity for all $z$ in $D$.*

Theorem A implies that the above definitions of $e^z$, $\sin z$, ... are the only ones which yield analytic functions and agree with the definitions for real variables.

Because of Theorem B, one can be sure that all familiar identities of trigonometry:

$$\sin^2 z + \cos^2 z = 1, \qquad \sin \left(\tfrac{1}{2}\pi - z\right) = \cos z, \ldots$$

---

* See Vol. 2, Part 1, Chapter 4 (translated by E. R. Hedrick and O. Dunkel), New York: Ginn and Co., 1916.

continue to hold for complex $z$. A general algebraic identity in $f(z)$, $g(z)$, $\ldots$ is obtained by equating to zero a sum of terms of the form $c[f(z)]^m[g(z)]^n \cdots$, where $c$ is a constant and each exponent is a positive integer or 0. Thus, in the two examples given, one has

$$[f(z)]^2 + [g(z)]^2 - 1 \equiv 0 \qquad [f(z) = \sin z,\ g(z) = \cos z],$$
$$f(z) - g(z) \equiv 0 \qquad [f(z) = \sin(\tfrac{1}{2}\pi - z),\ g(z) = \cos z].$$

To prove identities such as the following:

$$e^{z_1} \cdot e^{z_2} = e^{z_1 + z_2},$$

it may be necessary to apply Theorem B several times [see Probs. 2 and 3 below].

It should be remarked that, while $e^z$ is written as a power of $e$, it is best not to think of it as such. Thus $e^{1/2}$ has only one value, not two as would a usual complex root. To avoid confusion with the general power function, to be defined below, one often writes $e^z = \exp z$ and refers to $e^z$ as the *exponential function of z*.

The following new identities follow from (3–40) through (3–43):

$$\sinh iz = i \sin z, \qquad \cosh iz = \cos z,$$
$$e^{iz} = \cos z + i \sin z. \tag{3–46}$$

The first two of these show how closely the trigonometric and hyperbolic functions are related and explain the parallel between trigonometric and hyperbolic identities. Thus

$$\cos^2 z + \sin^2 z = 1$$

becomes

$$\cosh^2 (iz) - \sinh^2 (iz) = 1$$

or, on replacing $iz$ by $z$,

$$\cosh^2 z - \sinh^2 z = 1.$$

To obtain the real and imaginary parts of $\sin z$ we use the identity

$$\sin (z_1 + z_2) = \sin z_1 \cos z_2 + \cos z_1 \sin z_2,$$

which holds, by the reasoning described above, for all complex $z_1$ and $z_2$. Hence

$$\sin (x + iy) = \sin x \cos iy + \cos x \sin iy.$$

From (3–46), with $z$ replaced by $iy$, one has

$$\sinh y = -i \sin iy, \qquad \cosh y = \cos iy.$$

Hence
$$\sin z = \sin x \cosh y + i \cos x \sinh y. \tag{3–47}$$

Similarly one proves: $\cos z = \cos x \cosh y - i \sin x \sinh y$. From (3–46) one has
$$\sinh z = i \sin (-iz) = i \sin (y - ix).$$
Thus one finds
$$\sinh z = \sinh x \cos y + i \cosh x \sin y, \tag{3–48}$$
and similarly
$$\cosh z = \cosh x \cos y + i \sinh x \sin y.$$

From the definition of $e^z$ one finds that
$$e^{z+2\pi i} = e^z. \tag{3–49}$$

Thus the complex function $e^z$ has a period of $2\pi i$. Similarly, the function $e^{nz}$ has period $2\pi i/n$. This suggests using the complex exponential function as a basis for Fourier series. This is carried out in Section 7–17 of *Advanced Calculus*, where it is shown that every Fourier series can be written in terms of the functions $e^{inx}$ and $e^{-inx}$.

Other properties of the functions are listed in the problems which follow.

## PROBLEMS

1. Prove the following properties directly from the definitions of the functions:

   (a) $e^{z_1+z_2} = e^{z_1} \cdot e^{z_2}$  (b) $(e^z)^n = e^{nz}$  $(n = 1, 2, \ldots)$
   (c) $\sin (z_1 + z_2) = \sin z_1 \cos z_2 + \cos z_1 \sin z_2$

   (d) $\dfrac{d}{dz} e^z = e^z$

   (e) $\dfrac{d}{dz} \sin z = \cos z$,  $\dfrac{d}{dz} \cos z = -\sin z$
   (f) $\sin (z + \pi) = -\sin z$
   (g) $\sin (-z) = -\sin z$,  $\cos (-z) = \cos z$.

2. Prove the identity
$$e^{z_1+z_2} = e^{z_1} \cdot e^{z_2}$$

by application of Theorem B.

[*Hint: let $z_2 = x_2$, a fixed real number, $z_1 = z$, a variable complex number. Then $e^{z+x_2} = e^z \cdot e^{x_2}$ is an identity connecting analytic functions which is known to be true for $z$ real. Hence the identity is true for all complex $z$. Now proceed similarly with the identity: $e^{z_1+z} = e^{z_1} \cdot e^z$.*]

3. Prove the following identities by application of Theorem B (cf. Prob. 2):

(a) $\sin (z_1 + z_2) = \sin z_1 \cos z_2 + \cos z_1 \sin z_2$

(b) $\cos (z_1 + z_2) = \cos z_1 \cos z_2 - \sin z_1 \sin z_2$

(c) $e^{iz} = \cos z + i \sin z$          (d) $e^z = \cosh z + \sinh z$

(e) $(e^z)^n = e^{nz} \ (n = 1, 2, \ldots)$.

4. Evaluate the following complex numbers:

(a) $e^{1+\pi i}$      (b) $e^{2+7\pi i}$      (c) $e^{(1/2)\pi i}$      (d) $e^{(3/2)\pi i}$

(e) $e^{-(1/4)\pi i}$      (f) $\sin (1 + i)$      (g) $\cos (-i)$      (h) $\sinh (1 - i)$.

5. (a) Prove that $e^z$ has no complex zeros

(b) Show that $\sin z$ has only real zeros

(c) Show that $\cos z$ has only real zeros

(d) Find all zeros of $\sinh z$      (e) Find all zeros of $\cosh z$.

6. Determine where the following functions are analytic (cf. Prob. 5):

(a) $\tan z = \dfrac{\sin z}{\cos z}$            (b) $\cot z = \dfrac{\cos z}{\sin z}$

(c) $\sec z = \dfrac{1}{\cos z}$             (d) $\csc z = \dfrac{1}{\sin z}$

(e) $\tanh z = \dfrac{\sinh z}{\cosh z}$         (f) $\dfrac{\sin z}{z}$

(g) $\dfrac{e^z}{z \cos z}$                (h) $\dfrac{e^z}{\sin z + \cos z}$ .

## ANSWERS

4. (a) $-e$,      (b) $-e^2$,      (c) $i$,          (d) $-i$,      (e) $\frac{1}{2}\sqrt{2}\,(1 - i)$,

(f) $\dfrac{1}{2}\left[\left(e + \dfrac{1}{e}\right) \sin 1 + i\left(e - \dfrac{1}{e}\right) \cos 1\right]$,          (g) $\dfrac{1}{2}\left(e + \dfrac{1}{e}\right)$,

(h) $\dfrac{1}{2}\left[\left(e - \dfrac{1}{e}\right) \cos 1 - i\left(e + \dfrac{1}{e}\right) \sin 1\right]$.

5. (d) $n\pi i \ (n = 0, \pm 1, \pm 2, \ldots)$,      (e) $\frac{1}{2}\pi i + n\pi i \ (n = 0, \pm 1, \ldots)$.

6. The functions are analytic except at the following points:

(a) $\frac{1}{2}\pi + n\pi$,      (b) $n\pi$,          (c) $\frac{1}{2}\pi + n\pi$,      (d) $n\pi$,

(e) $\frac{1}{2}\pi i + n\pi i$,      (f) $0$,             (g) $0$, $\frac{1}{2}\pi + n\pi$,

(h) $-\frac{1}{4}\pi + n\pi$, where $n = 0, \pm 1, \pm 2, \ldots$

# 4 □ *The Logarithm and Related Functions*

## 4-1 □ INVERSE FUNCTIONS

If $w = f(z)$ is defined in a domain $D$ of the $z$ plane, then there is an associated "inverse function" $z = g(w)$ assigning to each $w$ the value (or values) of $z$ for which $f(z) = w$. However, unless $f(z)$ takes each value $w$ at most once in $D$, the "function" $g(w)$ is necessarily many-valued. For example, the inverse of $w = z^2$ is $z = \sqrt{w}$; for each $w$ other than 0 there are two square roots, so that $w$ is in general two-valued.

While we shall be concerned with formulas giving all values of the inverse function, it is not possible to use these as functions in the ordinary sense. Thus continuity, derivatives, etc. lose all their meaning if the value of the function for each $w$ is ambiguously defined. Hence it is necessary to select one of the many inverse values for each $w$. Such a selection leads to a "branch" of the inverse function. For example, one branch of $\sqrt{w}$ is defined as follows:

$$z = \sqrt{\rho}e^{i(\phi/2)}, \qquad 0 < \phi < 2\pi, \qquad \rho > 0,$$

where $\rho$, $\phi$ are polar coordinates in the $w$ plane:

$$w = \rho e^{i\phi}.$$

Thus a branch is a *single-valued* function, whose continuity and analyticity can be investigated. In general, it will be possible to represent the complete inverse function by several branches (perhaps infinitely many), each of which is continuous and, except for special points (the "branch points"), analytic in a domain. In this way the multiple-valued inverse function is replaced by *many single-valued functions.*

The expression "$f(z)$ is analytic in domain $D$" will be used *only when $f(z)$ is single-valued*. A more general interpretation of the term "analytic function" is given in Section 8–1.

This question has its counterpart for real variables. Thus $y = $ arc sin $x$ has infinitely many values for each $x$, as shown in Fig. 4–1. Individual branches $y_1(x)$, $y_2(x)$, ... are specified in a natural way as follows:

$$y_1 = \text{arc sin } x, \qquad -\tfrac{1}{2}\pi \leqq y \leqq \tfrac{1}{2}\pi,$$
$$y_2 = \text{arc sin } x, \qquad \tfrac{1}{2}\pi \leqq y \leqq \tfrac{3}{2}\pi,$$
$$y_3 = \text{arc sin } x, \qquad -\tfrac{3}{2}\pi \leqq y \leqq -\tfrac{1}{2}\pi,$$
$$\vdots$$

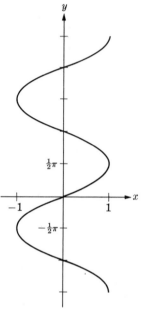

These are shown in Fig. 4–1. It is clear that infinitely many of these completely represent the inverse function. Each branch is continuous. Moreover, each branch has a continuous derivative except at the end points $x = \pm 1$. These points serve as branch points, at which the different branches join.

Another example from the theory of real variables, which is even more instructive for complex variables, is the function $\theta = \arg z$ as a function of $x$ and $y$. This is represented in Fig. 4–2. The surface is generated by a line moving parallel to the $xy$ plane; the line passes through the $\theta$ axis and through a helix about the $\theta$ axis. For each $(x, y)$ other than

FIG. 4–1. $y = $ arc sin $x$.

$(0, 0)$, infinitely many values of $\theta$ are obtained, each two values differing by a multiple of $2\pi$. The function can be built up of the following branches:

$$\theta_1 = \theta, \qquad -\pi < \theta < \pi; \qquad \theta_2 = \theta, \qquad 0 < \theta < 2\pi;$$
$$\theta_3 = \theta, \qquad -2\pi < \theta < 0; \; ...$$

The interval in each case specifies both the value of the function and the part of the $xy$ plane in which it is defined. Thus $\theta_1(x, y)$ is defined except for $y = 0$, $x \leqq 0$; $\theta_2(x, y)$ is defined except for $y = 0$, $x \geqq 0$. The branches are chosen here to overlap either for $y > 0$ or for $y < 0$; they could have been chosen to overlap only along single lines. Each branch is continuous and has continuous derivatives.

In this example, there is no branch point like that of the preceding example. However, the origin $(0, 0)$ is a common boundary point for all branches and would be termed a "logarithmic branch point."

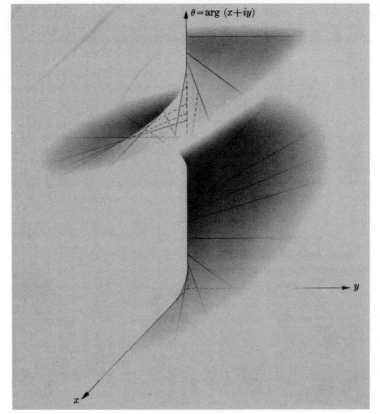

FIG. 4–2. $\theta = \arg(x + iy)$.

## 4-2 □ THE FUNCTION LOG $z$

The function $z = e^w$ is an analytic function of $w$. Its inverse is the logarithmic function of $z$; that is,

$$w = \log z, \quad \text{if} \quad z = e^w. \tag{4–20}$$

Hence

$$re^{i\theta} = e^{u+iv} = e^u e^{iv},$$

from which we conclude that

$$r = e^u, \quad v = \theta + 2n\pi \quad (n = 0, \pm 1, \pm 2, \ldots). \tag{4–21}$$

Accordingly,

$$w = u + iv = \log z = \log r + i(\theta + 2n\pi) \tag{4–22}$$

or, more simply,

$$w = \log|z| + i \arg z, \tag{4–23}$$

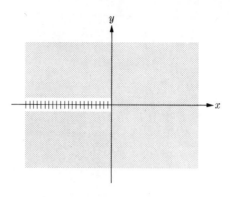

FIGURE 4–3

where log $|z|$ is the real logarithm of $|z|$ and arg $z$ is, as usual, defined only up to multiples of $2\pi$.

The complex logarithm is accordingly defined for each $z$ other than 0 and has infinitely many values for each $z$. We first select one branch of this function: the *principal value* of log $z$, by the following definition:

$$\text{Log } z = \log r + i\theta, \qquad -\pi < \theta < \pi, \qquad r > 0. \qquad (4\text{–}24)$$

This function is defined and continuous in the domain shown in Fig. 4–3. It is moreover an analytic function in the given domain, for $u = \log r$, $v = \theta$ and

$$\frac{\partial u}{\partial r} = \frac{1}{r} = \frac{1}{r}\frac{\partial v}{\partial \theta}, \qquad \frac{1}{r}\frac{\partial u}{\partial \theta} = 0 = -\frac{\partial v}{\partial r}.$$

Thus the Cauchy-Riemann equations in polar coordinates are satisfied and, by Theorem 25 above, the function is analytic. Furthermore, by (3–16),

$$\frac{dw}{dz} = e^{-i\theta}\left(\frac{\partial u}{\partial r} + i\frac{\partial v}{\partial r}\right) = \frac{1}{re^{i\theta}} = \frac{1}{z}. \qquad (4\text{–}25)$$

All values of log $z$ can be obtained from branches as follows:

$$
\begin{aligned}
f_1(z) &= \text{Log } z = \log r + i\theta, & -\pi < \theta < \pi, \ r > 0;\\
f_2(z) &= \log z = \log r + i\theta, & 0 < \theta < 2\pi, \ r > 0;\\
f_3(z) &= \log z = \log r + i\theta, & -2\pi < \theta < 0, \ r > 0;\\
f_4(z) &= \log z = \log r + i\theta, & \pi < \theta < 3\pi, \ r > 0;\\
&\vdots
\end{aligned}
$$

Each of these functions is analytic in the domain chosen and satisfies the equation:

$$\frac{d \log z}{dz} = \frac{1}{z}.$$

It should also be noted that

$$f_3(z) = f_2(z) - 2\pi i, \qquad f_4(z) = \text{Log } z + 2\pi i, \ldots$$

These branches are chosen to have overlapping domains and to give together all values of the inverse function. Their significance can be better understood by reference to the function arg $z$, which is the source of all the complications. This function was plotted in Section 4–1 and decomposed into branches in precisely the same manner as that used here for log $z$.

The choice of branches given here is arbitrary and they can be replaced by others in a great variety of ways. However, it should be noted that a branch of log $z$ will be analytic in a domain only if that domain contains no closed path $C$ enclosing the origin; for $\theta$ cannot be chosen to remain continuous on such a path. In general, if $D$ is any simply connected domain not containing the origin, an analytic branch of log $z$ can be defined in $D$, and all other branches of log $z$ in $D$ are obtained from this one branch by adding or subtracting a multiple of $2\pi i$.

One can obtain all values of log $z$ by the formula

$$\log z = \int_1^z \frac{dz}{z}, \tag{4–26}$$

where the path of integration is any path not through the origin. The integral on the right is independent of the path in any simply connected domain not containing the origin. In general, this integral gives

$$\int_1^z \frac{dz}{z} = \log z \Big|_1^z = \log |z| - \log 1 + i(\text{arg } z - \text{arg } 1)$$
$$= \log |z| + i\theta,$$

where $\theta$ is chosen as the total change in arg $z$ as this argument varies continuously on the path from 1 to $z$. Thus one choice of log 1 is given by

$$\oint_{|z|=1} \frac{dz}{z} = 2\pi i,$$

since arg $z$ increases by $2\pi$ on the path. The imaginary part of the integral $\int dz/z$ is given by

$$\text{Im} \int \frac{dx + i\, dy}{x + iy} = \int \frac{-y\, dx + x\, dy}{x^2 + y^2}.$$

This real line integral is discussed in Section 5–6 of *Advanced Calculus* and similar results are obtained.

**4–3 □ THE FUNCTIONS** $a^z$**,** $z^a$**,** $\sin^{-1} z$**,** $\cos^{-1} z$

The general exponential function $a^z$ is now defined, for $a \neq 0$, by the equation

$$a^z = e^{z \log a} = \exp (z \log a). \qquad (4\text{--}30)$$

Thus, for $z = 0$, $a^0 = 1$. Otherwise,

$$\log a = \log |a| + i \arg a$$

and one obtains many values:

$$a^z = \exp \{z[\log |a| + i(\theta + 2k\pi)]\} \quad (k = 0, \pm 1, \pm 2, \ldots),$$

where $\theta$ denotes one choice of $\arg a$. For example,

$$(1 + i)^i = \exp \left[ i \left\{ \log \sqrt{2} + i \left( \frac{\pi}{4} + 2k\pi \right) \right\} \right]$$

$$= \exp \left( -\frac{\pi}{4} - 2k\pi \right) (\cos \log \sqrt{2} + i \sin \log \sqrt{2}).$$

If $z$ is a positive integer $n$, $a^z$ reduces to $a^n$ and has only one value; the same holds for $z = -n$ and one has

$$a^{-n} = \frac{1}{a^n}. \qquad (4\text{--}31)$$

If $z$ is a fraction $p/q$ (in lowest terms), one finds that $a^z$ has $q$ distinct values, which are the $q$th roots of $a^p$.

If a fixed choice of $\log a$ is made in (4–30), then $a^z$ is simply $e^{cz}$, $c = \log a$, and is hence an analytic function of $z$ for all $z$. Each choice of $\log a$ determines such a function. If the principal value $\text{Log } a$ is used, one obtains the analytic function $\exp (z \text{ Log } a)$, called the *principal value of* $a^z$.

If $a$ and $z$ are interchanged in (4–30), one obtains the general power function:

$$z^a = e^{a \log z}. \qquad (4\text{--}32)$$

If an analytic branch of $\log z$ is chosen as above, then this function becomes an analytic function of an analytic function, and is hence analytic in the domain chosen. In particular, the *principal value* of $z^a$ is defined as the analytic function

$$z^a = e^{a \text{ Log } z},$$

in terms of the principal value of $\log z$.

For example, if $a = \frac{1}{2}$, one has

$$z^{1/2} = e^{(1/2)\log z} = e^{(1/2)(\log r + i\theta)} = e^{(1/2)\log r}e^{(1/2)i\theta} = \sqrt{r}\left(\cos\frac{\theta}{2} + i\sin\frac{\theta}{2}\right)$$

as in Section 1–2. If Log $z$ is used, then $\sqrt{z} = f_1(z)$ becomes analytic in the domain of Fig. 4–3. A second analytic branch $f_2(z)$ in the same domain is obtained by requiring that $\pi < \theta < 3\pi$. These are the only two analytic branches which can be obtained in this domain. It should be remarked that these two branches are related by the equation

$$f_2(z) = -f_1(z).$$

For $f_2$ is obtained from $f_1$ by increasing $\theta$ by $2\pi$, which replaces $e^{(1/2)i\theta}$ by

$$e^{(1/2)i(\theta+2\pi)} = e^{\pi i}e^{(1/2)i\theta} = -e^{(1/2)i\theta}.$$

Other branches of $\sqrt{z}$ can be obtained as follows:

$$f_3(z) = \sqrt{r}\,e^{(1/2)i\theta}, \qquad 0 < \theta < 2\pi,$$
$$f_4(z) = \sqrt{r}\,e^{(1/2)i\theta}, \qquad -2\pi < \theta < 0.$$

These assign two values to each $z$ other than the points of the *positive* real axis. We note that

$$f_4(z) = -f_3(z)$$

and that

$$f_3(z) = \pm f_1(z), \qquad f_4(z) = \mp f_1(z)$$

except on the $x$ axis.

The four branches described give together (with the duplications indicated) all values of the inverse of $z = w^2$ except the value $\sqrt{0} = 0$. The origin is a boundary point for the domains of all four branches and it is impossible to enlarge the domains to include this point while retaining analyticity. However, if one makes the definition

$$f_1(0) = f_2(0) = f_3(0) = f_4(0) = 0,$$

then all four branches remain *continuous* at the origin; that is,

$$\lim_{z\to 0} f(z) = 0$$

for $f = f_1, f_2, f_3$ or $f_4$, as $z$ approaches the origin from within the domain in which the function is defined. For each function is in absolute value equal to $\sqrt{r}$, which approaches 0 as $z$ approaches 0. The origin is a point at which all branches agree and it is a *branch point* of the inverse function.

The functions $\sin^{-1} z$ and $\cos^{-1} z$ are defined as the inverses of $\sin z$ and $\cos z$. One then finds

$$\sin^{-1} z = \frac{1}{i} \log [iz \pm \sqrt{1 - z^2}],$$

$$\cos^{-1} z = \frac{1}{i} \log [z \pm i\sqrt{1 - z^2}].$$

(4-33)

The proofs of these are left to the exercises. It can be shown that analytic branches of both these functions can be defined in each simply connected domain not containing the points $\pm 1$, which serve as branch points. For each $z$ other than $\pm 1$, one has two choices of $\sqrt{1 - z^2}$ and then an infinite sequence of choices of the logarithm, differing by multiples of $2\pi i$. This will be studied in Section 7–2 below.

**PROBLEMS**

1. Obtain all values:
   (a) $\log 2$      (b) $\log i$      (c) $\log (1 - i)$    (d) $i^i$
   (e) $(1 + i)^{2/3}$    (f) $i^{\sqrt{2}}$      (g) $\sin^{-1} 1$      (h) $\cos^{-1} 2$.

2. Prove the formulas (4–33).

3. (a) Evaluate $\sin^{-1} 0$, $\cos^{-1} 0$.
   (b) Find all zeros of $\sin z$ and $\cos z$ [cf. part (a)].

4. Prove the following identities in the sense that, for proper selection of values of the multiple-valued functions concerned, the equation is correct for each allowed choice of the variables:
   (a) $\log (z_1 \cdot z_2) = \log z_1 + \log z_2$    $(z_1 \neq 0, \quad z_2 \neq 0)$
   (b) $e^{\log z} = z$    $(z \neq 0)$        (c) $\log e^z = z$
   (d) $\log z_1^{z_2} = z_2 \log z_1$    $(z_1 \neq 0)$.

5. Determine all analytic branches of the multiple-valued functions in the domains given:
   (a) $\log z$,    $x < 0$           (b) $\sqrt[3]{z}$,    $x > 0$.

6. Prove that, for the analytic function $z^a$ (principal value),

$$\frac{d}{dz} z^a = \frac{a}{z} z^a = az^{a-1}.$$

7. Plot the functions $u = \text{Re}(\sqrt{z})$ and $v = \text{Im}(\sqrt{z})$ as functions of $x$ and $y$ and show the four branches described in the text.

**ANSWERS**

1. (a) $0.693 + 2n\pi i,$      (b) $i(\frac{1}{2}\pi + 2n\pi),$

   (c) $0.347 + i(\frac{7}{4}\pi + 2n\pi),$      (d) $\exp(-\frac{1}{2}\pi - 2n\pi),$

   (e) $\sqrt[3]{2} \exp\left(\frac{1}{6}\pi i + \frac{4n\pi}{3}i\right),$      (f) $\exp\left(\frac{\sqrt{2}}{2}\pi i + 2\sqrt{2}\,n\pi i\right),$

   (g) $\frac{1}{2}\pi + 2n\pi,$      (h) $2n\pi \pm 1.317i.$

The range of $n$ is $0, \pm 1, \pm 2, \ldots$ except in (e), where it is $0, 1, 2.$

3. (a) and (b) $n\pi$ and $\frac{1}{2}\pi + n\pi,$    $(n = 0, \pm 1, \pm 2, \ldots).$

5. (a) $\log r + i\theta,$      $\frac{1}{2}\pi + 2n\pi < \theta < \frac{3}{2}\pi + 2n\pi,$    $(n = 0, \pm 1, \pm 2, \ldots),$

   (b) $\sqrt[3]{r} \exp\left(\frac{i\theta}{3}\right),$    $-\frac{\pi}{2} + 2n\pi < \theta < \frac{\pi}{2} + 2n\pi,$    $(n = 0, 1, 2).$

# 5 □ Power Series

## 5-1 □ POWER SERIES AS ANALYTIC FUNCTIONS

We now proceed to enlarge the class of specific analytic functions still further by showing that every power series

$$\sum_{n=0}^{\infty} c_n(z - z_0)^n = c_0 + c_1(z - z_0) + \cdots + c_n(z - z_0)^n + \cdots$$

converging for some values of $z$ other than $z = z_0$ represents an analytic function.

Real power series are normally studied in the calculus and it is shown that each series has an *interval* of convergence. For complex power series the interval is replaced by a *circular domain* of convergence as in Fig. 5–1.

**Theorem 31.** *Every power series*

$$\sum_{n=0}^{\infty} c_n(z - z_0)^n \tag{5-10}$$

*has a radius of convergence $r^*$ such that the series converges absolutely when $|z - z_0| < r^*$, and diverges when $|z - z_0| > r^*$.*

*The number $r^*$ can be 0 (in which case the series converges only for $z = z_0$), a positive number, or $\infty$ (in which case the series converges for all z).*

*If $r^*$ is not 0 and $r_1$ is such that $0 < r_1 < r^*$, then the series converges uniformly for $|z - z_0| \leqq r_1$.*

*The number $r^*$ can be evaluated as follows:*

$$r^* = \lim_{n \to \infty} \left| \frac{c_n}{c_{n+1}} \right|, \quad \text{if the limit exists,}$$

$$r^* = \lim_{n \to \infty} \frac{1}{\sqrt[n]{|c_n|}}, \quad \text{if the limit exists,}$$

(5–11)

*and in any case by the formula*

$$r^* = \frac{1}{\overline{\lim_{n \to \infty}} \sqrt[n]{|c_n|}}.$$

(5–12)

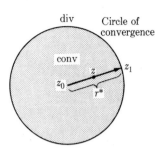

Fig. 5–1. Circle of convergence of a power series.

*Proof.* The series $\sum |c_n| r^n$ is a real power series and, hence, either diverges except for $r = 0$ or else has an interval of convergence which we can represent as $-r^* < r < r^*$, where $0 < r^* \le \infty$. When the series converges only at $r = 0$, we set $r^* = 0$. (See *Advanced Calculus*, pp. 350–351.)

We now assert that the complex series (5–10) converges absolutely for $|z - z_0| < r^*$. Indeed,

$$|c_n(z - z_0)^n| = |c_n|\,|z - z_0|^n,$$

so that the series of absolute values is simply the series $\sum |c_n| r^n$, with $r = |z - z_0|$. Therefore the series (5–10) converges absolutely for $|z - z_0| < r^*$. (When $r^* = 0$, we can only say: the series converges absolutely for $z = z_0$.) If $|z - z_0| \le r_1$, where $0 < r_1 < r^*$, then $|c_n(z - z_0)^n| \le |c_n| r_1^n$, so that by the $M$-test (Theorem 14, Section 2–3) the series converges uniformly in such a region.

Next we show that, if $r^* < \infty$, the series (5–10) cannot converge for $|z - z_0| > r^*$. Let us suppose the series does converge for one such value of $z$, say $z'$. Then, by Theorem 6 (Section 1–4),

$$\lim_{n \to \infty} c_n(z' - z_0)^n = 0,$$

(5–13)

for $c_n(z' - z_0)^n$ is the $n$-th term of the series (5–10) when $z = z'$. From (5–13) we conclude that

$$|c_n(z' - z_0)^n| < K, \quad n = 0, 1, 2, \ldots$$

for some constant $K$. Now, by assumption, $|z' - z_0| > r^*$. Hence, we can choose a real number $r$ such that $r^* < r < |z' - z_0|$. Now

$$|c_n r^n| = |c_n(z' - z_0)^n| \cdot \left| \frac{r}{z' - z_0} \right|^n < K \left| \frac{r}{z' - z_0} \right|^n = K s^n,$$

where $s = r/|z' - z_0|$, so that $0 < s < 1$. Therefore the series $\sum K s^n$ is a convergent geometric series and, by comparison with this series, the series $\sum |c_n| r^n$ converges. Since $r > r^*$, this is a contradiction. Accordingly, the series (5–10) must diverge for every $z'$ outside the circle $|z - z_0| = r^*$.

The expressions (5–11) for $r^*$ are obtained from the ratio and root tests applied to the real power series $\sum |c_n| r^n$; the expression given in (5–12) is also established in the theory of the real power series. (See *Advanced Calculus*, pp. 350–351.)

As for real variables, no general statement can be made about convergence on the boundary of the domain of convergence. This boundary is (when $r^* \neq 0$, $r^* \neq \infty$) a circle $|z - z_0| = r^*$, termed the *circle of convergence*. The series may converge at some points, all points, or no points of this circle.

EXAMPLE 1. $\sum_{n=1}^{\infty} z^n/n^2$. Formula (5–11) gives

$$r^* = \lim_{n \to \infty} \frac{(n+1)^2}{n^2} = 1.$$

The series converges absolutely on the circle of convergence, for, when $|z| = 1$, the series of absolute values is the convergent series $\sum (1/n^2)$.

EXAMPLE 2. $\sum_{n=0}^{\infty} z^n$. This complex geometric series converges for $|z| < 1$, as (5–11) shows. One has further

$$\sum_{n=0}^{\infty} z^n = \frac{1}{1-z} \quad (|z| < 1),$$

as shown in Section 2–3. On the circle of convergence, the series diverges everywhere, since the $n$th term fails to converge to 0.

EXAMPLE 3. $\sum_{n=1}^{\infty} z^n/n$. Again formula (5–11) gives the radius: $r^* = 1$. On the circle $|z| = 1$, the series is not absolutely convergent; for the series of absolute values is the divergent series $\sum (1/n)$. However, on this circle $z = \cos \theta + i \sin \theta$ and

$$\sum_{n=1}^{\infty} \frac{z^n}{n} = \sum_{n=1}^{\infty} \frac{(\cos \theta + i \sin \theta)^n}{n}$$

$$= \sum_{n=1}^{\infty} \frac{\cos n\theta}{n} + i \sum_{n=1}^{\infty} \frac{\sin n\theta}{n}.$$

The two real series are Fourier series. The imaginary part is the Fourier series of a "sawtooth wave" and, by the theory of Fourier series (*Advanced*

*Calculus*, pp. 410–412), it converges everywhere:

$$\sum_{n=1}^{\infty} \frac{\sin n\theta}{n} = \begin{cases} -\dfrac{\pi}{2} - \dfrac{\theta}{2}, & -\pi \leq \theta < 0, \\[2ex] \dfrac{\pi}{2} - \dfrac{\theta}{2}, & 0 < \theta \leq \pi, \end{cases}$$

and for $\theta = 0$, the series converges to 0. The real part is the series

$$\sum_{n=1}^{\infty} \frac{\cos n\theta}{n}.$$

This clearly diverges when $\theta = 0$. The series is the Fourier series of the function

$$\frac{1}{2} \log \frac{1}{2 - 2\cos\theta}$$

and can be shown to converge to this function except for $\theta = 0$, where the function becomes infinite [see K. Knopp, *Infinite Series*, page 402 and page 420 (London: Blackie, 1928)]. Hence the series $\sum(z^n/n)$ converges for $|z| \leq 1$ except for $z = 1$. It will later be seen that this series is the Taylor series of $\text{Log}\,[1/(1 - z)]$ and that

$$\text{Log}\,\frac{1}{1 - z} = \sum_{n=1}^{\infty} \frac{z^n}{n}, \qquad |z| \leq 1, \quad z \neq 1.$$

The third example reveals how delicate the investigation of the series on the circle of convergence can be. It also shows the close relationship between this problem and that of Fourier series.

**Theorem 32.** *A power series with nonzero convergence radius represents a continuous function within the circle of convergence.*

This follows from Theorem 15 (Section 2–3) and Theorem 31. If the series converges at a point $z = z_1$ of the circle of convergence $|z - z_0| = r^*$, then the sum $f(z)$ of the series is continuous in a certain sense at $z_1$: one has

$$\lim_{r \to r^*} f(z_0 + re^{i\theta_1}) = f(z_0 + r^* e^{i\theta_1}) = f(z_1)$$

as illustrated in Fig. 5–1. Thus $\lim f(z) = f(z_1)$ as $z$ approaches $z_1$ along a radius; one can even permit $z$ to approach $z_1$ along an arbitrary smooth path $C$ which is not tangent to the circle at $z_1$. This result is *Abel's theorem*, as extended by Stolz. For a proof one is referred to page 406 of the book by Knopp cited above.

**Theorem 33.** *A power series can be integrated term-by-term within the circle of convergence: that is, if $r^* \neq 0$ and*

$$f(z) = \sum_{n=0}^{\infty} c_n(z - z_0)^n, \qquad |z - z_0| < r^*,$$

*then, for every path $C$ inside the circle of convergence,*

$$\int_{\substack{z_1 \\ C}}^{z_2} f(z)\, dz = \sum_{n=0}^{\infty} c_n \int_{z_1}^{z_2} (z - z_0)^n\, dz = \sum_{n=0}^{\infty} c_n \left. \frac{(z - z_0)^{n+1}}{n + 1} \right|_{z_1}^{z_2},$$

*or in terms of indefinite integrals,*

$$\int f(z)\, dz = \sum_{n=0}^{\infty} c_n \frac{(z - z_0)^{n+1}}{n + 1} + \text{const}, \quad |z - z_0| < r^*.$$

*Proof.* By Theorem 20 (Section 2–5), we conclude that term-by-term integration along $C$ is permissible. However, since each term $c_n(z - z_0)^n$ is analytic, the integrals are independent of path, so that

$$\int_{z_1}^{z_2} f(z)\, dz$$

is independent of path. Hence

$$\int_{z_0}^{z} f(z)\, dz = F(z)$$

is well-defined for $|z - z_0| < r^*$. As in the proof of Theorem 29 above (Section 3–2), we reason that $F'(z) = f(z)$, so that $F(z)$ is an indefinite integral of $f(z)$ and is, incidentally, analytic. All indefinite integrals of $f(z)$ are given by $F(z) + \text{const}$ [cf. Prob. 5 following Section 3–3]. Now

$$F(z) = \int_{z_0}^{z} f(z)\, dz = \sum_{n=0}^{\infty} c_n \frac{(z - z_0)^{n+1}}{n + 1},$$

by term-by-term integration of the series. Hence we see that the theorem is proved.

**Theorem 34.** *A power series can be differentiated term-by-term; that is, if $r^* \neq 0$ and*

$$f(z) = \sum_{n=0}^{\infty} c_n(z - z_0)^n, \quad |z - z_0| < r^*,$$

*then*

$$f'(z) = \sum_{n=1}^{\infty} nc_n(z - z_0)^{n-1}, \quad |z - z_0| < r^*,$$

$$f''(z) = \sum_{n=2}^{\infty} n(n - 1)c_n(z - z_0)^{n-2}, \quad |z - z_0| < r^*$$

$$\vdots$$

*Hence every power series with nonzero convergence radius defines an analytic function $f(z)$ within the circle of convergence, and the power series is the Taylor series of $f(z)$:*

$$c_n = \frac{f^{(n)}(z_0)}{n!}.$$

*Proof.* We first verify that, if $b$ is any real number greater than 1, then $n < b^n$ for $n$ sufficiently large (in fact, $n/b^n \to 0$ as $n \to \infty$). Hence, for such $n$,

$$n|c_n| \, |z - z_0|^n \leqq |c_n| \, |b(z - z_0)|^n.$$

Thus under the assumptions made on the series for $f(z)$, the series $\sum nc_n(z - z_0)^n$ is absolutely convergent for $b|z - z_0| < r^*$, or $|z - z_0| < r^*/b$; since this holds for every $b > 1$, the series is absolutely convergent for $|z - z_0| < r^*$; since the series $\sum nc_n(z - z_0)^{n-1}$ differs from the series $\sum nc_n(z - z_0)^n$ only by a factor $(z - z_0)$, we conclude that this series also converges absolutely for $|z - z_0| < r^*$. From the inequality

$$|c_n| \, |z - z_0|^n \leqq n|c_n| \, |z - z_0|^n \quad \text{for } n \geqq 1,$$

we conclude, in the same way, that the series $\sum nc_n(z - z_0)^{n-1}$ cannot have radius of convergence larger than $r^*$. Hence the differentiated series has the same radius of convergence as the given power series. Let the sum of the differentiated series be $g(z)$:

$$g(z) = \sum_{n=1}^{\infty} nc_n(z - z_0)^{n-1}.$$

Then by Theorem 33 an indefinite integral of $g(z)$ is precisely the sum of the series for $f(z)$; that is,

$$f'(z) = g(z) = \sum_{n=1}^{\infty} nc_n(z - z_0)^{n-1}.$$

One can now differentiate as many times as desired. In general,

$$f^{(n)}(z) = n!c_n + (n+1)n(n-1)\cdots 2c_{n+1}(z-z_0)$$
$$+ (n+2)(n+1)\cdots 3c_{n+2}(z-z_0)^2 + \cdots.$$

On setting $z = z_0$, we find: $n!c_n = f^{(n)}(z_0)$, so that the series is the Taylor series:

$$f(z) = \sum_{n=0}^{\infty} f^{(n)}(z_0) \frac{(z-z_0)^n}{n!}.$$

**Theorem 35.**  *If two power series*

$$\sum_{n=0}^{\infty} c_n(z-z_0)^n, \qquad \sum_{n=0}^{\infty} C_n(z-z_0)^n$$

*have nonzero convergence radii and have equal sums wherever both series converge, then the series are identical: that is,*

$$c_n = C_n, \quad n = 0, 1, 2, \ldots$$

For if $f(z)$ denotes the common value of the sum, then $c_n = C_n = f^{(n)}(z_0)/n!$.

## PROBLEMS

1. Determine the radius of convergence for each of the following series:

(a) $\displaystyle\sum_{n=1}^{\infty} \frac{z^n}{n^3}$   (b) $\displaystyle\sum_{n=1}^{\infty} nz^n$   (c) $\displaystyle\sum_{n=0}^{\infty} 2^n(z-1)^n$   (d) $\displaystyle\sum_{n=1}^{\infty} \frac{z^n}{n^n}$.

2. Show that the series of Prob. 1(a) converges absolutely for all $z$ on the circle of convergence, while the series of Prob. 1(b) diverges everywhere on the circle of convergence.

3. Write the real and imaginary parts of the series of Prob. 1(a) for $|z| = 1$ as Fourier series.

4. (a) Solve the differential equation

$$\frac{dw}{dz} - w = 0$$

by setting $w = \sum_{n=0}^{\infty} c_n z^n$ and determining the coefficients $c_n$ so that the equation is satisfied.

(b) Solve the differential equation

$$(2z^3 - z^2)\frac{d^2w}{dz^2} - (6z^2 - 2z)\frac{dw}{dz} + (6z - 2)w = 0.$$

**ANSWERS**

1. (a) 1,    (b) 1,    (c) $\frac{1}{2}$,    (d) $\infty$.

3. $\sum_{n=1}^{\infty} \dfrac{\cos n\theta}{n^3}$, $\sum_{n=1}^{\infty} \dfrac{\sin n\theta}{n^3}$.

4. (a) $w = c_0 \left( 1 + z + \cdots + \dfrac{z^n}{n!} + \cdots \right)$,    (b) $w = c_1 z + c_2 (z^3 - z^2)$.

## 5–2 □ CAUCHY'S THEOREM FOR MULTIPLY CONNECTED DOMAINS

If $f(z)$ is analytic in a multiply connected domain $D$, then one cannot conclude that

$$\oint_C f(z)\, dz = 0$$

on every simple closed path $C$ in $D$. Thus, if $D$ is the doubly connected domain of Fig. 5–2 and $C$ is the curve $C_1$ shown, then the integral around $C$ need not be 0. However, by introducing cuts as in Fig. 5–2 and applying Cauchy's theorem to each of the two new simple closed paths formed, one concludes that

$$\oint_{C_1} f(z)\, dz = \oint_{C_2} f(z)\, dz; \qquad (5\text{–}20)$$

that is, the integral has the same value on all paths which go around the inner "hole" once in the positive direction. For a triply connected domain, as in Fig. 5–3, one obtains the equation:

$$\oint_{C_1} f(z)\, dz = \oint_{C_2} f(z)\, dz + \oint_{C_3} f(z)\, dz. \qquad (5\text{–}21)$$

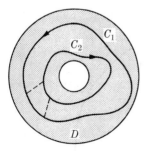
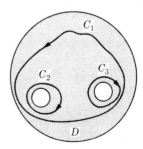

FIG. 5–2.  Cauchy theorem for doubly connected domain

FIG. 5–3.  Cauchy theorem for triply connected domain.

This can be written in the form

$$\oint_{C_1} f(z)\, dz + \oint_{C_2} f(z)\, dz + \oint_{C_3} f(z)\, dz = 0; \qquad (5\text{--}22)$$

this states that the integral around the complete boundary of a certain region in $D$ is equal to 0. More generally one has the following theorem:

**Theorem 36** (*Cauchy's theorem for multiply connected domains*). *Let $f(z)$ be analytic in a domain $D$ and let $C_1, \ldots, C_n$ be $n$ simple closed curves in $D$ which together form the boundary $B$ of a region $R$ contained in $D$. Then*

$$\int_B f(z)\, dz = 0,$$

*where the direction of integration on $B$ is such that the outer normal is $90°$ behind the tangent vector in the direction of integration.*

### 5–3 □ CAUCHY'S INTEGRAL FORMULA

Now let $D$ be a simply connected domain and let $z_0$ be a fixed point of $D$. If $f(z)$ is analytic in $D$, the function

$$\frac{f(z)}{z - z_0}$$

will fail to be analytic at $z_0$. Hence

$$\oint_C \frac{f(z)}{z - z_0}\, dz$$

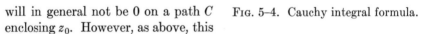

will in general not be 0 on a path $C$         FIG. 5–4. Cauchy integral formula.
enclosing $z_0$. However, as above, this
integral will have the same value on all paths $C$ about $z_0$. To determine this value, we reason that, if $C$ is a very small circle of radius $R$ about $z_0$, then $f(z_0)$ has, by continuity, approximately the constant value $f(z_0)$ on the path. This suggests that

$$\oint_C \frac{f(z)}{z - z_0}\, dz = f(z_0) \oint_{|z-z_0|=R} \frac{dz}{z - z_0} = f(z_0) \cdot 2\pi i,$$

since one finds

$$\oint_{|z-z_0|=R} \frac{dz}{z - z_0} = \int_0^{2\pi} \frac{Rie^{i\theta}}{Re^{i\theta}}\, d\theta = i \int_0^{2\pi} d\theta = 2\pi i,$$

with the aid of the substitution: $z - z_0 = Re^{i\theta}$. The correctness of the conclusion reached is the content of the following fundamental result:

**Theorem 37** (*Cauchy integral formula*).  *Let $f(z)$ be analytic in a domain D.  Let C be a simple closed curve in D, within which $f(z)$ is analytic, and let $z_0$ be inside C.  Then*

$$f(z_0) = \frac{1}{2\pi i} \oint_C \frac{f(z)}{z - z_0}\, dz. \qquad (5\text{-}30)$$

*Proof.*  The domain $D$ is not required to be simply connected, but since $f$ is analytic within $C$, the theorem concerns only a simply connected part of $D$, as shown in Fig. 5–4.  We reason as above to conclude that

$$\oint_C \frac{f(z)}{z - z_0}\, dz = \oint_{|z-z_0|=R} \frac{f(z)}{z - z_0}\, dz.$$

It remains to show that the integral on the right is indeed $f(z_0) \cdot 2\pi i$. Now, since $f(z_0) = \text{const}$,

$$\oint \frac{f(z_0)}{z - z_0}\, dz = f(z_0) \oint \frac{dz}{z - z_0} = f(z_0) \cdot 2\pi i,$$

where we integrate always on the circle $|z - z_0| = R$.  Hence, on the same path,

$$\oint \frac{f(z)}{z - z_0}\, dz - f(z_0) \cdot 2\pi i = \oint \frac{f(z) - f(z_0)}{z - z_0}\, dz. \qquad (5\text{-}31)$$

Now $|z - z_0| = R$ on the path and, since $f(z)$ is continuous at $z_0$, $|f(z) - f(z_0)| < \epsilon$ for $R < \delta$, for each preassigned $\epsilon > 0$.  Hence, by Theorem 19 (Section 2–5),

$$\left| \oint \frac{f(z) - f(z_0)}{z - z_0}\, dz \right| < \frac{\epsilon}{R} \cdot 2\pi R = 2\pi\epsilon.$$

Thus the absolute value of the integral can be made as small as desired by choosing $R$ sufficiently small.  But the integral has the same value for all choices of $R$.  This is possible only if the integral is 0 for all $R$.  Hence the left side of (5–31) is 0 and (5–30) follows.

The integral formula (5–30) is remarkable in that it expresses the values of the function $f(z)$ at points $z_0$ inside the curve $C$ in terms of the values along $C$ alone. If $C$ is taken as a circle: $z = z_0 + Re^{i\theta}$, then (5–30) reduces to the following:

$$f(z_0) = \frac{1}{2\pi} \int_0^{2\pi} f(z_0 + Re^{i\theta}) \, d\theta. \qquad (5\text{--}32)$$

Thus the *value of an analytic function at the center of a circle equals the average (arithmetic mean) of the values on the circumference.*

Just as with the Cauchy integral theorem, the Cauchy integral formula can be extended to multiply connected domains. Under the hypotheses of Theorem 36, one finds

$$f(z_0) = \frac{1}{2\pi i} \int_B \frac{f(z)}{z - z_0} \, dz = \frac{1}{2\pi i} \left[ \oint_{C_1} \frac{f(z)}{z - z_0} \, dz + \oint_{C_2} \frac{f(z)}{z - z_0} \, dz + \cdots \right],$$
$$(5\text{--}33)$$

where $z_0$ is any point inside the region $R$ bounded by $C_1$ (the outer boundary), $C_2$, ... $C_n$. The proof is left as an exercise (Prob. 6 below, following Section 5–4).

## 5–4 □ POWER SERIES EXPANSION OF GENERAL ANALYTIC FUNCTION

In Section 5–1 it was shown that every power series with nonzero convergence radius represents an analytic function. We now proceed to show that all analytic functions are obtainable in this way. If a function $f(z)$ is analytic in a domain $D$ of general shape, we cannot expect to represent $f(z)$ by one power series; for the power series converges only in a circular domain. However, we can show that, for each circular domain $D_0$ in $D$, there is a power series converging in $D_0$ whose sum is $f(z)$. Thus several (perhaps infinitely many) power series are needed to represent $f(z)$ throughout all of $D$.

**Theorem 38.** *Let $f(z)$ be analytic in the domain $D$. Let $z_0$ be in $D$ and let $R$ be the radius of the largest circle with center at $z_0$ and having its interior in $D$. Then there is a power series*

$$\sum_{n=0}^{\infty} c_n(z - z_0)^n$$

*which converges to $f(z)$ for $|z - z_0| < R$. Furthermore,*

$$c_n = \frac{f^{(n)}(z_0)}{n!} = \frac{1}{2\pi i} \oint_C \frac{f(z)}{(z - z_0)^{n+1}} \, dz, \qquad (5\text{--}40)$$

*where $C$ is a simple closed path in $D$ enclosing $z_0$ and within which $f(z)$ is analytic.*

*Proof.* For simplicity we take $z_0 = 0$. The general case can then be obtained by the substitution: $z' = z - z_0$. Let the circle $|z| \leq R$ be the largest circle with center at the origin and having its interior within $D$; the radius $R$ is then positive or $+\infty$ (in which case $D$ is the whole $z$ plane). Let $z_1$ be a point within this circle, so that $|z_1| < R$. Choose $R_2$ so that $|z_1| < R_2 < R$; see Fig. 5–5. Then $f(z)$ is analytic in a domain including the circle $C_2$: $|z| = R_2$ plus interior. Hence, by the Cauchy integral formula,

$$f(z_1) = \frac{1}{2\pi i} \oint_{C_2} \frac{f(z)}{z - z_1}\, dz.$$

Now the factor $1/(z - z_1)$ can be expanded in a geometric series:

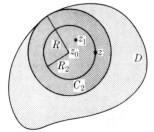

FIG. 5–5. Taylor series of an analytic function.

$$\frac{1}{z - z_1} = \frac{1}{z[1 - (z_1/z)]}$$

$$= \frac{1}{z}\left(1 + \frac{z_1}{z} + \cdots + \frac{z_1^n}{z^n} + \cdots\right).$$

The series can be considered as a power series in powers of $1/z$, for fixed $z_1$; it converges for $|z_1/z| < 1$ and converges uniformly for $|z_1/z| \leq |z_1|/R_2 < 1$. If one multiplies by $f(z)$, one finds

$$\frac{f(z)}{z - z_1} = \frac{f(z)}{z} + z_1\frac{f(z)}{z^2} + \cdots + z_1^n\frac{f(z)}{z^{n+1}} + \cdots;$$

since $f(z)$ is continuous for $|z| = R_2$, the series remains uniformly convergent on $C_2$; see the remark at the end of Section 2–3. One can hence integrate term-by-term on $C_2$ (Theorem 20, Section 2–5):

$$\frac{1}{2\pi i}\oint_{C_2}\frac{f(z)}{z - z_1}\,dz = \frac{1}{2\pi i}\oint_{C_2}\frac{f(z)}{z}\,dz + \frac{z_1}{2\pi i}\oint_{C_2}\frac{f(z)}{z^2}\,dz$$

$$+ \cdots + \frac{z_1^n}{2\pi i}\oint_{C_2}\frac{f(z)}{z^{n+1}}\,dz + \cdots.$$

The left-hand side is precisely $f(z_1)$, by the integral formula. Hence

$$f(z_1) = \sum_{n=0}^{\infty} c_n z_1^n, \qquad c_n = \frac{1}{2\pi i}\oint_{C_2}\frac{f(z)}{z^{n+1}}\,dz.$$

The path $C_2$ can be replaced by any path $C$ as described in the theorem, since $f(z)/z^{n+1}$ is analytic in $D$ except for $z = z_0 = 0$.

By Theorem 34, the series obtained is the Taylor series of $f$, so that

$$c_n = \frac{f^{(n)}(z_0)}{n!}, \qquad z_0 = 0.$$

The theorem is now completely proved.

The consequences of this theorem are far-reaching. First of all, not only does it guarantee that every analytic function is representable by power series but it ensures that the series converges to the function within each circular domain within the domain in which the function is given. Thus, *without further analysis*, we at once conclude that

$$e^z = 1 + z + \frac{z^2}{2!} + \cdots + \frac{z^n}{n!} + \cdots,$$

$$\sin z = z - \frac{z^3}{3!} + \frac{z^5}{5!} + \cdots + (-1)^{n+1} \frac{z^{2n+1}}{(2n+1)!} + \cdots,$$

$$\cos z = 1 - \frac{z^2}{2!} + \cdots + (-1)^n \frac{z^{2n}}{(2n)!} + \cdots,$$

for all $z$. A variety of other familiar expansions are obtained in the same way.

It should be recalled that a function $f(z)$ is defined to be analytic in a domain $D$ if $f(z)$ has a continuous derivative $f'(z)$ in $D$ (Section 3–1 above). By Theorem 38, $f(z)$ must have derivatives of all orders at every point of $D$. In particular, the derivative of an analytic function is itself analytic:

**Theorem 39.** *If $f(z)$ is analytic in domain $D$, then $f'(z)$, $f''(z)$, $\ldots$, $f^{(n)}(z)$, $\ldots$ exist and are analytic in $D$. Furthermore, for each $n$*

$$f^{(n)}(z_0) = \frac{n!}{2\pi i} \oint_C \frac{f(z)}{(z - z_0)^{n+1}} \, dz, \qquad (5\text{–}41)$$

*where $C$ is any simple closed path in $D$ enclosing $z_0$ and within which $f(z)$ is analytic.*

Equation (5–41) is a restatement of (5–40).

As pointed out in Section 3–1, one could define analyticity merely by requiring existence of $f'(z)$ and not its continuity. Cauchy's integral theorem and its consequence, the integral formula, can be proved without use of continuity of the derivative, so that Theorem 39 also holds. In other words, existence of the derivative of $f(z)$ is enough to guarantee continuity of $f'(z)$, $f''(z)$, $\ldots$ and convergence of the Taylor series. For details, see Chapter 3 of *Complex Analysis* by L. V. Ahlfors.

If in the proof of Theorem 38 one expands $1/(z - z_1)$ not in an infinite geometric series but in the finite series

$$\frac{1}{z - z_1} = \frac{1}{z}\left[1 + \frac{z_1}{z} + \cdots + \frac{z_1^n}{z^n} + \frac{z_1^{n+1}}{z^n(z - z_1)}\right]$$

and proceeds as before, one concludes that

$$f(z_1) = f(0) + z_1 f'(0) + \cdots + z_1^n \frac{f^{(n)}(0)}{n!} + \rho_n, \qquad (5\text{--}42)$$

where

$$\rho_n = \frac{z_1^{n+1}}{2\pi i} \oint_{C_2} \frac{f(z)}{z^{n+1}(z - z_1)}\, dz. \qquad (5\text{--}43)$$

This is a form of Taylor's Formula with Remainder. If the series has center $z_0$, one obtains the general formula:

$$f(z_1) = f(z_0) + (z_1 - z_0)f'(z_0) + \cdots + (z_1 - z_0)^n \frac{f^{(n)}(z_0)}{n!}$$

$$+ \frac{(z_1 - z_0)^{n+1}}{2\pi i} \oint_{C_2} \frac{f(z)}{(z - z_0)^{n+1}(z - z_1)}\, dz. \qquad (5\text{--}44)$$

The path $C_2$ can be replaced by any simple closed path in $D$ enclosing $z_0$ and $z_1$, within which $f(z)$ is analytic.

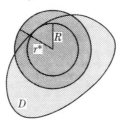

Fig. 5–6.  Analytic continuation.

*Circle of convergence of the Taylor series.* Theorem 38 guarantees convergence of the Taylor series of $f(z)$ about each $z_0$ in $D$ in the largest circular domain $|z - z_0| < R$ in $D$, as shown in Fig. 5–5. However, this does not mean that $R$ is the radius of convergence $r^*$ of the series, for $r^*$ can be larger than $R$, as suggested in Fig. 5–6. When this happens, the function $f(z)$ can be prolonged into a larger domain, while retaining analyticity. For example, if $f(z) = \text{Log } z \ (0 < \theta < \pi)$ is expanded in a Taylor series about the point $z = -1 + i$, the series has convergence radius $\sqrt{2}$, whereas $R = 1$ [Prob. 5(e) below].

The process of prolonging the function suggested here is called *analytic continuation*. It is discussed further in Section 8–1.

**PROBLEMS**

1. Evaluate with the aid of the Cauchy integral formula:

(a) $\dfrac{1}{2\pi i} \displaystyle\oint \dfrac{e^z}{z-2}\, dz$ on the circle: $|z-2| = 1$

(b) $\dfrac{1}{2\pi i} \displaystyle\oint \dfrac{z^2+4}{z}\, dz$ on the circle: $|z| = 1$

(c) $\dfrac{1}{2\pi i} \displaystyle\oint \dfrac{\sin z}{z}\, dz$ on the circle: $|z| = 4$

(d) $\displaystyle\oint \left( \dfrac{1}{z+1} + \dfrac{2}{z-3} \right) dz$ on the circle: $|z| = 4$

(e) $\displaystyle\oint \dfrac{1}{z^2-1}\, dz$ on the circle: $|z| = 2$

(f) $\displaystyle\oint \dfrac{1}{(z^2+1)(z^2+4)}\, dz$ on the circle: $|z| = \dfrac{3}{2}$.

2. (a) Compare the value of the function $e^z$ for $z = 0$ with the average of its values for $z = 1$, $z = i$, $z = -1$, $z = -i$. Interpret in terms of (5–32).

   (b) Show that, if $w = f(z) = z^2$, then

$$f(z_0) = \frac{f(z_0 + \Delta z) + f(z_0 + i\,\Delta z) + f(z_0 - \Delta z) + f(z_0 - i\,\Delta z)}{4}$$

   for every $z_0$ and every $\Delta z$. Interpret in terms of (5–32). Is the formula correct for $w = z^3$? for $w = z^4$?

3. It can be shown that the integral

$$\oint_C \sec z\, dz$$

   is equal to $-2\pi i$ if $C$ is a circle of radius 1 enclosing only one of the points $\frac{1}{2}\pi + 2n\pi$ ($n = 0, \pm 1, \ldots$) and is equal to $2\pi i$ if $C$ encloses only one of the points $\frac{3}{2}\pi + 2n\pi$. Evaluate this integral for the following choices of $C$:

   (a) $|z| = 1$,      (b) $|z| = 2$,      (c) $|z| = 10$,      (d) $|z-2| = 4$.

   Describe a path on which the integral has the value $10\pi i$.

4. Evaluate by (5–41):

(a) $\displaystyle\oint \dfrac{e^z}{z^5}\, dz$ on the circle: $|z| = 1$

(b) $\oint \dfrac{\sin z}{(z - \frac{1}{2}\pi)^2} dz$ on the circle: $|z| = 2$

(c) $\oint \dfrac{1}{z^2} dz$ on the circle: $|z| = 1$

(d) $\oint \dfrac{1}{z^2(z - 3)} dz$ on the circle: $|z| = 2$.

5. Expand in a Taylor series about the point indicated; determine the radius of convergence $r^*$ and the radius $R$ of the largest circle within which the series converges to the function:

(a) $e^z$ about $z = 1$

(b) $\dfrac{1}{z}$ about $z = 1$

(c) $\dfrac{1}{z - 2}$ about $z = 1$

(d) $\dfrac{1}{z(z - 2)}$ about $z = 1$

(e) $\operatorname{Log} z$ about $z = -1 + i$

(f) $\sqrt{z} = \sqrt{r} \exp{(\frac{1}{2}i\theta)}$,    $0 < \theta < 2\pi$,   about $z = 1 + i$

(g) $f(z) = \oint\limits_{|z_1|=1} \dfrac{dz_1}{z_1 - z}$,    $|z| < 1$,   about $z = 0$.

6. Prove (5–33) under the hypotheses stated in Theorem 36.

7. Prove *Cauchy's inequalities:*

$$|f^{(n)}(z_0)| \leqq \frac{Mn!}{R^n}    n = 0, 1, \ldots,$$

if $f(z)$ is analytic in a domain including the region $|z - z_0| \leqq R$ and $M$ is the maximum of $|f(z)|$ on the circle $|z - z_0| = R$.

[*Hint: take C to be the circle* $|z - z_0| = R$ *in* (5–41) *and estimate the integral as in the proof of the Cauchy integral formula.*]

8. A function $f(z)$ which is analytic in the whole $z$ plane is termed an *entire function* or an *integral function*. Examples are polynomials, $e^z$, $\sin z$, $\cos z$. Prove *Liouville's Theorem: If $f(z)$ is an entire function and $|f(z)| \leqq M$ for all $z$, where $M$ is constant, then $f(z)$ reduces to a constant.*

[*Hint: take $n = 1$ in the Cauchy inequalities of Prob. 7, to show that $f'(z_0) = 0$ for every $z_0$.*]

## ANSWERS

1. (a) $e^2$,     (b) 4,     (c) 0,     (d) $6\pi i$,     (e) 0,     (f) 0.

2. (a) average is 1.04.

3. (a) 0,     (b) 0,     (c) 0,     (d) $2\pi i$.

4. (a) $\frac{1}{12}\pi i$,     (b) 0,     (c) 0,     (d) $-\frac{2}{9}\pi i$.

5. (a) $\displaystyle\sum_{n=0}^{\infty} \frac{e(z-1)^n}{n!}$,   $R = r^* = \infty$;

   (b) $\displaystyle\sum_{n=0}^{\infty} (-1)^n (z-1)^n$,   $R = r^* = 1$;

   (c) $\displaystyle -\sum_{n=0}^{\infty} (z-1)^n$,   $R = r^* = 1$;

   (d) $\displaystyle -\sum_{n=0}^{\infty} (z-1)^{2n}$,   $R = r^* = 1$;

   (e) $\displaystyle \log\sqrt{2} + \tfrac{3}{4}\pi i - \sum_{n=1}^{\infty} \left(\frac{1+i}{2}\right)^n \frac{(z+1-i)^n}{n}$,     $R = 1$,     $r^* = \sqrt{2}$;

   (f) $\sqrt[4]{2}\,\exp\left(\tfrac{1}{8}\pi i\right)$

   $\displaystyle \times\left[1 + \frac{1-i}{4}(z-1-i) - \sum_{n=2}^{\infty} \frac{(i-1)^n \cdot 1\cdot 3\cdot 5\cdots(2n-3)}{4^n n!}(z-1-i)^n\right]$,

   $R = 1$,     $r^* = \sqrt{2}$;     (g) $2\pi i$,     $R = 1$,     $r^* = \infty$.

## 5–5 □ PROPERTIES OF REAL AND IMAGINARY PARTS OF ANALYTIC FUNCTIONS

The properties of analytic functions derived above lead to properties of the two real functions of two real variables:

$$u = u(x, y) = \mathrm{Re}[f(z)], \qquad v = v(x, y) = \mathrm{Im}[f(z)].$$

The analyticity of $f(z)$ was seen to imply existence and continuity of derivatives of all orders for $f(z)$. Since

$$f'(z) = \frac{\partial u}{\partial x} + i\frac{\partial v}{\partial x} = \frac{\partial v}{\partial y} - i\frac{\partial u}{\partial y},$$

$$f''(z) = \frac{\partial^2 u}{\partial x^2} + i\frac{\partial^2 v}{\partial x^2} = \frac{\partial^2 v}{\partial y\,\partial x} - i\frac{\partial^2 u}{\partial y\,\partial x} = \cdots,$$

and so on, one concludes that *u and v have continuous partial derivatives of all orders.*

Now the Cauchy-Riemann equations:

$$\frac{\partial u}{\partial x} = \frac{\partial v}{\partial y}, \qquad \frac{\partial u}{\partial y} = -\frac{\partial v}{\partial x} \tag{5–50}$$

can be differentiated to give

$$\frac{\partial^2 u}{\partial x^2} = \frac{\partial^2 v}{\partial x\,\partial y}, \qquad \frac{\partial^2 u}{\partial y^2} = -\frac{\partial^2 v}{\partial y\,\partial x}.$$

Adding these, we find

$$\frac{\partial^2 u}{\partial x^2} + \frac{\partial^2 u}{\partial y^2} = 0, \tag{5–51}$$

since

$$\frac{\partial^2 v}{\partial x\,\partial y} = \frac{\partial^2 v}{\partial y\,\partial x}.$$

Similarly one proves:

$$\frac{\partial^2 v}{\partial x^2} + \frac{\partial^2 v}{\partial y^2} = 0. \tag{5–52}$$

**Theorem 40.** *The real and imaginary parts of an analytic function are harmonic functions of $x$ and $y$; that is, if $w = f(z)$ is analytic in the domain $D$, then $u = \mathrm{Re}[f(z)]$ and $v = \mathrm{Im}[f(z)]$ are harmonic in $D$.*

If $u$ and $v$ are harmonic functions related by (5–50) in a domain, then $v$ is said to be a "harmonic conjugate" of $u$ in this domain and one terms the pair $u$, $v$ a pair of conjugate harmonic functions. Thus the real and imaginary parts of an analytic function form a pair of conjugate harmonic functions. Conversely, by Theorem 22 (Section 3–1), if $u$, $v$ form a pair of conjugate harmonic functions, then they can be interpreted as the real and imaginary parts of an analytic function $u + iv = f(z)$.

It should be noted that the Cauchy-Riemann equations are not symmetrical, so that, while $v$ is conjugate to $u$, $u$ *is conjugate to* $-v$.

If only the function $u = \mathrm{Re}[f(z)]$ is known, one can recover $v$, on the basis of (5–50), by a line integration:

$$v = \int_{z_1}^{z} \left( -\frac{\partial u}{\partial y}\, dx + \frac{\partial u}{\partial x}\, dy \right) + \text{const.} \tag{5–53}$$

For this integral is simply $\int dv$, by (5–50):

$$dv = \frac{\partial v}{\partial x}\, dx + \frac{\partial v}{\partial y}\, dy = -\frac{\partial u}{\partial y}\, dx + \frac{\partial u}{\partial x}\, dy. \tag{5–54}$$

With $dv$ given, $v$ is determined up to an additive constant, so that (5–53) gives all solutions.

If $u$ is given only as a harmonic function in a *simply connected* domain $D$, then (5–53) can be used to construct a conjugate harmonic function $v$, so that $u + iv = f(z)$ is analytic in $D$. For this integral is independent of the path by (5–51) and hence does define a function $v$. Since (5–54) must then hold, the Cauchy-Riemann equations follow and $v$ is conjugate to $u$. If $D$ is not simply connected, the integral may depend on the path, so that a multiple-valued function is obtained; this is illustrated by the function $\log z$, for which $u = \frac{1}{2} \log (x^2 + y^2)$ is harmonic except at the origin. Such multiple-valued functions are far from being useless, since one can build them up out of analytic branches, as was done for $\log z$ in Section 4–2 above.

The function $u$ can be obtained from $v$ by a similar formula:

$$ u = \int_{z_1}^{z} \frac{\partial v}{\partial y}\, dx - \frac{\partial v}{\partial x}\, dy + \text{const.} $$

### 5–6 □ POISSON INTEGRAL FORMULA

The Cauchy integral formula can be applied to obtain valuable relations for harmonic functions:

**Theorem 41.** *Let $w = u + iv = f(z)$ be analytic in a domain including the circle $|z| = R$ plus interior. Then for $z_0 = r_0 e^{i\theta_0}$ inside this circle,*

$$ u(z_0) = \frac{1}{2\pi} \int_0^{2\pi} \frac{R^2 - r_0^2}{R^2 + r_0^2 - 2Rr_0 \cos (\theta_0 - \theta)}\, u(Re^{i\theta})\, d\theta, \qquad (5\text{–}60) $$

*and similarly*

$$ v(z_0) = \frac{1}{2\pi} \int_0^{2\pi} \frac{R^2 - r_0^2}{R^2 + r_0^2 - 2Rr_0 \cos (\theta_0 - \theta)}\, v(Re^{i\theta})\, d\theta. \qquad (5\text{–}61) $$

*Furthermore,*

$$ v(z_0) = \frac{1}{2\pi} \int_0^{2\pi} \frac{2Rr_0 \sin (\theta_0 - \theta)}{R^2 + r_0^2 - 2Rr_0 \cos (\theta_0 - \theta)}\, u(Re^{i\theta})\, d\theta + v(0), $$

$$ (5\text{–}62) $$

*and (5–60) and (5–62) are obtained by taking real and imaginary parts in the equation:*

$$ f(z_0) = \frac{1}{2\pi} \int_0^{2\pi} \frac{z + z_0}{z - z_0}\, u(z)\, d\theta + iv(0), \quad z = Re^{i\theta}. \qquad (5\text{–}63) $$

Equation (5–60) is known as the *Poisson integral formula* for the harmonic function $u$. This will be studied further in Section 7–3. It expresses the values of $u$ inside the circle in terms of its values on the boundary, just as does the Cauchy integral formula for an analytic function. Equation (5–61) merely restates (5–60) for the harmonic function $v$. However, (5–62) expresses the values of $v$ directly in terms of the boundary values of the conjugate function.

*Proof of Theorem 41.*    The Cauchy integral formula for the circle $C: |z| = R$ gives

$$f(z_0) = \frac{1}{2\pi i} \oint_C \frac{f(z)}{z - z_0}\, dz. \quad (5\text{–}64)$$

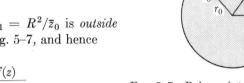

Now the point $z_1 = R^2/\bar{z}_0$ is *outside* $C$, as shown in Fig. 5–7, and hence

$$\frac{f(z)}{z - z_1}$$

FIG. 5–7.  Poisson integral formula.

is analytic within $C$. Accordingly, for $z_0 \neq 0$,

$$0 = \oint_C \frac{f(z)}{z - z_1}\, dz = \oint_C \frac{f(z)}{z - (R^2/\bar{z}_0)}\, dz. \quad (5\text{–}65)$$

If we set $z = Re^{i\theta}$ in (5–64), so that $dz = i\,Re^{i\theta}\,d\theta = iz\,d\theta$, we find

$$f(z_0) = \frac{1}{2\pi} \int_0^{2\pi} \frac{z}{z - z_0}\,(u + iv)\, d\theta. \quad (5\text{–}64')$$

If we make the same substitution in (5–65), we find

$$0 = \frac{1}{2\pi} \int_0^{2\pi} \frac{z}{z - (R^2/\bar{z}_0)}\,(u + iv)\, d\theta. \quad (5\text{–}65')$$

We now take conjugates in (5–65'); on using the relation $z \cdot \bar{z} = R^2$, we find

$$0 = \frac{1}{2\pi} \int_0^{2\pi} \frac{-z_0}{z - z_0}\,(u - iv)\, d\theta. \quad (5\text{–}66)$$

This relation is clearly valid also for $z_0 = 0$. On subtracting (5–66) from (5–64'), we obtain the equation

$$f(z_0) = \frac{1}{2\pi} \int_0^{2\pi} \frac{z + z_0}{z - z_0} u(z) \, d\theta + \frac{i}{2\pi} \int_0^{2\pi} v(z) \, d\theta. \qquad (5\text{--}67)$$

If we take real parts here, we obtain at once:

$$u(z_0) = \frac{1}{2\pi} \int_0^{2\pi} \operatorname{Re}\left(\frac{z + z_0}{z - z_0}\right) u(z) \, d\theta, \quad z = Re^{i\theta}, \quad z_0 = r_0 e^{i\theta_0}.$$

This gives the desired integral formula (5–60). Since $v$ is the real part of the analytic function $v - iu$, a similar formula (5–61) holds for $v$. If we set $z_0 = 0$ in (5–61), we find

$$v(0) = \frac{1}{2\pi} \int_0^{2\pi} v(Re^{i\theta}) \, d\theta. \qquad (5\text{--}68)$$

Hence (5–67) reduces to (5–63); on taking imaginary parts in (5–63) we find (5–62). The theorem is thus proved.

Equation (5–68) is itself of interest. It states that, just as for analytic functions, *the value of a harmonic function at the center of a circle equals the average of the values on the circumference;* cf. (5–32) above.

It is of great significance that the Poisson integral formula (5–60) remains correct for an arbitrary function $u$ which is continuous for $|z| \leq R$ and harmonic only for $|z| < R$ (Prob. 9 below). In fact, if $h(\theta)$ is a *piecewise* continuous function of $\theta$ for $0 \leq \theta \leq 2\pi$ and $h(0) = h(2\pi)$, the equation

$$u(r_0 e^{i\theta}) = \frac{1}{2\pi} \int_0^{2\pi} \frac{R^2 - r_0^2}{R^2 + r_0^2 - 2Rr_0 \cos(\theta_0 - \theta)} h(\theta) \, d\theta \qquad (5\text{--}69)$$

*defines* a harmonic function $u$ in the region $|z| < R$ having the boundary values $h(\theta)$; that is, if we set $u(Re^{i\theta}) = h(\theta)$, then $u$ is harmonic for $|z| < R$ and continuous for $|z| \leq R$ except where $h$ is discontinuous. This question will be studied further in Section 7–3.

From the fact that the analytic function $f(z)$ can be expanded in a Taylor series, one concludes that $u(x, y) = \operatorname{Re}[f(z)]$ and $v(x, y) = \operatorname{Im}[f(z)]$ or, in general, any harmonic function can be expanded in a Taylor series in $x$ and $y$; the series will converge in a circular domain as for $f(z)$. Thus from the expansion

$$e^z = 1 + z + \frac{z^2}{2} + \cdots + \frac{z^n}{n!} + \cdots,$$

one concludes that

$$u = e^x \cos y = \mathrm{Re}(e^z) = 1 + x + \frac{x^2 - y^2}{2!} + \cdots$$
$$+ \frac{\mathrm{Re}(x + iy)^n}{n!} + \cdots.$$

If polar coordinates are used, one has

$$e^z = 1 + r(\cos\theta + i\sin\theta) + \cdots + \frac{r^n(\cos n\theta + i\sin n\theta)}{n!} + \cdots ;$$

accordingly,

$$u = e^{r\cos\theta}\cos(r\sin\theta) = 1 + r\cos\theta + \cdots + \frac{r^n\cos n\theta}{n!} + \cdots.$$

This represents $u$ as a Fourier series in $\theta$ with coefficients which depend on $r$.

The Cauchy-Riemann equations appear in a slightly different form in the theory of vector fields: namely, as the conditions that a vector field in the plane have divergence 0 and curl **0**. Thus let $\mathbf{V} = u\mathbf{i} - v\mathbf{j}$ (where $\mathbf{i}$, $\mathbf{j}$, $\mathbf{k}$ are the unit vectors of vector analysis). Then

$$\mathrm{div}\,\mathbf{V} = \frac{\partial u}{\partial x} - \frac{\partial v}{\partial y}, \qquad \mathrm{curl}\,\mathbf{V} = \left(-\frac{\partial v}{\partial x} - \frac{\partial u}{\partial y}\right)\mathbf{k}.$$

Hence the conditions: $\mathrm{div}\,\mathbf{V} = 0$ and $\mathrm{curl}\,\mathbf{V} = \mathbf{0}$, reduce to

$$\frac{\partial u}{\partial x} = \frac{\partial v}{\partial y}, \qquad \frac{\partial u}{\partial y} = -\frac{\partial v}{\partial x};$$

these are the Cauchy-Riemann equations. This connection with vector theory is basic for applications in hydrodynamics and electromagnetism; it will be considered further in Section 7–5.

**PROBLEMS**

1. Show that the slope of a curve: $u(x, y) = \mathrm{const}$ is given by

$$y' = -\frac{\partial u/\partial x}{\partial u/\partial y}.$$

Hence show that, if $u$, $v$ form a pair of conjugate harmonic functions, then the curves $v = \mathrm{const}$ are orthogonal to the curves $u = \mathrm{const}$. Are there any exceptional points?

2. Plot the level curves of $u = \mathrm{Re}[f(z)]$ and $v = \mathrm{Im}[f(z)]$ for

(a) $f(z) = z^2$

(b) $f(z) = z^3$

(c) $f(z) = 3iz - 1 - i$

(d) $f(z) = \log z$ (any branch)

(e) $f(z) = e^z$

(f) $f(z) = \dfrac{1}{z}$.

3. (a) Expand in power series in powers of $x$ and $y$:

$$u = \frac{1 - x}{(1 - x)^2 + y^2} = \mathrm{Re}\left(\frac{1}{1 - z}\right),$$

$$v = \frac{y}{(1 - x)^2 + y^2} = \mathrm{Im}\left(\frac{1}{1 - z}\right).$$

(b) Write the series (a) in polar coordinates.

4. (a) Expand $y = e^x \cos x$ in a Taylor series in the real variable $x$.

[*Hint: use the series for $e^x \cos y$ given above.*]

(b) Expand $y = e^{\cos x} \cos (\sin x)$ in a Fourier series.

5. Show that the following functions are harmonic, and obtain the conjugate functions by line integration:

(a) $u = 5x - 3y$

(b) $u = 2xy$

(c) $u = \dfrac{y}{x^2 + y^2}$

(d) $e^x(x \cos y - y \sin y)$.

6. Show that, if $u(x, y)$ is harmonic in domain $D$, then the functions

$$\frac{\partial u}{\partial x}, \quad \frac{\partial u}{\partial y}, \quad \frac{\partial^2 u}{\partial x^2}, \quad \frac{\partial^2 u}{\partial x\,\partial y}, \quad \frac{\partial^2 u}{\partial y^2}, \quad \frac{\partial^3 u}{\partial x^3}, \quad \cdots$$

are all harmonic in $D$. If $v$ is conjugate to $u$, what function is conjugate to $\partial^2 u/\partial x^2$?

7. Let $u(x, y)$ and $v(x, y)$ be a pair of conjugate harmonic functions in a domain $D$ and let $u + iv = f(z)$.

(a) Show that $J = \dfrac{\partial(u, v)}{\partial(x, y)} = |f'(z)|^2$.

(b) Show that, if $f'(z_0) \neq 0$, then the equations

$$u = u(x, y), \qquad v = v(x, y)$$

can be solved uniquely for $x$ and $y$ in terms of $u$ and $v$ in a neighborhood of $(x_0, y_0)$, so that the equations define a one-to-one mapping of this neighborhood into the $uv$ plane (cf. Section 2–8 of *Advanced Calculus*).

(c) Show that the inverse mapping of (b):

$$x = x(u, v), \qquad y = y(u, v)$$

satisfies the Cauchy-Riemann equations:

$$\frac{\partial x}{\partial u} = \frac{\partial y}{\partial v}, \qquad \frac{\partial x}{\partial v} = -\frac{\partial y}{\partial u},$$

so that the inverse function $z = z(w)$ is analytic near the given point.

(d) Show that the inverse mapping $z(w)$ of (b) and (c) satisfies the condition:

$$\frac{dz}{dw} = \frac{1}{dw/dz}.$$

8. Let $\phi(u, v)$ be a harmonic function in domain $D_w$ of the $w$ plane and let $w = f(z)$ be analytic in domain $D_z$ of the $z$ plane, with values in $D_w$.

(a) Show that $\phi[u(x, y), v(x, y)]$ satisfies the equation

$$\frac{\partial^2 \phi}{\partial x^2} + \frac{\partial^2 \phi}{\partial y^2} = |f'(z)|^2 \left( \frac{\partial^2 \phi}{\partial u^2} + \frac{\partial^2 \phi}{\partial v^2} \right).$$

(b) Show that $\phi[u(x, y), v(x, y)]$ is a harmonic function of $x$ and $y$ in $D_z$.

9. *Integrals depending on a parameter.* Let $g(z_1, z_2) = g(x_1 + iy_1, x_2 + iy_2)$ be a function of two complex variables $z_1, z_2$. Continuity for such a function is defined precisely as for real variables; it can also be defined by requiring that $u = \text{Re}[g]$ and $v = \text{Im}[g]$ be continuous in $x_1, y_1, x_2, y_2$. Let $g$ be defined for $z_1$ on a path $C$ in the $z_1$ plane and $z_2$ in a domain $D$ of the $z_2$ plane and let $g$ be continuous in both variables. Moreover, let $g$ be analytic in $z_2$ for each $z_1$ and let the derivative $\partial g/\partial z_2$ be continuous in both variables. Then the integrals

$$F(z_2) = \int_C g(z_1, z_2)\, dz_1, \qquad \int_C \frac{\partial g}{\partial z_2} (z_1, z_2)\, dz_1$$

are well-defined. Moreover, Leibnitz's rule is applicable (Section 4–12 of *Advanced Calculus*):

(a) $\dfrac{d}{dz_2} \displaystyle\int_C g(z_1, z_2)\, dz_1 = \int_C \frac{\partial g}{\partial z_2} (z_1, z_2)\, dz_1,$

for the line integral can be written in terms of two real line integrals and then, by use of a parameter $t$, in terms of two real integrals with respect to $t$. By Leibnitz's rule, the Cauchy-Riemann equations are satisfied by

$$u = \text{Re}[F(z_2)] \quad \text{and} \quad v = \text{Im}[F(z_2)],$$

so that $F(z_2)$ is analytic. Since $F'(z_2) = \partial u/\partial x_2 + i \, \partial v/\partial x_2$, (a) reduces to two identities in real variables.

(b) Apply the rule (a) to prove formulas (5–41) from (5–30).

(c) Prove that, if $F(z)$ is continuous on the path $C$, then

$$\int_C \frac{F(z)}{z - z_0} \, dz$$

defines an analytic function $f(z_0)$ in each domain not meeting $C$. The functions $f$ obtained in different domains need not be related, as the following example shows:

$$\oint_{|z|=1} \frac{1}{z - z_0} \, dz = \begin{cases} 2\pi i, & |z_0| < 1, \\ 0, & |z_0| > 1. \end{cases}$$

(d) Let $h(\theta)$ be continuous for $0 \leq \theta \leq 2\pi$ and let $h(0) = h(2\pi)$. Prove that

$$f(z_0) = \frac{1}{2\pi} \int_0^{2\pi} \frac{z + z_0}{z - z_0} h(\theta) \, d\theta, \quad z = Re^{i\theta},$$

is analytic for $|z_0| < R$ and hence that

$$u(z_0) = \frac{1}{2\pi} \int_0^{2\pi} \frac{R^2 - r_0^2}{R^2 + r_0^2 - 2Rr_0 \cos(\theta_0 - \theta)} h(\theta) \, d\theta,$$

$$v(z_0) = \frac{1}{2\pi} \int_0^{2\pi} \frac{2Rr_0 \sin(\theta_0 - \theta)}{R^2 + r_0^2 - 2Rr_0 \cos(\theta_0 - \theta)} h(\theta) \, d\theta$$

are harmonic for $|z_0| < R$.

(e) Let the function $h(\theta)$ of part (d) have a continuous derivative. Show by integration by parts that

$$v(z_0) = -\frac{1}{\pi} \int_0^{2\pi} \log \frac{1}{|z - z_0|} h'(\theta) \, d\theta, \quad z = Re^{i\theta}.$$

This is a representation of the harmonic function $v$ as a *logarithmic potential of a mass distribution on the circle* $|z| = R$.

**ANSWERS**

3. (a) $u = 1 + x + (x^2 - y^2) + (x^3 - 3xy^2) + \cdots$

$$+ \left[ x^n - \frac{n(n-1)}{2!} x^{n-2} y^2 + \frac{n(n-1)(n-2)(n-3)}{4!} x^{n-4} y^4 + \cdots \right] + \cdots,$$

$v = y + 2xy + (3x^2 y - y^3) + \cdots$

$$+ \left[ nx^{n-1} y - \frac{n(n-1)(n-2)}{3!} x^{n-3} y^3 + \cdots \right] + \cdots; \ x^2 + y^2 < 1;$$

(b) $u = 1 + r \cos \theta + \cdots + r^n \cos n\theta + \cdots,$
    $v = r \sin \theta + \cdots + r^n \sin n\theta + \cdots.$

4. (a) $1 + x + \cdots + \dfrac{(\sqrt{2}\,x)^n}{n!} \cos \left( \tfrac{1}{4} n\pi \right) + \cdots,$

   (b) $1 + \cos x + \cdots + \dfrac{\cos nx}{n!} + \cdots.$ Both series converge for all $x$.

5. (a) $v = 3x + 5y + \text{const},$ \qquad (b) $v = y^2 - x^2 + \text{const},$

   (c) $v = \dfrac{x}{x^2 + y^2} + \text{const},$ \qquad (d) $e^x(x \sin y + y \cos y).$

# 6 □ *Laurent Series and Residues*

## 6–1 □ POWER SERIES IN POSITIVE AND NEGATIVE POWERS. LAURENT EXPANSION

We have shown that every power series $\sum a_n(z - z_0)^n$ with nonzero convergence radius represents an analytic function and that every analytic function can be built up out of such series. It thus appears unnecessary to seek other explicit expressions for analytic functions. However, the power series represent the function only in circular domains and are hence awkward for representing a function in a more complicated type of domain. It is therefore worthwhile to consider other types of representations.

A series of form

$$\sum_{n=0}^{\infty} \frac{b_n}{(z - z_0)^n} = b_0 + \frac{b_1}{z - z_0} + \cdots + \frac{b_n}{(z - z_0)^n} + \cdots \qquad (6\text{-}10)$$

will also represent an analytic function in a domain where the series converges, for the substitution: $z_1 = 1/(z - z_0)$ reduces this series to an ordinary power series:

$$\sum_{n=0}^{\infty} b_n z_1^n.$$

If this series converges for $|z_1| < r^*$, then its sum is an analytic function $f(z_1)$; hence the series (6–10) converges, for

$$|z - z_0| > r_1^* = \frac{1}{r^*}, \qquad (6\text{-}11)$$

to the analytic function

$$g(z) = f\left(\frac{1}{z - z_0}\right).$$

88

The value $z_1 = 0$ corresponds to $z = \infty$, in a limiting sense, and accordingly we can also say: $g(z)$ is analytic at $\infty$ and $g(\infty) = b_0$. This will be justified more fully in Section 6–3.

The domain of convergence of the series (6–10) is the region (6–11), which is the *exterior* of a circle. It can happen that $r_1^* = 0$, in which case the series converges for all $z$ except $z_0$; if $r_1^* = \infty$, the series diverges for all $z$ (except $z = \infty$, as above).

If we add to a series (6–10) a power series in positive powers of $z - z_0$:

$$\sum_{n=0}^{\infty} a_n(z - z_0)^n = a_0 + a_1(z - z_0) + \cdots,$$

converging for $|z - z_0| < r_2^*$, one obtains a sum

$$\sum_{n=0}^{\infty} \frac{b_n}{(z - z_0)^n} + \sum_{n=0}^{\infty} a_n(z - z_0)^n. \quad (6\text{–}12)$$

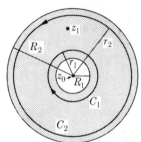

Fig. 6–1. Laurent's theorem.

If $r_1^* < r_2^*$, the sum converges and represents an analytic function $f(z)$ in the *annular domain:*

$$r_1^* < |z - z_0| < r_2^*,$$

as shown in Fig. 6–1; each series has an analytic sum in this domain, so that the sum of the two series is analytic there. We can write this sum in the more compact form (after some relabeling):

$$f(z) = \sum_{n=-\infty}^{\infty} a_n(z - z_0)^n, \quad (6\text{–}13)$$

though this should be interpreted as the sum of two series as in (6–12).

In this way we build up a new class of analytic functions, each defined in a ring-shaped domain. Every function analytic in such a domain can be obtained in this way:

**Theorem 42** (Laurent's theorem).  *Let $f(z)$ be analytic in the ring:* $R_1 < |z - z_0| < R_2$. *Then*

$$f(z) = \sum_{n=-\infty}^{\infty} a_n(z - z_0)^n$$

$$= [a_0 + a_1(z - z_0) + \cdots] + \left[ \frac{a_{-1}}{z - z_0} + \frac{a_{-2}}{(z - z_0)^2} + \cdots \right],$$

*where*

$$a_n = \frac{1}{2\pi i} \oint_C \frac{f(z)}{(z - z_0)^{n+1}} \, dz \qquad (6\text{--}14)$$

*and $C$ is any simple closed curve separating $|z - z_0| = R_1$ from $|z - z_0| = R_2$. The series converge uniformly for $R_1 < k_1 \leqq |z - z_0| \leqq k_2 < R_2$.*

*Proof.* For simplicity we take $z_0 = 0$. Let $z_1$ be any point of the ring and choose $r_1, r_2$ so that $R_1 < r_1 < |z_1| < r_2 < R_2$, as in Fig. 6–1. We then apply the Cauchy integral formula in general form [(5–33) above] to the region bounded by $C_1$: $|z| = r_1$ and $C_2$: $|z| = r_2$. Hence

$$f(z_1) = \frac{1}{2\pi i} \oint_{C_2} \frac{f(z)}{z - z_1} \, dz - \frac{1}{2\pi i} \oint_{C_1} \frac{f(z)}{z - z_1} \, dz. \qquad (6\text{--}15)$$

The first term can be replaced by a power series

$$\sum_{n=0}^{\infty} a_n z_1^n, \qquad a_n = \frac{1}{2\pi i} \oint_{C_2} \frac{f(z)}{z^{n+1}} \, dz,$$

as in the proof of Theorem 38 (Section 5–4). For the second term, the series expansion

$$\frac{1}{z - z_1} = -\frac{1}{z_1} \left( \frac{1}{1 - (z/z_1)} \right) = -\frac{1}{z_1} - \frac{z}{z_1^2} - \frac{z^2}{z_1^3} \cdots ,$$

valid for $|z_1| > |z| = r_1$, leads similarly to the series

$$\sum_{n=1}^{\infty} \frac{b_n}{z_1^n} = \sum_{n=-\infty}^{-1} a_n z_1^n, \qquad a_n = \frac{1}{2\pi i} \oint_{C_1} \frac{f(z)}{z^{n+1}} \, dz.$$

Hence

$$f(z_1) = \sum_{n=-\infty}^{\infty} a_n z_1^n, \qquad a_n = \frac{1}{2\pi i} \oint_C \frac{f(z)}{z^{n+1}} \, dz;$$

the path $C_2$ or $C_1$ can be replaced by any path $C$ separating $|z| = R_1$ from $|z| = R_2$, since the function integrated is analytic throughout the annulus. The uniform convergence follows as for ordinary power series (Theorem 31, Section 5–1). The theorem is now established.

Laurent's theorem continues to hold when $R_1 = 0$ or $R_2 = \infty$ or both. In the case $R_1 = 0$, the Laurent expansion represents a function $f(z)$ analytic in a *deleted neighborhood of $z_0$*, i.e., in the circular domain $|z - z_0| < R_2$ minus its center $z_0$. If $R_2 = \infty$, we can say similarly that the series represents $f(z)$ in a *deleted neighborhood of $z = \infty$*.

*Remark.* Laurent's theorem does not provide a series expansion for $\log z$ in a ring: $R_1 < |z| < R_2$, for $\log z$ cannot be defined as an analytic function throughout such a ring.

## 6–2 □ ISOLATED SINGULARITIES OF AN ANALYTIC FUNCTION. ZEROS AND POLES

Let $f(z)$ be defined and analytic in domain $D$. We say that $f(z)$ has an *isolated singularity* at the point $z_0$ if $f(z)$ is analytic throughout a neighborhood of $z_0$ except at $z_0$ itself; that is, to use the term mentioned at the end of the preceding section, $f(z)$ is analytic in a deleted neighborhood of $z_0$, but not at $z_0$. The point $z_0$ is then a boundary point of $D$ and would be called an *isolated boundary point* (see Fig. 6–2).

A deleted neighborhood:

$$0 < |z - z_0| < R_2$$

forms a special case of the annular domain for which Laurent's theorem is applicable. Hence in this deleted neighborhood $f(z)$ has a representation as a Laurent series:

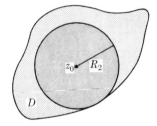

$$f(z) = \sum_{n=-\infty}^{\infty} a_n(z - z_0)^n.$$

FIG. 6–2. Isolated singularity.

The form of this series leads to a classification of isolated singularities into three fundamental types:

*Case I. No terms in negative powers of $z - z_0$ appear.* In this case the series is a Taylor series and represents a function analytic in a neighborhood of $z_0$. Thus the singularity can be removed by setting $f(z_0) = a_0$. We call this a *removable singularity* of $f(z)$. It is illustrated by

$$\frac{\sin z}{z} = 1 - \frac{z^2}{3!} + \frac{z^4}{5!} \cdots$$

at $z = 0$. In practice, one automatically removes the singularity by defining the function properly.

*Case II. Only a finite number of negative powers of $z - z_0$ appear.* Thus one has

$$f(z) = \frac{a_{-N}}{(z - z_0)^N} + \cdots + \frac{a_{-1}}{z - z_0} + a_0 + \cdots + a_n(z - z_0)^n + \cdots$$

$$(6\text{–}20)$$

with $N \geqq 1$ and $a_{-N} \neq 0$. Here $f(z)$ is said to have a *pole of order N* at $z_0$. One can write

$$f(z) = \frac{1}{(z - z_0)^N} g(z), \qquad g(z) = a_{-N} + a_{-N+1}(z - z_0) + \cdots, \quad (6\text{–}21)$$

so that $g(z)$ is analytic for $|z - z_0| < R_2$ and $g(z_0) \neq 0$. Conversely, every function $f(z)$ representable in the form (6–21) has a pole of order $N$ at $z_0$. Poles are illustrated by rational functions of $z$, such as

$$\frac{z - 2}{(z^2 + 1)(z - 1)^3},$$

which has poles of order 1 at $\pm i$ and of order 3 at $z = 1$.

The rational function

$$\frac{a_{-N}}{(z - z_0)^N} + \cdots + \frac{a_{-1}}{z - z_0} = p(z) \qquad (6\text{–}22)$$

is termed the *principal part* of $f(z)$ at the pole $z_0$. Thus $f(z) - p(z)$ is analytic at $z_0$.

*Case III. Infinitely many negative powers of $z - z_0$ appear.* In this case $f(z)$ is said to have an *essential singularity* at $z_0$. This is illustrated by the function

$$f(z) = e^{1/z} = 1 + \frac{1}{z} + \frac{1}{2!} \frac{1}{z^2} + \frac{1}{3!} \frac{1}{z^3} + \cdots,$$

which has an essential singularity at $z = 0$.

In Case I, $f(z)$ has a definite finite limit at $z_0$ and accordingly $|f(z)|$ is bounded near $z_0$; that is, there is a real constant $M$ such that $|f(z)| < M$ for $z$ sufficiently close to $z_0$. In Case II,

$$\lim_{z \to z_0} f(z) = \infty$$

and it is customary to assign the value $\infty$ (complex) to $f(z)$ at a pole. At an essential singularity, $f(z)$ has a very complicated discontinuity; one can in fact, for every complex number $c$, find a sequence $z_n$ converging to $z_0$ such that

$$\lim_{n \to \infty} f(z_n) = c;$$

(see Prob. 13 below). Since Cases I, II, III are mutually exclusive, it follows that, if $|f(z)|$ is bounded near $z_0$, then $z_0$ must be a removable singularity and, if $\lim f(z) = \infty$ at $z_0$, then $z_0$ must be a pole.

Let $f(z)$ be analytic at a point $z_0$ and let $f(z_0) = 0$, so that $z_0$ is a zero of $f(z)$. The Taylor series about $z_0$ has the form

$$f(z) = a_N(z - z_0)^N + a_{N+1}(z - z_0)^{N+1} + \cdots,$$

where $N \geq 1$ and $a_N \neq 0$, or else $f(z) \equiv 0$ in a neighborhood of $z_0$; it will be seen that the latter case can occur only if $f(z) \equiv 0$ throughout the domain in which it is given. If now $f(z)$ is not identically 0, then

$$f(z) = (z - z_0)^N h(z), \qquad h(z) = a_N + a_{N+1}(z - z_0) + \cdots,$$

$$h(z_0) = \frac{f^{(N)}(z_0)}{N!} = a_N \neq 0.$$

We say that $f(z)$ has a zero of *order* $N$ or *multiplicity* $N$ at $z_0$. For example, $1 - \cos z$ has a zero of order 2 at $z = 0$, since

$$1 - \cos z = \frac{z^2}{2} - \frac{z^4}{24} + \cdots.$$

*If $f(z)$ has a zero of order $N$ at $z_0$, then*

$$F(z) = \frac{1}{f(z)}$$

*has a pole of order $N$ at $z_0$ and conversely.* For, if $f$ has a zero of order $N$, then

$$f(z) = (z - z_0)^N h(z)$$

as above, with $h(z_0) \neq 0$. It follows from continuity that $h(z) \neq 0$ in a sufficiently small neighborhood of $z_0$. Hence $g(z) = 1/h(z)$ is analytic in the neighborhood and $g(z_0) \neq 0$. Now in this neighborhood, except for $z_0$,

$$F(z) = \frac{1}{f(z)} = \frac{1}{(z - z_0)^N h(z)} = \frac{g(z)}{(z - z_0)^N},$$

so that $F$ has a pole at $z_0$. The converse is proved in the same way.

It remains to consider the case when $f \equiv 0$ in a neighborhood of $z_0$. This is covered by the following theorem.

**Theorem 43.** *The zeros of an analytic function are isolated, unless the function is identically zero; that is, if $f(z)$ is analytic in domain $D$ and $f(z)$ is not identically zero, then for each zero $z_0$ of $f(z)$ there is a deleted neighborhood of $z_0$ in which $f(z) \neq 0$.*

*Proof.* Let $E_1$ denote the set of all points $z_1$ in $D$ for which $f(z) \equiv 0$ in a neighborhood of $z_1$; let $E_2$ denote the rest of $D$. Let it be assumed that neither $E_1$ nor $E_2$ forms all of $D$. Then $E_1$ is an open set, by its very definition (Section 2–1).

*The set $E_2$ is also open.* Let $z_2$ be in $E_2$. If $f(z_2) = 0$, then, as above, $f(z) = (z - z_2)^N h(z)$, where $h(z)$ is analytic at $z_2$ and $h(z_2) \neq 0$. It follows from the continuity of $h(z)$ that $h(z) \neq 0$ in some neighborhood of $z_2$. Hence $f(z) \neq 0$ in this neighborhood, except at $z_2$, and every point of the neighborhood belongs to $E_2$. Similarly, if $f(z_2) \neq 0$, then $f(z) \neq 0$ in a neighborhood of $z_2$ and every point of the neighborhood belongs to $E_2$. Therefore $E_2$ is open.

Accordingly, the domain $D$ is composed of two open sets $E_1$, $E_2$ without common point. As pointed out in a footnote in Section 2–1, this is impossible. Accordingly, either $E_1$ is all of $D$—that is, $f(z) \equiv 0$, or $E_2$ is all of $D$—that is, each zero of $f(z)$ is isolated.

## 6–3 □ THE COMPLEX NUMBER ∞

The complex number ∞ has been introduced several times in connection with limiting processes, for example, in the discussion of poles in the preceding section. In each case ∞ has appeared in a natural way as the limiting position of a point receding indefinitely from the origin. We can incorporate this number into the complex number system with special algebraic rules:

$$\frac{z}{\infty} = 0 \quad (z \neq \infty), \qquad z \pm \infty = \infty \quad (z \neq \infty), \qquad \frac{z}{0} = \infty \quad (z \neq 0),$$

$$z \cdot \infty = \infty \quad (z \neq 0), \qquad \frac{\infty}{z} = \infty \quad (z \neq \infty). \tag{6-30}$$

Expressions such as $\infty + \infty$, $\infty - \infty$, $\infty/\infty$ are not defined.

A function $f(z)$ is said to be analytic in a deleted neighborhood of ∞ if $f(z)$ is analytic for $|z| > R_1$ for some $R_1$. In this case the Laurent expansion with $R_2 = \infty$ and $z_0 = 0$ is available and one has

$$f(z) = \sum_{n=-\infty}^{\infty} a_n z^n, \quad |z| > R_1.$$

If there are no *positive* powers of $z$ here, $f(z)$ is said to have a *removable singularity* at ∞ and we make $f$ *analytic at* ∞ by defining $f(\infty) = a_0$:

$$f(z) = a_0 + \frac{a_{-1}}{z} + \cdots + \frac{a_{-n}}{z^n} + \cdots, \quad |z| > R_1;$$
$$f(\infty) = a_0. \tag{6-31}$$

This is clearly equivalent to the statement that, if one sets $z_1 = 1/z$, then $f(z)$ becomes a function of $z_1$ with removable singularity at $z_1 = 0$.

If a finite number of positive powers occur, one has, for $N \geqq 1$,

$$f(z) = a_N z^N + \cdots + a_1 z + a_0 + \frac{a_{-1}}{z} + \cdots,$$

$$= z^N h(z), \qquad h(z) = a_N + \frac{a_{N-1}}{z} + \cdots, \tag{6-32}$$

where $h(z)$ is analytic at $\infty$ and $h(\infty) = a_N \neq 0$. In this case $f(z)$ is said to have a *pole of order* $N$ at $\infty$. The same holds for $f(1/z_1)$ at $z_1 = 0$. Furthermore,

$$\lim_{z \to \infty} f(z) = \infty. \tag{6-33}$$

If infinitely many positive powers appear, $f(z)$ is said to have an *essential singularity* at $z = \infty$.

If $f(z)$ is analytic at $\infty$ as in (6–31) and $f(\infty) = a_0 = 0$, then $f(z)$ is said to have a *zero* at $z = \infty$. If $f$ is not identically zero, then necessarily some $a_{-N} \neq 0$ and

$$f(z) = \frac{a_{-N}}{z^N} + \frac{a_{-N-1}}{z^{N+1}} + \cdots, \qquad |z| > R_1$$

$$= \frac{1}{z^N} g(z), \qquad g(z) = a_{-N} + \frac{a_{-N-1}}{z} + \cdots. \tag{6-34}$$

Thus $g(z)$ is analytic at $\infty$ and $g(\infty) = a_{-N} \neq 0$. We say that $f(z)$ has a zero of order (or multiplicity) $N$ at $\infty$. We can then show that, if $f(z)$ has a zero of order $N$ at $\infty$, then $1/f(z)$ has a pole of order $N$ at $\infty$, and conversely.

The significance of the complex number $\infty$ can be shown geometrically by the device of *stereographic projection*, i.e., a projection of the plane onto a sphere tangent to the plane at $z = 0$, as shown in Fig. 6–3. The sphere is given in $xyt$ space by

$$x^2 + y^2 + (t - \tfrac{1}{2})^2 = \tfrac{1}{4}, \tag{6-35}$$

so that the radius is $\tfrac{1}{2}$. $N$ denotes the "north pole" of the sphere, the point $(0, 0, 1)$. If $N$ is joined to an arbitrary point $z$ in the $xy$ plane, the line segment $Nz$ will meet the sphere at one other point $P$, which is the projection of $z$ on the sphere. For example,

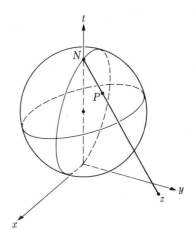

FIG. 6–3. Stereographic projection.

the points of the circle: $|z| = 1$ project on the "equator" of the sphere, i.e., the great circle: $t = \frac{1}{2}$. As $z$ recedes to infinite distance from the origin, $P$ approaches $N$ as limiting position. *Thus $N$ corresponds to the complex number $\infty$.*

One refers to the $z$ plane plus the number $\infty$ as the *extended $z$ plane*. To emphasize that $\infty$ is *not* included, we refer to the *finite $z$ plane*.

## PROBLEMS

1. Prove the validity of the *binomial expansion*

$$(1 + z)^m = 1 + \frac{m}{1} z + \frac{m(m-1)}{1 \cdot 2} z^2 + \cdots$$

$$+ \frac{m(m-1) \cdots (m-n+1)}{n!} z^n + \cdots$$

for $|z| < 1$, where $m$ is an arbitrary complex number and the principal value of $(1 + z)^m$ is chosen.

2. Expand in Laurent series or Taylor series as indicated:

(a) $\dfrac{1}{z-2}$ for $|z| < 2$   $\left[\text{Hint: } \dfrac{1}{z-2} = \dfrac{-1}{2[1-(z/2)]}.\right]$

(b) $\dfrac{1}{z-2}$ for $|z| > 2$   $\left[\text{Hint: } \dfrac{1}{z-2} = \dfrac{1}{z[1-(2/z)]}.\right]$

(c) $\dfrac{1}{(z-1)(z-2)}$ for $|z| < 1$   [*Hint: use partial fractions.*]

(d) $\dfrac{1}{(z-1)(z-2)}$ for $1 < |z| < 2$

(e) $\dfrac{1}{(z-1)^2}$ for $|z| < 1$     [*Hint: use Prob. 1.*]

(f) $\dfrac{1}{(z-1)^2}$ for $|z| > 1$   $\left[\text{Hint: } \dfrac{1}{(z-1)^2} = \dfrac{1}{z^2[1-(1/z)]^2}.\right]$

(g) $\dfrac{1}{(z-a)^m}$ for $|z| < |a|$,   $m = 1, 2, \ldots$

(h) $\dfrac{1}{(z-a)^m}$ for $|z| > |a|$,   $m = 1, 2, \ldots$

3. Expand in Laurent series at the isolated singularity given and state the type of singularity:

(a) $\dfrac{e^z}{z}$ at $z = 0$;    (b) $\dfrac{1 - \cos z}{z}$ at $z = 0$;

(c) $\dfrac{1}{z(z-1)^2}$ at $z = 1$     [*Hint: set $z_1 = z - 1$ and expand about $z_1 = 0$.*]

(d) csc $z$ at $z = 0$

[*Hint:*

$$\operatorname{csc} z = \frac{1}{\sin z} = \frac{1}{z - z^3/3! + \cdots}.$$

*Hence there is a first order pole at $z = 0$. Now set*

$$\operatorname{csc} z = \frac{1}{z - z^3/3! + \cdots} = \frac{a_{-1}}{z} + a_0 + a_1 z + \cdots$$

*and determine the coefficients $a_{-1}, a_0, \ldots$ so that*

$$1 = \left(z - \frac{z^3}{3!} + \cdots\right)\left(\frac{a_{-1}}{z} + a_0 + \cdots\right).\Big]$$

(e) csc $z$ at $z = \pi$     [*Hint: set $z_1 = z - \pi$ and proceed as in (d).*]

(f) cot $z$ at $z = 0$.

4. Let $f(z)$ be analytic for $|z| < R$ except for poles at $z_1, \ldots, z_k$. Let the principal part of $f(z)$ at $z_1$ be $p_1(z)$, at $z_2$ be $p_2(z)$, etc.

(a) Show that $f(z) - p_1(z) - p_2(z) - \cdots - p_k(z)$ is analytic for $|z| < R$ except for removable singularities, and can be represented by a Taylor series:

$$f(z) - p_1(z) - \cdots - p_k(z) = \sum_{n=0}^{\infty} a_n z^n, \quad |z| < R.$$

(b) Let $R_1$ be the maximum of $|z_1|, \cdots, |z_k|$, so that $f(z)$ is analytic for $R_1 < |z| < R$. Show that the Laurent expansion of $f(z)$ in this annulus is given by

$$f(z) = \sum_{n=-\infty}^{\infty} a_n z^n, \quad R_1 < |z| < R,$$

where the terms $a_0 + a_1 z + \cdots$ are obtained as in part (a) and

$$p_1(z) + \cdots + p_k(z) = \sum_{n=-\infty}^{-1} a_n z^n$$

is the Laurent expansion of $p_1(z) + \cdots + p_k(z)$ about $\infty$.

5. Expand csc $z$ in a Laurent series for $\pi < |z| < 2\pi$.

[*Hint: proceed as in Prob. 3(d) and (e) to find the principal parts $p_1(z)$, $p_2(z)$, $p_3(z)$ at $0$, $\pi$, $-\pi$ respectively. Set*]

$$\frac{1}{\sin z} - p_1(z) - p_2(z) - p_3(z) = \sum_{n=0}^{\infty} a_n z^n$$

*as in Prob. 4(a) and determine $a_0$, $a_1$, ... so that this is an identity; this requires clearing of denominators and replacement of $\sin z$ by $z - (z^3/3!) + \cdots$. Now proceed as in Prob. 4(b).*]

6. Expand in Laurent series in the annulus given:

    (a)  $\sec z$,  $\frac{1}{2}\pi < |z| < \frac{3}{2}\pi$

    (b)  $\dfrac{z}{z^2 - 1}$,  $1 < |z - 2| < 3$    [*Hint: set $z_1 = z - 2$.*]

    (c)  $\dfrac{e^z}{z - 1}$,  $|z| > 1$.

7. Let $A(z)$ and $B(z)$ be analytic at $z = z_0$; let $A(z_0) \neq 0$ and let $B(z)$ have a zero of order $N$ at $z_0$, so that

$$f(z) = \frac{A(z)}{B(z)} = \frac{a_0 + a_1(z - z_0) + \cdots}{b_N(z - z_0)^N + b_{N+1}(z - z_0)^{N+1} + \cdots}$$

has a pole of order $N$ at $z_0$. Show that the principal part of $f(z)$ at $z_0$ is

$$\frac{a_0}{b_N} \frac{1}{(z - z_0)^N} + \frac{a_1 b_N - a_0 b_{N+1}}{b_N^2} \frac{1}{(z - z_0)^{N-1}} + \cdots$$

and obtain the next term explicitly.

[*Hint: set*

$$\frac{a_0 + a_1(z - z_0) + \cdots}{b_N(z - z_0)^N + b_{N+1}(z - z_0)^{N+1} + \cdots} = \frac{c_{-N}}{(z - z_0)^N} + \frac{c_{-N+1}}{(z - z_0)^{N-1}} + \cdots,$$

*multiply across, and solve for $c_{-N}$, $c_{-N+1}$, ....*]

8. Find principal parts at the points indicated, with the aid of the result of Prob. 7:

    (a)  $\csc z$ at $z = 0$             (b)  $\csc z$ at $z = \pi$

    (c)  $\tan z$ at $z = \dfrac{\pi}{2}$        (d)  $\dfrac{z}{z^2 + 1}$ at $z = i$

    (e)  $\dfrac{z}{(z^4 - 1)^2}$ at $z = i$      (f)  $\tan^2 z$ at $z = \dfrac{\pi}{2}$.

9. Let $f(z)$ be a rational function in lowest terms:

$$f(z) = \frac{a_0 z^n + a_1 z^{n-1} + \cdots + a_n}{b_0 z^m + b_1 z^{m-1} + \cdots + b_m},\qquad a_0 b_0 \neq 0.$$

The *degree* $d$ of $f(z)$ is defined to be the larger of $m$ and $n$. Assuming the fundamental theorem of algebra, show that $f(z)$ has precisely $d$ zeros and $d$ poles in the extended $z$ plane, a pole or zero of order $N$ being counted as $N$ poles or zeros.

10. Locate all zeros and poles in the extended $z$ plane (cf. Prob. 9):

(a) $\dfrac{z^2 - 1}{z^2 + 1}$

(b) $\dfrac{z - 1}{z^3 + 1}$

(c) $\dfrac{(z - 1)^2(z + 2)^3}{z}$

(d) $\dfrac{1}{(z - 1)^3}$.

11. Let $z_1 = x_1 + iy_1$ project on the point $(x, y, t)$ under the stereographic projection described above. Show that

(a) $x = \dfrac{x_1}{1 + x_1^2 + y_1^2}$, $\quad y = \dfrac{y_1}{1 + x_1^2 + y_1^2}$, $\quad t = \dfrac{x_1^2 + y_1^2}{1 + x_1^2 + y_1^2}$

(b) a circle in the $z_1$ plane projects on a circle

(c) $\bar{z}_1$ projects on $(x, -y, t)$, $-z_1$ projects on $(-x, -y, t)$, $-1/\bar{z}_1$ projects on the point diametrically opposite to $(x, y, t)$.

12. Prove *Riemann's theorem: If* $|f(z)|$ *is bounded in a deleted neighborhood of an isolated singularity* $z_0$, *then* $z_0$ *is a removable singularity of* $f(z)$.

[*Hint: proceed as in Prob. 7 following Section 5–4, with the aid of (6–14), to show that* $a_n = 0$ *for* $n < 0$.]

13. Prove the *Theorem of Weierstrass and Casorati: If* $z_0$ *is an essential singularity of* $f(z)$, $c$ *is an arbitrary complex number, and* $\epsilon > 0$, *then* $|f(z) - c| < \epsilon$ *for some* $z$ *in every neighborhood of* $z_0$.

[*Hint: if the property fails, then* $1/[f(z) - c]$ *is analytic and bounded in absolute value in a deleted neighborhood of* $z_0$. *Now apply Prob. 12 and conclude that* $f(z)$ *has a pole or removable singularity at* $z_0$.]

## ANSWERS

2. (a) $-\displaystyle\sum_{n=0}^{\infty} \dfrac{z^n}{2^{n+1}}$,

(b) $\displaystyle\sum_{n=0}^{\infty} \dfrac{2^n}{z^{n+1}}$,

(c) $\displaystyle\sum_{n=0}^{\infty} z^n \left(1 - \dfrac{1}{2^{n+1}}\right)$,

(d) $-\displaystyle\sum_{n=0}^{\infty} \dfrac{z^n}{2^{n+1}} - \sum_{n=1}^{\infty} \dfrac{1}{z^n}$,

(e) $\displaystyle\sum_{n=0}^{\infty} (n + 1)z^n$,

(f) $\displaystyle\sum_{n=2}^{\infty} \dfrac{n - 1}{z^n}$,

(g) $\dfrac{1}{(-a)^m}\left[1+\displaystyle\sum_{n=1}^{\infty}\dfrac{m(m+1)\,\cdots\,(m+n-1)}{n!}\,\dfrac{z^n}{a^n}\right],$

(h) $\dfrac{1}{z^m}+\displaystyle\sum_{n=1}^{\infty}\dfrac{m(m+1)\,\cdots\,(m+n-1)}{n!}\,\dfrac{a^n}{z^{m+n}}.$

3. (a) $\displaystyle\sum_{n=0}^{\infty}\dfrac{z^{n-1}}{n!}$, pole of order 1;

(b) $\displaystyle\sum_{n=1}^{\infty}\dfrac{(-1)^{n-1}}{(2n)!}\,z^{2n-1}$, removable;

(c) $\displaystyle\sum_{n=0}^{\infty}(-1)^n(z-1)^{n-2}$, pole of order 2;

(d) $\dfrac{1}{z}+\dfrac{1}{6}z+\dfrac{7}{360}z^3+\cdots$, pole of order 1;

(e) $-\dfrac{1}{z-\pi}-\dfrac{1}{6}(z-\pi)-\dfrac{7}{360}(z-\pi)^3+\cdots$, pole of order 1;

(f) $\dfrac{1}{z}-\dfrac{1}{3}z-\dfrac{1}{45}z^3+\cdots$, pole of order 1.

5. $-\dfrac{1}{z}-2\displaystyle\sum_{n=1}^{\infty}\dfrac{\pi^{2n}}{z^{2n+1}}+\left(\dfrac{1}{6}-\dfrac{2}{\pi^2}\right)z+\left(\dfrac{7}{360}-\dfrac{2}{\pi^4}\right)z^3+\cdots.$

6. (a) $-\pi\displaystyle\sum_{n=0}^{\infty}\dfrac{\pi^{2n}}{4^n z^{2n+2}}+1-\dfrac{4}{\pi}+\left(\dfrac{1}{2}-\dfrac{16}{\pi^3}\right)z^2+\cdots,$

(b) $\dfrac{1}{2}\displaystyle\sum_{n=1}^{\infty}\dfrac{(-1)^{n+1}}{(z-2)^n}+\dfrac{1}{6}\displaystyle\sum_{n=0}^{\infty}\dfrac{(-1)^n}{3^n}(z-2)^n,$

(c) $\displaystyle\sum_{n=0}^{\infty}\left[e-\left(1+1+\dfrac{1}{2!}+\cdots+\dfrac{1}{n!}\right)\right]z^n+e\displaystyle\sum_{n=1}^{\infty}\dfrac{1}{z^n}.$

7. $\dfrac{a_2 b_N^2 - a_1 b_N b_{N+1} - a_0 b_{N+2} b_N + a_0 b_{N+1}^2}{b_N^3 (z-z_0)^{N-2}}.$

8. (a) $\dfrac{1}{z},$      (b) $\dfrac{-1}{z-\pi},$      (c) $-\dfrac{1}{z-\frac{1}{2}\pi},$

(d) $\dfrac{1}{2}\dfrac{1}{z-i},$      (e) $\dfrac{-i}{16}\dfrac{1}{(z-i)^2}+\dfrac{1}{8}\dfrac{1}{z-i},$      (f) $\dfrac{1}{(z-\frac{1}{2}\pi)^2}.$

10. Zeros: (a) $\pm 1,$             (b) $1,\infty,\infty,$
                (c) $1,1,-2,-2,-2,$       (d) $\infty,\infty,\infty;$

     poles: (a) $\pm i,$             (b) $-1,\frac{1}{2}\pm\frac{1}{2}\sqrt{3}\,i,$
              (c) $0,\infty,\infty,\infty,\infty,$      (d) $1,1,1.$

## 6–4 □ RESIDUES

Let $f(z)$ be analytic throughout a domain $D$ except for an isolated singularity at a certain finite point $z_0$ of $D$. The integral

$$\oint_C f(z)\, dz$$

will not in general be 0 on a simple closed path in $D$. However, the integral will have the same value on all curves $C$ which enclose $z_0$ and no other singularity of $f$. This value, divided by $2\pi i$, is known as the *residue* of $f(z)$ at $z_0$ and is denoted by Res $[f(z), z_0]$. Thus

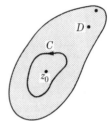

$$\text{Res } [f(z), z_0] = \frac{1}{2\pi i} \oint_C f(z)\, dz \quad (z_0 \text{ finite}),$$

$$(6\text{--}40)$$

where the integral is taken on any path $C$ in $D$ within which $f(z)$ is analytic except at $z_0$ (Fig. 6–4).

Fig. 6–4.  Residue.

**Theorem 44.** *The residue of $f(z)$ at a finite point $z_0$ is given by the equation*

$$\text{Res } [f(z), z_0] = a_{-1}, \qquad (6\text{--}41)$$

*where*

$$f(z) = \cdots + \frac{a_{-N}}{(z - z_0)^N} + \cdots + \frac{a_{-1}}{z - z_0} + a_0 + a_1(z - z_0) + \cdots$$

$$(6\text{--}42)$$

*is the Laurent expansion of $f(z)$ at $z_0$.*

*Proof.* To evaluate the integral (6–40), we choose as $C$ a circle $|z - z_0| = k$ in $D$ enclosing no singularity other than $z_0$. The Laurent series converges uniformly on $C$, by Theorem 42, and hence one can integrate (6–42) term by term. But

$$\oint \frac{1}{(z - z_0)^n}\, dz = \int_0^{2\pi} \frac{kie^{i\theta}}{k^n e^{ni\theta}}\, d\theta = \begin{cases} 0, & n \neq 1, \\ 2\pi i, & n = 1, \end{cases}$$

so that

$$\oint_C f(z)\, dz = 2\pi i a_{-1}.$$

It should be noted that this relation is the case $n = -1$ of (6–14).

EXAMPLE 1.   $\operatorname{Res}\left[\dfrac{1}{z^2(z-1)}, 0\right] = -1$, since

$$\frac{1}{z^2(z-1)} = -\frac{1}{z^2} - \frac{1}{z} - 1 - \cdots - z^n - \cdots, \quad 0 < |z| < 1.$$

EXAMPLE 2.   $\operatorname{Res}\left[\dfrac{1}{z^2(z^2-1)}, 0\right] = 0$, since

$$\frac{1}{z^2(z^2-1)} = -\frac{1}{z^2} - 1 - z^2 - \cdots - z^{2n} - \cdots, \quad 0 < |z| < 1.$$

Thus the residue can be 0, even though $f(z)$ has a nonremovable singularity at $z_0$.

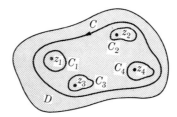

FIG. 6–5.  Cauchy residue theorem.

If $C$ is a simple closed path in $D$, within which $f(z)$ is analytic except for isolated singularities at $z_1, \ldots, z_k$, then by Theorem 36 (Section 5–2)

$$\oint_C f(z)\, dz = \oint_{C_1} f(z)\, dz + \cdots + \oint_{C_k} f(z)\, dz,$$

where $C_1$ encloses only the singularity at $z_1$, $C_2$ encloses only $z_2$, . . . as in Fig. 6–5. One thus obtains the following basic theorem:

**Theorem 45** (Cauchy's residue theorem).  *If $f(z)$ is analytic in a domain $D$ and $C$ is a simple closed curve in $D$ within which $f(z)$ is analytic except for isolated singularities at $z_1, \ldots, z_k$, then*

$$\oint_C f(z)\, dz = 2\pi i \{\operatorname{Res}[f(z), z_1] + \cdots + \operatorname{Res}[f(z), z_k]\}. \qquad (6\text{–}43)$$

This theorem permits rapid evaluation of integrals on closed paths, wherever it is possible to compute the coefficient $a_{-1}$ of the Laurent expansion at each singularity inside the path. Various techniques for obtaining the Laurent expansion are illustrated in the problems preceding this section. However, if one wishes only the term in $(z - z_0)^{-1}$ of the expansion, various simplifications are possible. We give several rules here:

*Rule I. At a simple pole $z_0$* (i.e., a pole of first order),

$$\text{Res}\,[f(z), z_0] = \lim_{z \to z_0} (z - z_0) f(z).$$

*Rule II. At a pole $z_0$ of order $N$ ($N = 2, 3, \ldots$),*

$$\text{Res}\,[f(z), z_0] = \lim_{z \to z_0} \frac{g^{(N-1)}(z)}{(N - 1)!},$$

*where* $g(z) = (z - z_0)^N f(z)$.

*Rule III. If $A(z)$ and $B(z)$ are analytic in a neighborhood of $z_0$, $A(z_0) \neq 0$, and $B(z)$ has a zero at $z_0$ of order 1, then*

$$f(z) = \frac{A(z)}{B(z)}$$

*has a pole of first order at $z_0$ and*

$$\text{Res}\,[f(z), z_0] = \frac{A(z_0)}{B'(z_0)}.$$

*Rule IV. If $A(z)$ and $B(z)$ are as in Rule III, but $B(z)$ has a zero of second order at $z_0$, so that $f(z)$ has a pole of second order at $z_0$, then*

$$\text{Res}\,[f(z), z_0] = \frac{6A'B'' - 2AB'''}{3B''^2}, \tag{6–44}$$

*where $A$ and the derivatives $A'$, $B''$, $B'''$ are evaluated at $z_0$.*

*Proofs of rules.* Let $f(z)$ have a pole of order $N$:

$$f(z) = \frac{1}{(z - z_0)^N} [a_{-N} + a_{-N+1}(z - z_0) + \cdots] = \frac{1}{(z - z_0)^N} g(z),$$

where

$$g(z) = (z - z_0)^N f(z), \qquad g(z_0) = a_{-N},$$

and $g$ is analytic at $z_0$. The coefficient of $(z - z_0)^{-1}$ in the Laurent series for $f(z)$ is the coefficient of $(z - z_0)^{N-1}$ in the Taylor series for $g(z)$. This coefficient, which is the residue sought, is

$$\frac{g^{(N-1)}(z_0)}{(N - 1)!} = \lim_{z \to z_0} \frac{g^{(N-1)}(z)}{(N - 1)!}.$$

For $N = 1$ this gives Rule I; for $N = 2$ or higher, we obtain Rule II.

Rules III and IV follow from the identity

$$\frac{A(z)}{B(z)} = \frac{a_0 + a_1(z - z_0) + \cdots}{b_N(z - z_0)^N + b_{N+1}(z - z_0)^{N+1} + \cdots}$$

$$= \frac{a_0}{b_N} \frac{1}{(z - z_0)^N} + \frac{a_1 b_N - a_0 b_{N+1}}{b_N^2} \frac{1}{(z - z_0)^{N-1}} + \cdots$$

derived in Prob. 7 above. For a first order pole, $N = 1$ and the residue is

$$\frac{a_0}{b_1} = \frac{A(z_0)}{B'(z_0)}.$$

For a second order pole, $N = 2$ and the residue is $(a_1 b_2 - a_0 b_3)/b_2^2$. Since

$$a_0 = A(z_0), \qquad a_1 = A'(z_0), \qquad b_2 = \frac{B''(z_0)}{2!}, \qquad b_3 = \frac{B'''(z_0)}{3!},$$

this reduces to the expression (6–44). As indicated in Prob. 7, the procedure is easily generalized to take care of a pole of third or higher order; it is also easily modified to cover the case when $A(z)$ has a zero of order $M$ at $z_0$, while $B(z)$ has a zero of order $N$, and $N > M$ (see Prob. 9 below).

EXAMPLE 3

$$\oint_{|z|=2} \frac{ze^z}{z^2 - 1} \, dz = 2\pi i \{ \text{Res} \, [f(z), 1] + \text{Res} \, [f(z), -1] \}.$$

Since $f(z)$ has first order poles at $\pm 1$, one finds by Rule I

$$\text{Res} \, [f(z), 1] = \lim_{z \to 1} (z - 1) \cdot \frac{ze^z}{z^2 - 1} = \lim_{z \to 1} \frac{ze^z}{z + 1} = \frac{e}{2},$$

$$\text{Res} \, [f(z), -1] = \lim_{z \to -1} (z + 1) \cdot \frac{ze^z}{z^2 - 1} = \lim_{z \to -1} \frac{ze^z}{z - 1} = \frac{-e^{-1}}{-2}.$$

Accordingly,

$$\oint_{|z|=2} \frac{ze^z}{z^2 - 1} \, dz = 2\pi i \left( \frac{e}{2} + \frac{e^{-1}}{2} \right) = 2\pi i \cosh 1.$$

Rule III could also have been used:

$$\text{Res} \, [f(z), 1] = \frac{ze^z}{2z} \Big|_{z=1} = \frac{e}{2},$$

$$\text{Res} \, [f(z), -1] = \frac{ze^z}{2z} \Big|_{z=-1} = \frac{-e^{-1}}{-2}.$$

This is simpler than Rule I, since the expression

$$\frac{A(z)}{B'(z)},$$

once computed, serves for all poles of the prescribed type.

EXAMPLE 4

$$\oint_{|z|=2} \frac{z}{z^4 - 1} \, dz = 2\pi i \{\text{Res}\,[f(z),\,1] + \text{Res}\,[f(z),\,-1] \\ + \text{Res}\,[f(z),\,i] + \text{Res}\,[f(z),\,-i]\}.$$

All poles are of first order. Rule III gives

$$\frac{A(z)}{B'(z)} = \frac{z}{4z^3} = \frac{1}{4z^2}$$

as the expression for the residue at any one of the four points. Moreover, $z^4 = 1$ at each pole, so that

$$\frac{1}{4z^2} = \frac{z^2}{4z^4} = \frac{z^2}{4}.$$

Hence

$$\oint_{|z|=2} \frac{z}{z^4 - 1} \, dz = \frac{2\pi i}{4}[1 + 1 - 1 - 1] = 0.$$

EXAMPLE 5

$$\oint_{|z|=2} \frac{e^z}{z(z-1)^2} \, dz = 2\pi i \{\text{Res}\,[f(z),\,0] + \text{Res}\,[f(z),\,1]\}.$$

At the first order pole $z = 0$, application of Rule I gives the residue: 1. At the second order pole $z = 1$, Rule II gives

$$\text{Res}\,[f(z),\,1] = \frac{d}{dz}\left(\frac{e^z}{z}\right)\Bigg|_{z=1} = \frac{e^z(z-1)}{z^2}\Bigg|_{z=1} = 0.$$

Rule IV could also be used, with $A = e^z$, $B = z^3 - 2z^2 + z$:

$$\text{Res}\,[f(z),\,1] = \frac{6e^z(6z-4) - 2e^z \cdot 6}{3(6z-4)^2}\Bigg|_{z=1} = 0.$$

Accordingly,

$$\oint_{|z|=2} \frac{e^z}{z(z-1)^2} \, dz = 2\pi i(1 + 0) = 2\pi i.$$

EXAMPLE 6

$$\oint_{|z|=2} \frac{\tan z}{z}\, dz = 2\pi i\{\mathrm{Res}\,[f(z), \tfrac{1}{2}\pi] + \mathrm{Res}\,[f(z), -\tfrac{1}{2}\pi]\},$$

for the singularity at $z = 0$ is removable and the only other singularities within the path are $\pm\tfrac{1}{2}\pi$. At these points $\cos z$ has a first order zero (since its derivative, $-\sin z$, is not zero at either point), so that $\tan z$ has a first order pole. Rule I gives

$$\mathrm{Res}\,[f(z), \tfrac{1}{2}\pi] = \lim_{z\to(1/2)\pi} \frac{(z - \tfrac{1}{2}\pi)\tan z}{z}.$$

Here no cancellation is possible, unless series are introduced:

$$\frac{(z - \tfrac{1}{2}\pi)\tan z}{z} = \frac{(z - \tfrac{1}{2}\pi)\sin z}{z\cos z} = \frac{(z - \tfrac{1}{2}\pi)\sin z}{z[-(z - \tfrac{1}{2}\pi) + \tfrac{1}{6}(z - \tfrac{1}{2}\pi)^3 + \cdots]}$$

$$= \frac{\sin z}{z[-1 + \tfrac{1}{6}(z - \tfrac{1}{2}\pi)^2 + \cdots]}.$$

We can now take the limit and find

$$\mathrm{Res}\,[f(z), \tfrac{1}{2}\pi] = \frac{1}{-\tfrac{1}{2}\pi}.$$

Rule III would give, with $A = \sin z$, $B = z\cos z$,

$$\mathrm{Res}\,[f(z), \tfrac{1}{2}\pi] = \left.\frac{\sin z}{\cos z - z\sin z}\right|_{z=(1/2)\pi} = \frac{1}{-\tfrac{1}{2}\pi}.$$

The two methods are essentially the same here. However, we have at once

$$\mathrm{Res}\,[f(z), -\tfrac{1}{2}\pi] = \left.\frac{\sin z}{\cos z - z\sin z}\right|_{z=-(1/2)\pi} = \frac{-1}{-\tfrac{1}{2}\pi}.$$

Accordingly,

$$\oint_{|z|=2} \frac{\tan z}{z}\, dz = 2\pi i\left(-\frac{2}{\pi} + \frac{2}{\pi}\right) = 0.$$

This example shows that the effectiveness of Rule I and, even more so, of Rule II is greatly reduced if no cancellation is possible. It is of interest to note that, when this difficulty arises, one can obtain the limit by the familiar procedure for indeterminate forms, as shown in Prob. 11 below.

## 6–5 □ RESIDUE AT INFINITY

Let $f(z)$ be analytic for $|z| > R$. The *residue of* $f(z)$ *at* $\infty$ is defined as follows:

$$\text{Res}\,[f(z),\,\infty] = \frac{1}{2\pi i} \oint_C f(z)\,dz,$$

where the integral is taken in the *negative* direction on a simple closed path $C$, in the domain of analyticity of $f(z)$, and *outside* of which $f(z)$ has no singularity other than $\infty$. This is suggested in Fig. 6–6. Theorem 44 has an immediate extension to this case:

**Theorem 44a.** *The residue of* $f(z)$ *at* $\infty$ *is given by the equation:*

$$\text{Res}\,[f(z),\,\infty] = -a_{-1}, \tag{6–50}$$

*where* $a_{-1}$ *is the coefficient of* $z^{-1}$ *in the Laurent expansion of* $f(z)$ *at* $\infty$ :

$$f(z) = \cdots + \frac{a_{-n}}{z^n} + \cdots + \frac{a_{-1}}{z} + a_0 + a_1 z + \cdots. \tag{6–51}$$

The proof is the same as for Theorem 44, since only the term in $z^{-1}$ contributes to the integral. It should be stressed that presence of a residue at $\infty$ is not related to presence of a pole or essential singularity at $\infty$; that is, $f(z)$ can have a nonzero residue whether or not there is a pole or essential singularity. The pole or essential singularity at $\infty$ is due to the *positive powers* of $z$, not to negative powers (Section 6–3). Thus the function

$$e^{1/z} = 1 + \frac{1}{z} + \frac{1}{2!z^2} + \cdots$$

is analytic at $\infty$, but has the residue $-1$ there.

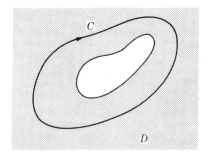

FIG. 6–6.   Residue at infinity.

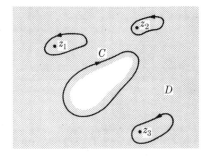

FIG. 6–7. Residue theorem for exterior.

Cauchy's residue theorem has also an extension to include $\infty$:

**Theorem 45a.**  *Let $f(z)$ be analytic in a domain $D$ which includes a deleted neighborhood of $\infty$.  Let $C$ be a simple closed path in $D$ outside of which $f(z)$ is analytic except for isolated singularities at $z_1, \ldots, z_k$.  Then*

$$\oint_C f(z) \, dz = 2\pi i \{\operatorname{Res}[f(z), z_1] + \cdots + \operatorname{Res}[f(z), z_k]$$
$$+ \operatorname{Res}[f(z), \infty]\}. \qquad (6\text{--}52)$$

The proof, which is like that of Theorem 45, is left as an exercise (Prob. 6 below).  It is to be emphasized that the integral on $C$ is taken in the *negative* direction (see Fig. 6–7) and that the *residue at $\infty$ must be included* on the right.

For a particular integral

$$\oint_C f(z) \, dz$$

on a simple closed path $C$ one has now two modes of evaluation: the integral equals $2\pi i$ times the sum of the residues inside the path (provided there are only a finite number of singularities there), and it also equals *minus* $2\pi i$ times the sum of the residues outside the path plus that at $\infty$ (provided there are only a finite number of singularities in the exterior domain).  One can evaluate the integral both ways to check results.  The principle involved here is summarized in the theorem:

**Theorem 46.**  *If $f(z)$ is analytic in the extended $z$ plane except for a finite number of singularities, then the sum of all residues of $f(z)$ (including $\infty$) is zero.*

To evaluate residues at $\infty$, one can formulate a set of rules like the ones above.  However, the following two rules are adequate for most purposes:

*Rule V.  If $f(z)$ has a zero of first order at $\infty$, then*

$$\operatorname{Res}[f(z), \infty] = -\lim_{z \to \infty} z f(z).$$

*If $f(z)$ has a zero of second or higher order at $\infty$, the residue at $\infty$ is 0.*

*Rule VI.*  $\operatorname{Res}[f(z), \infty] = -\operatorname{Res}\left[\dfrac{1}{z^2} f\left(\dfrac{1}{z}\right), 0\right].$

The proof of Rule V is left as an exercise (Prob. 10 below).  To prove Rule VI, we write

$$f(z) = \cdots + a_n z^n + \cdots + a_1 z + a_0 + \frac{a_{-1}}{z} + \frac{a_{-2}}{z^2} + \cdots, \quad |z| > R.$$

Then

$$f\left(\frac{1}{z}\right) = \cdots + \frac{a_n}{z^n} + \cdots + \frac{a_1}{z} + a_0 + a_{-1} z + a_{-2} z^2 + \cdots,$$

$$0 < |z| < \frac{1}{R},$$

$$\frac{1}{z^2} f\left(\frac{1}{z}\right) = \cdots + \frac{a_0}{z^2} + \frac{a_{-1}}{z} + a_{-2} + \cdots.$$

Hence

$$\text{Res}\left[\frac{1}{z^2} f\left(\frac{1}{z}\right), 0\right] = a_{-1},$$

and the rule follows.  This result reduces the problem to evaluation of a residue at 0, to which Rules I to IV are applicable.

EXAMPLE 1.  We consider the integral

$$\oint_{|z|=2} \frac{z}{z^4 - 1}\, dz$$

of Example 4 in the preceding section.  There is no singularity outside the path other than $\infty$, and at $\infty$ the function has a zero of order 3; hence the integral is 0.

EXAMPLE 2

$$\oint_{|z|=2} \frac{1}{(z + 1)^4 (z^2 - 9)(z - 4)}\, dz.$$

Here there is a fourth order pole inside the path, at which evaluation of the residue is tedious.  Outside the path there are first order poles at $\pm 3$ and 4 and a zero of order 7 at $\infty$.  Hence, by Rule I,

$$\oint_{|z|=2} \frac{1}{(z + 1)^4 (z^2 - 9)(z - 4)}\, dz =$$

$$-2\pi i \left( \frac{1}{4^4 6(-1)} + \frac{1}{(-2)^4(-6)(-7)} + \frac{1}{5^4 \cdot 7} \right).$$

## 6-6 □ LOGARITHMIC RESIDUES—ARGUMENT PRINCIPLE

Let $f(z)$ be analytic in a domain $D$. Then

$$\frac{f'(z)}{f(z)} \tag{6-60}$$

is analytic in $D$ except at the zeros of $f(z)$. If an analytic branch of $\log f(z)$ is chosen in part of $D$ [necessarily excluding the zeros of $f(z)$], then

$$\frac{d}{dz} \log f(z) = \frac{f'(z)}{f(z)}.$$

For this reason the expression (6-60) is termed the *logarithmic derivative* of $f(z)$. Its value is demonstrated by the following theorem.

**Theorem 47.** *Let $f(z)$ be analytic in domain $D$. Let $C$ be a simple closed path in $D$ within which $f(z)$ is analytic except for a finite number of poles and let $f(z) \neq 0$ on $C$. Then*

$$\frac{1}{2\pi i} \oint_C \frac{f'(z)}{f(z)}\, dz = N_0 - N_p,$$

*where $N_0$ is the total number of zeros of $f$ inside $C$ and $N_p$ is the total number of poles of $f$ inside $C$, zeros and poles being counted according to their multiplicities.*

*Proof.* The logarithmic derivative $f'/f$ has isolated singularities precisely at the zeros and poles of $f$. At a zero $z_0$,

$$f(z) = (z - z_0)^N g(z), \quad g(z_0) \neq 0,$$
$$f'(z) = (z - z_0)^N g'(z) + N(z - z_0)^{N-1} g(z),$$
$$\frac{f'(z)}{f(z)} = \frac{(z - z_0)^N g'(z) + N(z - z_0)^{N-1} g(z)}{(z - z_0)^N g(z)} = \frac{g'(z)}{g(z)} + \frac{N}{z - z_0}.$$

Hence the logarithmic derivative has a pole of first order, with residue $N$ equal to the multiplicity of the zero. A similar analysis applies to the poles of $f$, with $N$ replaced by $-N$. The theorem then follows from the Cauchy residue theorem (Theorem 45), provided we show that there are only a finite number of singularities. The poles of $f$ are finite in number by assumption. If there were infinitely many zeros of $f$, then one could select a sequence $z_n = x_n + iy_n$ of distinct zeros inside $C$. Such a sequence would have to have at least one limiting value $z_0$, i.e., a point $z_0$, every neighborhood of which contains infinitely many members of the sequence (see pp. 59–61 of *Complex Analysis* by L. V. Ahlfors). If $f(z_0) = 0$, then $f(z) \neq 0$ in a deleted neighborhood of $z_0$, by Theorem 43; if $f(z_0) \neq 0$, then $f(z) \neq 0$ in a neighborhood of $z_0$ by continuity; if $z_0$ is a pole, then $f$ approaches $\infty$ as $z$ approaches $z_0$, so that $f(z) \neq 0$ in a suitable neighborhood of $z_0$. Thus $z_0$ cannot be a limiting value of zeros, and there can only be a finite number of zeros in all. The theorem is proved.

As $z$ traces the path $C$, the point $w = f(z)$ traces a path $C_w$ in the $w$ plane. We can change variables as in Section 3–3 above and write

$$\frac{1}{2\pi i} \oint_C \frac{f'(z)}{f(z)}\,dz = \frac{1}{2\pi i} \int_{C_w} \frac{dw}{w}.$$

The path $C_w$ will be a closed path, but it may cross itself many times. By assumption, $f(z) \neq 0$ on $C$, so that $C_w$ does not pass through the origin of the $w$ plane. As remarked in Section 4–2, the integral

$$\int_{C_w}{}_{w_1}^{w_2} \frac{dw}{w} = \log w_2 - \log w_1$$

measures the total change in $\log w$ as $\log w$ varies continuously on the path. If $w_1 = w_2$, then

$$\log w_2 - \log w_1 = \log |w_2| + i \arg w_2 - (\log |w_1| + i \arg w_1)$$
$$= i(\arg w_2 - \arg w_1).$$

Hence on a closed path $C_w$, the integral

$$\int_{C_w} \frac{dw}{w}$$

is pure imaginary and measures $i$ times the total change in $\arg w$ as $\arg w$ varies continuously on the path. This total change in $\arg w$ must be a multiple of $2\pi$, since $w_1 = w_2$, and it can be considered as a measure of the number of times the path $C_w$ winds around the origin in the $w$ plane (Fig. 6–8). Also,

$$\int_{C_w} \frac{dw}{w} = i \int_{C_w} \frac{-v\,du + u\,dv}{u^2 + v^2}.$$

The integral on the right is a Kronecker integral (see Sections 5–6 and 5–14 of *Advanced Calculus*).

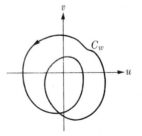

Fig. 6–8. Argument principle.

We summarize these various interpretations of the theorem:

$$\frac{1}{2\pi i} \oint_{C_z} \frac{f'(z)}{f(z)} \, dz = \frac{1}{2\pi} \text{ [increase in arg } f(z) \text{ on path]}$$

$$= N_0 - N_p = \frac{1}{2\pi i} \int_{C_w} \frac{dw}{w} = \frac{1}{2\pi} \int_{C_w} \frac{-v \, du + u \, dv}{u^2 + v^2}.$$

$$(6\text{--}61)$$

The statement

$$\frac{1}{2\pi} \text{ [increase in arg } f(z) \text{ on path]} = N_0 - N_p \qquad (6\text{--}62)$$

is known as the *argument principle*. This is of great value in finding roots of analytic functions.

**Theorem 48.** *Let $f(z)$ be analytic in domain $D$. Let $C_z$ be a simple closed path in $D$, within which $f(z)$ is analytic. If the function $f(z)$ maps the curve $C_z$ in a one-to-one fashion onto a simple closed path $C_w$ in the $w$ plane and $f'(z) \neq 0$ inside $C_z$, then $f(z)$ maps the interior of $C_z$ in a one-to-one fashion onto the entire interior of $C_w$.*

*Proof.* We first remark that the Jacobian of the transformation from the $xy$ plane to the $uv$ plane is

$$J = \frac{\partial(u, v)}{\partial(x, y)} = \begin{vmatrix} \dfrac{\partial u}{\partial x} & \dfrac{\partial u}{\partial y} \\ \dfrac{\partial v}{\partial x} & \dfrac{\partial v}{\partial y} \end{vmatrix} = \left(\frac{\partial u}{\partial x}\right)^2 + \left(\frac{\partial v}{\partial x}\right)^2 = |f'(z)|^2. \qquad (6\text{--}63)$$

Hence $J > 0$. It then follows [see Section 5–14 of *Advanced Calculus*] that, as $z$ traces $C_z$ in the positive direction, $w = f(z)$ traces $C_w$ in the positive direction. Hence, if $w_0$ is a point interior to $C_w$ (Fig. 6–9),

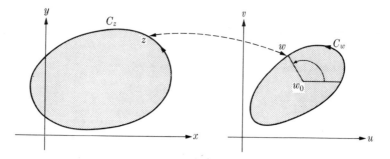

Fig. 6–9. One-to-one mapping.

arg $(w - w_0) = $ arg $[f(z) - w_0]$ increases by precisely $2\pi$. We apply the argument principle to the function $f(z) - w_0$ and, since this function has no poles inside $C_z$, conclude that

$$N_0 = \frac{1}{2\pi} \cdot 2\pi = 1;$$

that is, $f(z) - w_0$ has precisely one root $z_0$ inside $C_z$. Accordingly, an inverse transformation $z = z(w)$ is defined inside $C_w$ and, reversing the roles of $z$ and $w$ (cf. Prob. 7 following Section 5–6), we conclude that the correspondence between interiors is one-to-one.

**Corollary.**  *Let $f(z)$ be analytic in domain $D_z$ and map $D_z$ in a one-to-one fashion into the $w$ plane. Then $f'(z) \neq 0$ in $D_z$.*

*Proof.*  If $f'(z_0) = 0$, then choose a circle $C_z$ about $z_0$ lying with its interior in $D_z$. The function $f(z)$ maps $C_z$ onto $C_w$ as in the above theorem and, as in the above proof, $N_0 = 1$ for the function $f(z) - w_0$. However, since $f'(z_0) = 0$, $f(z) - w_0$ has a double root at $z_0$, so that $N_0 \geq 2$. This is a contradiction, hence $f'(z) \neq 0$ in $D_z$.

*Remark.*  Because of (6–63), the condition $f'(z) \neq 0$ is equivalent to the condition $J \neq 0$, which is sufficient to ensure a one-to-one transformation in a *sufficiently small neighborhood of a given point* (see *Advanced Calculus*, Section 2–8). The condition $f'(z) \neq 0$ in $D_z$ is not sufficient to guarantee a one-to-one transformation throughout all of $D_z$. For example, $w = z^2$ satisfies this condition for $z \neq 0$, but the transformation is not one-to-one, since the inverse is the two-valued function $z = \sqrt{w}$. Sufficient conditions for a one-to-one mapping, supplementing Theorem 48, are given in Section 7–1.

Both Theorems 47 and 48 can be extended to multiply connected domains (Prob. 7 below). The argument principle and Theorem 48 can also be extended, by a limiting process, to the case in which $f(z)$ is analytic only inside $C_z$ and continuous on $C_z$ plus interior; the requirement of analyticity of $f(z) = u + iv$ in Theorem 48 can even be replaced by the condition that $J = \partial(u, v)/\partial(x, y)$ be everywhere positive (or everywhere negative) inside $C_z$.

## PROBLEMS

1. Evaluate the following integrals on the paths given:

(a) $\oint \dfrac{z}{z + 1}\, dz, \quad |z| = 2$      (b) $\oint \dfrac{z}{z^3 + 1}\, dz, \quad |z| = 2$

(c) $\oint \dfrac{e^z}{z^2 - 1}\, dz, \quad |z| = 2$      (d) $\oint \dfrac{1}{z^4 + 1}\, dz, \quad |z - 1| = 2$

(e) $\oint \dfrac{1}{2z^2 + 3z - 2}\, dz, \quad |z| = 1$      (f) $\oint \dfrac{1}{z^2(z + 1)}\, dz, \quad |z| = 2$

(g) $\oint \dfrac{\sin z}{(z - 1)^2(z^2 + 9)}\, dz, \quad |z| = 2$

(h) $\oint \tan^2 z\, dz, \quad |z| = 10$      (i) $\oint \dfrac{z^7}{(z^4 + 1)^2}\, dz, \quad |z| = 2$

(j) $\oint \dfrac{4z^3 + 2z}{z^4 + z^2 + 1}\, dz, \quad |z| = 2$

(k) $\oint \dfrac{e^z}{z^3}\, dz, \quad |z| = 1$      (l) $\oint \dfrac{1}{(z - 1)^3(z - 7)}\, dz, \quad |z| = 2.$

2. Determine which of the following transformations from the $z$ plane to the $w$ plane is one-to-one in the domain given:

  (a) $w = z^2, \quad |z| < 1$
  (b) $w = z^2, \quad 0 < x < 1, \quad 0 < y < 1$
  (c) $w = e^z, \quad 0 < x < 1, \quad 0 < y < \pi$
  (d) $w = \sin z, \quad -\tfrac{1}{2}\pi < x < \tfrac{1}{2}\pi, \quad 0 < y < k.$

3. If a proper rational function $f(z)$ has only poles of first order:

$$f(z) = \frac{b_0 z^n + \cdots + b_{n-1} z + b_n}{(z - z_1)(z - z_2) \cdots (z - z_k)} \quad (n < k,\ z_1, \ldots, z_k \text{ distinct}),$$

then expansion of $f(z)$ in partial fractions:

$$f(z) = \frac{c_1}{z - z_1} + \cdots + \frac{c_k}{z - z_k}$$

requires only determination of the numbers $c_1, \ldots, c_k$, which are the residues of $f(z)$ at the poles. Apply this to obtain the partial expansions of the following functions:

(a) $\dfrac{1}{z^2 - 4}$      (b) $\dfrac{z + 1}{(z - 1)(z - 2)(z - 3)}$

(c) $\dfrac{z^2}{z^5 + 1}$      (d) $\dfrac{1}{z^n - 1}.$

4. Prove: Every proper rational function $f(z)$ has a partial fraction expansion.

[*Hint: let $p_1(z), \ldots, p_n(z)$ be the principal parts of $f(z)$ at its poles. Then $g(z) = f(z) - p_1(z) - p_2(z) - \cdots - p_n(z)$ is rational and has no poles. Show that $g(z)$ must be identically 0.*]

5. Prove the Fundamental Theorem of Algebra: *Every polynomial of degree at least 1 has a zero.*

[*Hint: show that* $\text{Res}[f'(z)/f(z), \infty]$ *is not* 0, *is in fact minus the degree* $n$ *of the polynomial* $f(z)$. *Then use Theorem 47 to show that* $f$ *has* $n$ *zeros.*]

6. Prove Theorem 45a.

7. Formulate and prove Theorem 47 for integration around the boundary $B$ of a region $R$ in $D$, bounded by simple closed curves $C_1, \ldots, C_k$.

8. Extend Rule IV of Section 6–4 to the case in which $B(z)$ has a third order zero.

[*Hint: use Prob. 7 following Section 6–3.*]

9. Extend Rule IV of Section 6–4 to the case in which $A(z)$ has a first order zero at $z_0$ and $B(z)$ has a second order zero.

10. Prove Rule V of Section 6–5.

11. Prove de l'Hôpital's rule for analytic functions: If $A(z)$ and $B(z)$ have zeros at $z_0$, then

$$\lim_{z \to z_0} \frac{A(z)}{B(z)} = \lim_{z \to z_0} \frac{A'(z)}{B'(z)},$$

provided the limit exists.

[*Hint: let* $A(z)$ *have a zero of multiplicity* $N$, $B(z)$ *one of multiplicity* $M$ *at* $z_0$. *Show that the limit of both sides is* 0 *if* $N > M$, *is* $A^N(z_0)/B^N(z_0)$ *if* $N = M$, *is* $\infty$ *if* $N < M$.]

12. Evaluate the following integral, applying Rule II and de l'Hôpital's rule (Prob. 11):

$$\oint \csc^3 z \, dz \quad \text{on } |z| = 1.$$

**ANSWERS**

1. (a) $-2\pi i$          (b) 0,
  (c) $2\pi i \sinh 1$,          (d) 0,
  (e) $\dfrac{2\pi i}{5}$,          (f) 0,
  (g) $2\pi i(0.1 \cos 1 - 0.02 \sin 1)$,          (h) 0,
  (i) $2\pi i$,          (j) $8\pi i$,
  (k) $\pi i$,          (l) $-\dfrac{\pi i}{108}$.

2. All except (a) are one-to-one.

3. (a) $\dfrac{1}{4}\dfrac{1}{z-2} - \dfrac{1}{4}\dfrac{1}{z+2}$ ;

     (b) $\dfrac{1}{z-1} - \dfrac{3}{z-2} + \dfrac{2}{z-3}$ ;

(c) $-\dfrac{1}{5}\left[\dfrac{z_2}{z-z_1} + \dfrac{z_5}{z-z_2} + \dfrac{z_3}{z-z_3} + \dfrac{z_1}{z-z_4} + \dfrac{z_4}{z-z_5}\right]$,

$$z_k = \exp\left(\dfrac{k\pi i}{5}\right), \qquad k = 1,3,5,7,9;$$

(d) $\dfrac{1}{n}\left[\dfrac{z_1}{z-z_1} + \cdots + \dfrac{z_n}{z-z_n}\right]$,    $z_k = \exp\left(\dfrac{2k\pi i}{n}\right), \qquad k = 1,\ldots,n.$

8. $\dfrac{120A''B'''^2 - 60A'B'''B^{iv} - 12AB'''B^v + 15AB^{iv2}}{40B'''^3}$

9. $\dfrac{2A'}{B''}$.                      12. $\pi i$.

## 6–7 □ APPLICATION OF RESIDUES TO EVALUATION OF REAL INTEGRALS

A variety of real definite integrals between special limits can be evaluated with the aid of residues.

For example, an integral

$$\int_0^{2\pi} R(\sin\theta, \cos\theta)\, d\theta,$$

where $R$ is a rational function of $\sin\theta$ and $\cos\theta$, is converted to a complex line integral by the substitution:

$$z = e^{i\theta}, \qquad dz = ie^{i\theta}\, d\theta = iz\, d\theta,$$

$$\cos\theta = \frac{e^{i\theta} + e^{-i\theta}}{2} = \frac{1}{2}\left(z + \frac{1}{z}\right),$$

$$\sin z = \frac{e^{i\theta} - e^{-i\theta}}{2i} = \frac{1}{2i}\left(z - \frac{1}{z}\right);$$

the path of integration is the circle: $|z| = 1$.

EXAMPLE 1

$$\int_0^{2\pi} \frac{1}{\cos\theta + 2}\, d\theta.$$

The substitution reduces this to

$$\oint_{|z|=1} \frac{-2i}{z^2 + 4z + 1}\, dz = 4\pi\, \mathrm{Res}[1/(z^2 + 4z + 1), -2 + \sqrt{3}],$$

since $-2 + \sqrt{3}$ is the only root of the denominator inside the circle. Accordingly,

$$\int_0^{2\pi} \frac{1}{\cos \theta + 2} \, d\theta = \frac{2\pi}{\sqrt{3}}.$$

The substitution can be summarized in the one rule:

$$\int_0^{2\pi} R(\sin \theta, \cos \theta) \, d\theta = \oint_{|z|=1} R\left(\frac{z^2 - 1}{2iz}, \frac{z^2 + 1}{2z}\right) \frac{dz}{iz}. \qquad (6\text{--}70)$$

The complex integral can be evaluated by residues, provided $R$ has no poles on the circle $|z| = 1$.

A second example is provided by integrals of the type

$$\int_{-\infty}^{\infty} f(x) \, dx.$$

We illustrate the procedure with an example and formulate a general principle below.

EXAMPLE 2. $\int_{-\infty}^{\infty} dx/(x^4 + 1)$. This integral can be regarded as a line integral of $f(z) = 1/(z^4 + 1)$ along the real axis. The path is not closed (unless one adjoins $\infty$), but we show that it acts like a closed path "enclosing" the upper half-plane, so that the integral along the path equals the sum of the residues in the upper half-plane.

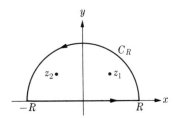

FIG. 6–10.  Evaluation of $\int_{-\infty}^{\infty} f(x) \, dx$ by residues.

To establish this, we consider the integral of $f(z)$ on the semicircular path $C_R$ shown in Fig. 6–10. When $R$ is sufficiently large, the path encloses the two poles: $z_1 = \exp(\frac{1}{4}i\pi)$, $z_2 = \exp(\frac{3}{4}i\pi)$ of $f(z)$. Hence

$$\oint_{C_R} f(z) \, dz = 2\pi i\{\text{Res}[f(z), z_1] + \text{Res}[f(z), z_2]\}.$$

As $R$ increases, the integral on $C_R$ cannot change, since it always equals the sum of the residues times $2\pi i$. Hence

$$\oint_{C_R} f(z)\, dz = \lim_{R \to \infty} \oint_{C_R} f(z)\, dz = \lim_{R \to \infty} \int_{-R}^{R} \frac{dx}{x^4 + 1} + \lim_{R \to \infty} \int_{D_R} \frac{1}{z^4 + 1}\, dz,$$

where $D_R$ is the semicircle: $z = Re^{i\theta}$, $0 \leq \theta \leq \pi$. The limit of the first term is the integral desired (since the limits at $+\infty$ and $-\infty$ exist separately, as required; cf. Section 4–4 of *Advanced Calculus*). The limit of the second term is 0, since on $D_R$

$$\left| \frac{1}{z^4 + 1} \right| \leq \frac{1}{|z|^4 - 1} = \frac{1}{R^4 - 1}$$

by (1–15) and

$$\left| \int_{D_R} \frac{1}{z^4 + 1}\, dz \right| \leq \frac{\pi R}{R^4 - 1}.$$

Accordingly,

$$\int_{C_R} f(z)\, dz = \int_{-\infty}^{\infty} \frac{dx}{x^4 + 1} = 2\pi i \{\mathrm{Res}[f(z), z_1] + \mathrm{Res}[f(z), z_2]\}.$$

By Rule III above, the sum of the residues is

$$\frac{1}{4z_1^3} + \frac{1}{4z_2^3} = -\frac{1}{4}(z_1 + z_2) = -\frac{\sqrt{2}}{4} i$$

and hence

$$\int_{-\infty}^{\infty} \frac{dx}{x^4 + 1} = \frac{\pi \sqrt{2}}{2}.$$

We now formulate the general principle:

**Theorem 49.** *Let $f(z)$ be analytic in a domain $D$ which includes the real axis and all of the half-plane $y > 0$ except for a finite number of points. If*

$$\lim_{R \to \infty} \int_0^{\pi} f(Re^{i\theta}) Re^{i\theta}\, d\theta = 0 \tag{6–71}$$

*and*

$$\int_{-\infty}^{\infty} f(x)\, dx \tag{6–72}$$

*exists, then*

$$\int_{-\infty}^{\infty} f(x)\, dx = 2\pi i \{\text{sum of residues of } f(z) \text{ in the upper half-plane}\}.$$
$$\tag{6–73}$$

The proof is a repetition of the reasoning used in the above example. It is of interest to note that, even though the integral (6–72) fails to exist as improper integral, condition (6–71) implies that

$$\lim_{R \to \infty} \int_{-R}^{R} f(x) \, dx \qquad (6\text{–}74)$$

exists. Thus, while the integral from 0 to $+\infty$ and the integral from $-\infty$ to 0 may be meaningless, the symmetric limit (6–74) may exist. This is illustrated by

$$\int_{-\infty}^{\infty} \frac{x^5}{x^4 + 1} \, dx$$

[to which (6–71) can be shown to apply]. When (6–74) exists, it is termed the *Cauchy principal value* of the integral and is denoted by

$$(P) \int_{-\infty}^{\infty} f(x) \, dx.$$

In order to apply Theorem 49, it is necessary to have simple criteria to guarantee that (6–71) holds. We list two such criteria here:

I. *If $f(z)$ is rational and has a zero of order greater than 1 at $\infty$, then* (6–71) *holds.*

For, when $|z|$ is sufficiently large,

$$f(z) = \frac{a_{-N}}{z^N} + \frac{a_{-N-1}}{z^{N+1}} + \cdots, \quad N > 1,$$

so that $zf(z)$ has a zero at infinity. Now, by (2–59),

$$\left| \int_{0}^{\pi} f(Re^{i\theta}) Re^{i\theta} \, d\theta \right| \leqq \int_{0}^{\pi} |zf(z)| \, d\theta,$$

so that the integral must converge to 0 as $R \to \infty$.

II. *If $g(z)$ is rational and has a zero of order 1 or greater at $\infty$, then* (6–71) *holds for* $f(z) = e^{miz}g(z), \ m > 0$.

For a proof, and further criteria, we refer to page 115 of the treatise of Whittaker and Watson.* Rule II makes possible the evaluation of the integral

$$\int_{-\infty}^{\infty} g(x)e^{mix} \, dx = \int_{-\infty}^{\infty} g(x) \cos mx \, dx + i \int_{-\infty}^{\infty} g(x) \sin mx \, dx,$$

provided both real integrals exist.

---

* *A Course of Modern Analysis*, 4th ed. Cambridge: Cambridge University Press, 1940.

EXAMPLE 3. The integrals

$$\int_{-\infty}^{\infty} \frac{x \cos x}{x^2 + 1} \, dx \quad \text{and} \quad \int_{-\infty}^{\infty} \frac{x \sin x}{x^2 + 1} \, dx$$

both exist by the Corollary to Theorem 51 of Section 6–22 of *Advanced Calculus*. Hence

$$\int_{-\infty}^{\infty} \frac{xe^{ix}}{x^2 + 1} \, dx = 2\pi i \operatorname{Res}\left[\frac{ze^{iz}}{z^2 + 1}, i\right] = \frac{\pi i}{e}.$$

Taking real and imaginary parts, we find

$$\int_{-\infty}^{\infty} \frac{x \cos x}{x^2 + 1} \, dx = 0, \qquad \int_{-\infty}^{\infty} \frac{x \sin x}{x^2 + 1} \, dx = \frac{\pi}{e}.$$

Since the first integral is an integral of an *odd* function, the value of 0 could be predicted.

## PROBLEMS

1. Evaluate the following integrals:

(a) $\displaystyle\int_0^{2\pi} \frac{1}{5 + 3\sin\theta} \, d\theta$

(b) $\displaystyle\int_0^{2\pi} \frac{1}{5 - 4\cos\theta} \, d\theta$

(c) $\displaystyle\int_0^{2\pi} \frac{1}{(\cos\theta + 2)^2} \, d\theta$

(d) $\displaystyle\int_0^{2\pi} \frac{1}{(3 + \cos^2\theta)^2} \, d\theta.$

2. Evaluate the following integrals:

(a) $\displaystyle\int_{-\infty}^{\infty} \frac{1}{x^2 + x + 1} \, dx$

(b) $\displaystyle\int_{-\infty}^{\infty} \frac{1}{(x^2 + 1)(x^2 + 4)} \, dx$

(c) $\displaystyle\int_{-\infty}^{\infty} \frac{1}{x^6 + 1} \, dx$

(d) $\displaystyle\int_0^{\infty} \frac{1}{(x^2 + 1)^2} \, dx.$

3 Evaluate the following integrals:

(a) $\displaystyle\int_{-\infty}^{\infty} \frac{\cos x}{x^2 + 4} \, dx$

(b) $\displaystyle\int_{-\infty}^{\infty} \frac{\sin 2x}{x^2 + x + 1} \, dx$

(c) $\displaystyle\int_0^{\infty} \frac{x^3 \sin x}{x^4 + 1} \, dx$

(d) $\displaystyle\int_0^{\infty} \frac{x^2 \cos 3x}{(x^2 + 1)^2} \, dx.$

4. Prove that $\displaystyle\int_0^{\infty} \frac{\sin x}{x} \, dx = \frac{1}{2}\pi.$

[*Hint: let C be a path formed of the semicircular paths $D_r$: $|z| = r$ and $D_R$: $|z| = R$, where $0 \leq \theta \leq \pi$ and $0 < r < R$, plus the intervals $-R \leq x \leq -r, r \leq x \leq R$ on the real axis. Show that*

$$\lim_{r \to 0} \int_{D_r}^{r} \frac{e^{iz} - 1}{z} dz = 0.$$

*Use this result and criterion II above to conclude that*

$$\lim_{r \to 0} \int_{D_r}^{r} \frac{e^{iz}}{z} dz = -\pi i, \qquad \lim_{R \to \infty} \int_{D_R}^{-R} \frac{e^{iz}}{z} dz = 0.$$

*Accordingly,*

$$\lim_{R \to \infty} \left\{ \lim_{r \to 0} \oint_C \frac{e^{iz}}{z} dz \right\} = \lim_{R \to \infty} \left\{ \lim_{r \to 0} \left[ \int_{-R}^{-r} \frac{e^{ix}}{x} dx + \int_{r}^{R} \frac{e^{ix}}{x} dx \right] \right\} - \pi i.$$

*The left-hand side is zero by the Cauchy Integral Theorem. Show that the imaginary part of the right-hand side has the value $2 \int_0^\infty (\sin x/x) dx - \pi$.]*

## ANSWERS

1. (a) $\dfrac{\pi}{2}$,         (b) $\dfrac{2}{3}\pi$,         (c) $\dfrac{4\pi}{3\sqrt{3}}$,         (d) $\dfrac{7\pi\sqrt{3}}{72}$.

2. (a) $\dfrac{2\pi\sqrt{3}}{3}$,         (b) $\dfrac{\pi}{6}$,         (c) $\dfrac{2\pi}{3}$,         (d) $\dfrac{\pi}{4}$.

3. (a) $\frac{1}{2}\pi e^{-2}$,         (b) $-2\dfrac{\sqrt{3}}{3}\pi e^{-\sqrt{3}} \sin 1$,         (c) $\frac{1}{2}\pi e^{-(1/2)\sqrt{2}} \cos(\frac{1}{2}\sqrt{2})$,

   (d) $-\frac{1}{2}\pi e^{-3}$.

# 7 □ Conformal Mapping

## 7-1 □ DEFINITION OF CONFORMAL MAPPING

As pointed out in Section 2–1, a function $w = f(z)$ can be interpreted as a *transformation* or *mapping* from the $z$ plane to the $w$ plane. The term "mapping" is really justified only when the correspondence between $z$ values and $w$ values is one-to-one, i.e., to each $z$ of a domain $D_z$ corresponds just one $w = f(z)$ of a domain $D_w$ and conversely. The domain $D_w$ is then a distorted picture or "image" of the domain $D_z$; circles in $D_z$ correspond to closed curves in $D_w$, triangles in $D_z$ to curvilinear triangles in $D_w$, as illustrated in Fig. 7–1.

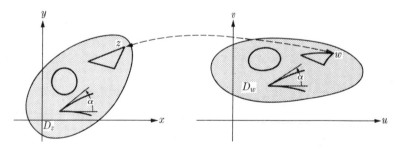

FIG. 7–1.  Conformal mapping.

If $f(z)$ is analytic, such a mapping has an additional property, that of being *conformal*. A mapping from $D_z$ to $D_w$ is termed *conformal* if to each pair of curves in $D_z$ intersecting at angle $\alpha$ there corresponds a pair of curves in $D_w$ intersecting at angle $\alpha$. The mapping is termed *conformal* and *sense-preserving* if the angles are equal and have the same sign, as illustrated in Fig. 7–1.

**Theorem 50.**  *Let $w = f(z)$ be analytic in the domain $D_z$, and map $D_z$ in a one-to-one fashion on a domain $D_w$. If $f'(z) \neq 0$ in $D_z$, then $f(z)$ is conformal and sense-preserving.*

*Proof.*  Let $z(t) = x(t) + iy(t)$ be parametric equations of a smooth curve through $z_0$ in $D_z$. By proper choice of parameter (e.g., by using arc length) we can ensure that the tangent vector

$$\frac{dz}{dt} = \frac{dx}{dt} + i\frac{dy}{dt}$$

is not 0 at $z_0$. The given curve corresponds to a curve $w = w(t)$ in the $w$ plane, with tangent vector

$$\frac{dw}{dt} = \frac{dw}{dz}\frac{dz}{dt}$$

as in Section 3–3 above.  Hence

$$\arg\frac{dw}{dt} = \arg\frac{dw}{dz} + \arg\frac{dz}{dt}.$$

This equation asserts that, at $w_0 = f(z_0)$, the argument of the tangent vector differs from that of $dz/dt$ by the angle $\arg f'(z_0)$, which is *independent of the particular curve chosen through $z_0$.* Accordingly, as the direction of the curve through $z_0$ is varied, the direction of the corresponding curve through $w_0$ must vary through the same angle (in magnitude and sign). The theorem is thus established.

Conversely, it can be shown that all conformal and sense-preserving maps $w = f(z)$ are given by analytic functions; more explicitly, if $u$ and $v$ have continuous first partial derivatives in $D_z$ and $J = \partial(u, v)/\partial(x, y) \neq 0$ in $D_z$, then the fact that the mapping by $w = u + iv = f(z)$ is conformal and sense-preserving implies that $u_x = v_y$, $u_y = -v_x$, so that $w$ is analytic (see pp. 70–71 of *Complex Analysis* by L. V. Ahfors). From this geometric characterization it is also clear that the inverse of a one-to-one conformal, sense-preserving mapping has the same property and *is itself analytic.*

If $f'(z_0) = 0$ at a point $z_0$ of $D_z$, then $\arg f'(z_0)$ has no meaning and the argument above breaks down. One can in fact show that conformality breaks down at $z_0$ and, in fact, the transformation is not one-to-one in any neighborhood of $z_0$, by the Corollary to Theorem 48 in Section 6–6; see also Prob. 14 below.

In practice, the term "conformal" is used loosely to mean "conformal and sense-preserving"; that will be done here. It should be noted that a reflection, such as the mapping $w = \bar{z}$, is conformal but sense-reversing.

*Tests for one-to-one-ness.* For the applications of conformal mapping, it is crucial that the mapping be one-to-one in the domain chosen. In most examples, the mapping will also be defined and continuous on the boundary of the domain; failure of one-to-one-ness on the boundary is less serious.

By the Corollary to Theorem 48, if $f'(z) = 0$ at some point of the domain, then the mapping cannot be one-to-one. One should therefore verify that $f'(z) \neq 0$ in the domain as a first step. Even if this is satisfied, the mapping need not be one-to-one and one must apply additional tests. The following are useful tests for one-to-one-ness:

I. *Explicit formula for the inverse function.* If an explicit formula for the inverse function $z = z(w)$ is available and one can show that, by this formula, there is at most one $z$ in $D_z$ for each $w$, then the mapping must be one-to-one. For example, $w = z^2$ is one-to-one in the *first quadrant* of the $z$ plane, for to each $w$ there is at most one square root $\sqrt{w}$ in the quadrant. As $z$ varies over $D_z$, $w$ varies over $D_w$: the upper half-plane $v > 0$, as will be seen below.

II. *Analysis of level curves of $u$ and $v$.* One can verify one-to-one-ness and at the same time obtain a very clear picture of the mapping by plotting the level curves: $u(x, y) = c_1$, $v(x, y) = c_2$. If for arbitrary choice of $c_1, c_2$ the loci $u = c_1$, $v = c_2$ intersect at most once in $D_z$, then the mapping from $D_z$ to the $uv$ plane is one-to-one.

III. *One-to-one-ness on the boundary.* This is the test formulated in Theorem 48: if $f(z)$ is analytic in $C$ plus interior $D_z$ and one-to-one on $C$, then $f(z)$ is one-to-one on $D_z$. As remarked above, it is sufficient that $f$ be continuous on $C$ plus interior, and analytic on the interior; in various important examples this is the case, analyticity being violated at one or more points on the boundary. One can also reason thus: if one can show that, for every simple closed curve $C'$ approximating the boundary sufficiently closely, $f$ is one-to-one on $C'$, then $f$ must be one-to-one in $D_z$; for, if $f$ fails to be one-to-one in $D_z$, then $f(z_1) = f(z_2)$ for two points $z_1, z_2$ of $D_z$. A curve $C'$ sufficiently close to the boundary would enclose both $z_1$ and $z_2$, so that the failure of one-to-one-ness would have to reveal itself on $C'$. Other natural extensions of the principle will be pointed out in the examples to follow.

IV. *Real or imaginary part maxima and minima on the boundary.* Let $f(z)$ be analytic in domain $D_z$, bounded by the simple closed curve $C$. Let $u = \mathrm{Re}[f(z)]$ be continuous in $D_z$ plus $C$. *If $u$ has precisely one relative maximum and one relative minimum on $C$, then $w = f(z)$ is one-to-one in $D_z$.* A similar criterion holds for $v = \mathrm{Im}[f(z)]$. Furthermore, the same conclusion holds for mappings: $u = u(x, y)$, $v = v(x, y)$ by *nonanalytic* functions, provided the Jacobian $J = \partial(u, v)/\partial(x, y)$ is always positive (or always negative) in $D_z$. For a proof see the author's paper: *Close-to-convex Schlicht Functions.**

V. Let $f(z) = u + iv$ be analytic in $D_z$ and let $D_z$ be *convex;* that is, for each pair of points $z_1$, $z_2$ of $D_z$, let the line segment from $z_1$ to $z_2$ lie in $D_z$. If real constants $a$, $b$ can be found such that

$$a\frac{\partial u}{\partial x} + b\frac{\partial u}{\partial y} > 0 \text{ in } D_z,$$

then $f$ is one-to-one in $D_z$ (see Prob. 15 below, following Section 7–2).

VI. Let $f(z) = u + iv$ be analytic in $D_z$ and let $D_z$ be the half-plane: $y > 0$. If a complex constant $c$ and a real number $a$ can be found, such that

$$\text{Re}[c(z - a)f'(z)] > 0$$

in $D_z$, then $f$ is one-to-one in $D_z$ (see Prob. 16 below, following Section 7–2).

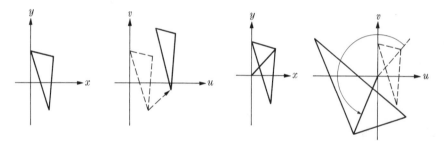

FIG. 7–2.   Translation.          Fig. 7–3.   Rotation-stretching.

## 7–2 □ EXAMPLES OF CONFORMAL MAPPING

EXAMPLE 1. *Translations.* The general form is

$$w = z + a + bi \quad (a, b \text{ real constants}).$$

Each point $z$ is displaced through the vector $a + bi$, as in Fig. 7–2.

EXAMPLE 2. *Rotation-stretchings.* The general form is

$$w = Ae^{i\alpha}z \quad (A, \alpha \text{ real constants}, A > 0).$$

---

* *Michigan Mathematical Journal*, Vol. 1 (1952), pp. 169–185.

If one writes $z = re^{i\theta}$, $w = \rho e^{i\phi}$, so that $\rho$, $\phi$ are polar coordinates in the $w$ plane, then one has

$$\rho = Ar, \qquad \phi = \theta + \alpha.$$

Thus distances from the origin are stretched in the ratio $A$ to 1, while all figures are rotated about the origin through the angle $\alpha$ (Fig. 7–3).

EXAMPLE 3. *The general linear integral transformation*

$$w = az + b \quad (a, b \text{ complex constants}). \tag{7–20}$$

This is equivalent to a rotation-stretching, as in Example 2, with $a = Ae^{i\alpha}$, followed by a translation through the vector $b$.

EXAMPLE 4. *The reciprocal transformation*

$$w = \frac{1}{z}.$$

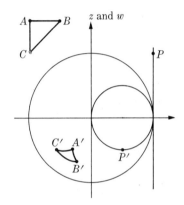

In polar coordinates one has

$$\rho = \frac{1}{r}, \qquad \phi = -\theta.$$

Thus this transformation involves both a reflection in the real axis and "inversion" in the circle of radius 1 about the origin (Fig. 7–4). Figures outside the circle correspond to smaller ones inside. It can be shown that circles (including straight lines,

FIG. 7–4. The transformation $w = \dfrac{1}{z}$.

as "circles through $\infty$") correspond to circles (Prob. 5 below). Thus the line $x = 1$ becomes the circle

$$(u - \tfrac{1}{2})^2 + v^2 = \tfrac{1}{4}.$$

EXAMPLE 5. *The general linear fractional transformation*

$$w = \frac{az + b}{cz + d} \quad (a, b, c, d \text{ complex constants}),$$

$$\begin{vmatrix} a & b \\ c & d \end{vmatrix} \neq 0. \tag{7–21}$$

If $ad - bc$ were equal to 0, $w$ would reduce to a constant; hence this is ruled out. Examples 1, 2, 3, and 4 are special cases of (7–21). Moreover,

the general transformation (7–21) is equivalent to a succession of transformations,

$$z_1 = cz + d, \qquad z_2 = \frac{1}{z_1}, \qquad w = \frac{a}{c} + \frac{bc - ad}{c} z_2 \qquad (7\text{–}22)$$

of the types of Examples 3 and 4; if $c = 0$, (7–21) is already of type
(7–20).

The transformation (7–21) is analytic except for $z = -d/c$. It is one-
to-one, for Eq. (7–21) can be solved for $z$, to give the inverse:

$$z = \frac{-dw + b}{cw - a}, \qquad (7\text{–}23)$$

which is single-valued; $w$ has a pole at $z = -d/c$ and $z$ has a pole at
$w = a/c$; in other words, $z = -d/c$ corresponds to $w = \infty$ and $z = \infty$
corresponds to $w = a/c$. If one includes these values, then the transformation (7–21) is a *one-to-one transformation of the extended plane on itself.*
When $c = 0$, $z = \infty$ corresponds to $w = \infty$.

Since the transformations (7–22) all have the property of mapping
circles (including straight lines) on circles, the general transformation
(7–21) has also this property. By considering special domains bounded
by circles and lines, one obtains a variety of interesting one-to-one mappings. The following three are important cases:

EXAMPLE 6. *Unit circle on unit circle.* The transformations

$$w = e^{i\alpha} \frac{z - z_0}{1 - \bar{z}_0 z} \qquad (\alpha \text{ real}, \ |z_0| < 1) \qquad (7\text{–}24)$$

all map $|z| \leq 1$ on $|w| \leq 1$ and every linear fractional (or even one-to-one
conformal) transformation of $|z| \leq 1$ on $|w| \leq 1$ has this form (see Prob.
11 below).

EXAMPLE 7. *Half-plane on half-plane.* The transformations

$$w = \frac{az + b}{cz + d} \qquad (a, b, c, d \text{ real and } ad - bc > 0) \qquad (7\text{–}25)$$

all map $\text{Im}(z) \geq 0$ on $\text{Im}(w) \geq 0$ and every linear fractional transformation
of $\text{Im}(z) \geq 0$ on $\text{Im}(w) \geq 0$ has this form (see Prob. 12 below).

EXAMPLE 8. *Half-plane on unit circle.* The transformations

$$w = e^{i\alpha} \frac{z - z_0}{z - \bar{z}_0} \qquad (\alpha \text{ real}, \ \text{Im}(z_0) > 0) \qquad (7\text{–}26)$$

all map $\text{Im}(z) \geqq 0$ on $|w| \leqq 1$ and every linear fractional transformation of $\text{Im}(z) \geqq 0$ on $|w| \leqq 1$ has this form (see Prob. 13 below).

EXAMPLE 9.  *The transformation*

$$w = z^2.$$

Here the transformation is not one-to-one in the whole $z$ plane, for the inverse is $z = \sqrt{w}$ and has two values for each $w$.  In polar coordinates one has

$$\rho = r^2, \qquad \phi = 2\theta.$$

Thus each sector in the $z$ plane with vertex at the origin and angle $\alpha$ is mapped onto a sector in the $w$ plane with vertex at $w = 0$ and angle $2\alpha$. In particular the half-plane $D_z$: $\text{Im}(z) > 0$ is mapped on the $w$ plane minus the positive real axis, as shown in Fig. 7–5.  Since the two square roots of $w$ are negatives of each other, each $w$ has at most one square root in $D_z$, so that the mapping is one-to-one.  The structure of the level curves:

$$u = x^2 - y^2 = \text{const}, \qquad v = 2xy = \text{const},$$

shown in Fig. 7–5, also reveals the one-to-one-ness, in accordance with test II of Section 7–1.  Test V gives the inequality: $ax - by > 0$.  Such an inequality is satisfied in each half-plane bounded by a line through the origin; hence $w = z^2$ is one-to-one in every such half-plane.

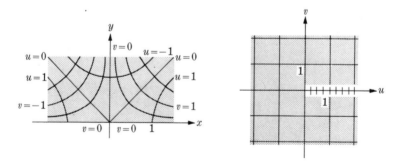

FIG. 7–5.  The transformation $w = z^2$.

It should be noted that $dw/dz = 0$ for $z = 0$ and that the mapping is not conformal at this point; the angles between curves are *doubled*.

EXAMPLE 10.  *The transformations*

$$w = z^n \quad (n = 2, 3, 4, \ldots).$$

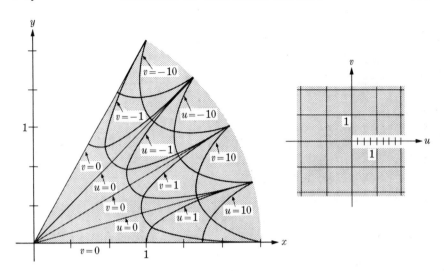

FIG. 7–6.  The transformation $w = z^n$.

Here the inverse $z = w^{1/n}$ is $n$-valued.  In polar coordinates

$$\rho = r^n, \qquad \phi = n\theta,$$

so that each sector is expanded by a factor of $n$.  One obtains a one-to-one
mapping by restricting to a sector: $0 < \arg z < 2\pi/n$, as illustrated in
Fig. 7–6.  The one-to-one-ness follows from the explicit formula:

$$r = \sqrt[n]{\rho}, \qquad \theta = \frac{\phi}{n}, \quad 0 < \phi < 2\pi$$

for the inverse function, or by one of the other tests.  Actually $n$ need not
be an integer; for $n$ any positive real number, similar results hold.

EXAMPLE 11.  *The exponential transformation*

$$w = e^z.$$

Here the inverse $z = \log w$ has infinitely many values.  In polar coordinates:

$$\rho = e^x, \qquad \phi = y + 2n\pi \quad (n = 0, 1, 2, \ldots).$$

This shows that lines $x = $ const, in the $z$ plane become circles $\rho = $ const, in
the $w$ plane, while lines $y = $ const, become rays: $\phi = $ const.  One obtains a
one-to-one mapping by restricting $z$ to a strip: $-\pi < y < \pi$, which is then
mapped onto the $w$ plane minus the negative real axis, as shown in Fig. 7–7.

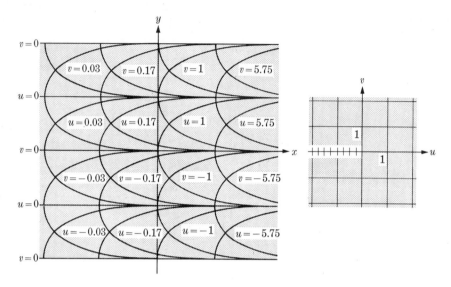

FIG. 7–7.   The transformation $w = e^z$.

EXAMPLE 12.  *The transformation*

$$w = \sin z.$$

Here the inverse

$$z = \sin^{-1} w = \frac{1}{i} \log (iw + \sqrt{1 - w^2})$$

is infinitely multiple-valued.  One obtains a one-to-one mapping by restricting $z$ to the strip $-\frac{1}{2}\pi < x < \frac{1}{2}\pi$, as the structure of the level curves of Fig. 7–8 reveals.  One can also verify that $v = \cos x \sinh y$ has precisely one maximum and one minimum on each rectangle with vertices $(\pm\frac{1}{2}\pi, \pm k)$; hence by test IV we conclude that the mapping is one-to-one inside each such rectangle, and accordingly in the whole strip.  Test V is also applicable, with $a = 1$ and $b = 0$.

EXAMPLE 13.  *The transformation*

$$w = z + \frac{1}{z}.$$

The inverse is the two-valued solution of the quadratic equation

$$z^2 - zw + 1 = 0.$$

The mapping is one-to-one in the domain: $|z| > 1$, as the accompanying Fig. 7–9 reveals (see also Prob. 3 following Section 7–7).

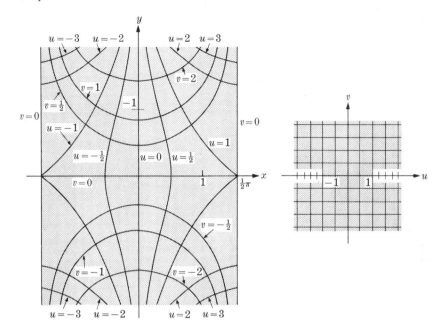

Fig. 7–8.   The transformation $w = \sin z$.

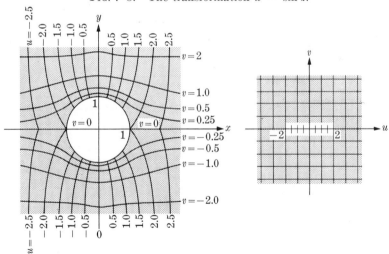

Fig. 7–9.   The transformation $w = z + (1/z)$.

A variety of other mappings can be obtained by applying first one of the above mappings and then a second one, since an analytic function of an analytic function is analytic. Also each of the inverses of the above transformations is analytic and one-to-one in the appropriate domain in the $w$ plane. Section 7–8 discusses general classes of mappings.

**PROBLEMS**

1. Determine the images of the circle $|z - 1| = 1$ and the line $y = 1$ under the following transformations:

   (a) $w = 2z$               (b) $w = z + 3i - 1$        (c) $w = 2iz$

   (d) $w = \dfrac{1}{z}$             (e) $w = \dfrac{z + i}{z - i}$          (f) $w = z^2$.

2. For each of the following transformations verify that the transformation is one-to-one in the given domain, determine the corresponding domain in the $w$ plane, and plot the level curves of $u$ and $v$:

   (a) $w = \sqrt{z} = \sqrt{r}e^{i\theta/2}, \quad -\pi < \theta < \pi$

   (b) $w = \dfrac{z - i}{z + i}, \quad |z| < 1$       (c) $w = \dfrac{1}{z}, \quad 1 < x < 2$

   (d) $w = \operatorname{Log} z, \quad \operatorname{Im}(z) > 0$     (e) $w = \operatorname{Log} \dfrac{z - 1}{z + 1}, \quad \operatorname{Im}(z) > 0$

      [Hint: use test $VI$, with $c = i$ and $a = 0$.]

   (f) $w = z + \dfrac{1}{z}, \quad \operatorname{Im}(z) > 0$

      [Hint: use test $VI$ with $c = -i$ and $a = 0$.]

   (g) $w = z - \dfrac{1}{z}, \quad |z| > 1$

   (h) $w = \operatorname{Log} \dfrac{z}{z + 1} - 2 \operatorname{Log} z, \quad \operatorname{Im}(z) > 0$

      [Hint: use test $V$, with $a = 0$ and $b = -1$.]

   (i) $w = e^z + z, \quad -\pi < y < \pi$.

3. Verify the mapping onto the domain shown and the level curves of $u$ and $v$ for the transformations of

   (a) Fig. 7–5,  (b) Fig. 7–6,  (c) Fig. 7–7,  (d) Fig. 7–8,  (e) Fig. 7–9.

4. By combining particular transformations given above determine a one-to-one conformal mapping of

   (a) the quadrant $x > 0, \quad y > 0$ onto the domain $|w| < 1$

   (b) the sector $0 < \theta < \tfrac{1}{3}\pi$ on the quadrant $u > 0, \quad v > 0$

   (c) the half-plane $y > 0$ on the strip $0 < v < \pi$

   (d) the half-strip $-\tfrac{1}{2}\pi < x < \tfrac{1}{2}\pi, \quad y > 0$ on the quadrant $u > 0, \quad v > 0$

(e) the domain $r > 1$, $\quad 0 < \theta < \pi$ on the strip $0 < v < \pi$

(f) the strip $1 < x + y < 2$ on the half-plane $v > 0$

(g) the half-plane $x + y + 1 > 0$ on the quadrant $u > 0$, $\quad v > 0$.

5. (a) Show that the equation of an arbitrary circle or straight line can be written in the form

$$a z\bar{z} + b z + \bar{b}\bar{z} + c = 0 \quad (a, c \text{ real}).$$

  (b) Using the result of (a), show that circles or lines become circles or lines under the transformation $w = 1/z$.

6. If $w = f(z)$ is a linear fractional function (7–21), show that $f'(z) \neq 0$.

7. A point where $f'(z) = 0$ is called a *critical point* of the analytic function $f(z)$. Locate the critical points of the following functions and show that none lies within the domain of the corresponding mapping in Examples 11, 12, 13:

  (a) $w = e^z$ $\qquad\qquad$ (b) $w = \sin z$ $\qquad\qquad$ (c) $w = z + \dfrac{1}{z}$.

8. (a) Show that the determinant of coefficients of the inverse (7–23) of the transformation (7–21) is not zero. Thus the *inverse of a linear fractional transformation is linear fractional.*

  (b) Show that, if

$$w_1 = \frac{az + b}{cz + d}, \qquad w_2 = \frac{a_1 w_1 + b_1}{c_1 w_1 + d_1}$$

  are linear fractional transformations: $w_1 = f(z)$, $w_2 = g(w_1)$, then $w_2 = g[f(z)]$ is linear fractional. Thus a *linear fractional transformation followed by a linear fractional transformation gives rise to a linear fractional transformation.*

9. The *cross-ratio* of four complex numbers $z_1$, $z_2$, $z_3$, $z_4$, denoted by $[z_1, z_2, z_3, z_4]$, is defined as follows:

$$[z_1, z_2, z_3, z_4] = \frac{z_1 - z_3}{z_1 - z_4} \div \frac{z_2 - z_3}{z_2 - z_4}.$$

This is meaningful, provided at least three of the four numbers are distinct; if $z_1 = z_4$ or $z_2 = z_3$ it has the value $\infty$; the expression remains meaningful if one, but only one, of the numbers is $\infty$.

(a) Prove that, if $z_1$, $z_2$, $z_3$ are distinct, then

$$w = [z, z_1, z_2, z_3]$$

defines a linear fractional function of $z$.

(b) Prove that, if $w = f(z)$ is a linear fractional function and $w_1 = f(z_1)$, $w_2 = f(z_2)$, $w_3 = f(z_3)$, $w_4 = f(z_4)$, then

$$[z_1, z_2, z_3, z_4] = [w_1, w_2, w_3, w_4],$$

provided at least three of $z_1, z_2, z_3, z_4$ are distinct. Thus the cross-ratio is invariant under a linear fractional transformation.

(c) Let $z_1, z_2, z_3$ be distinct and let $w_1, w_2, w_3$ be distinct. Prove that there is one and only one linear fractional transformation $w = f(z)$ such that $f(z_1) = w_1$, $f(z_2) = w_2$, $f(z_3) = w_3$, namely the transformation defined by the equation

$$[z, z_1, z_2, z_3] = [w, w_1, w_2, w_3].$$

(d) Using the result of (c) find linear fractional transformations taking each of the following triples of $z$ values into the corresponding $w$'s:

(i) $z = 1, i, 0$;     $w = 0, i, 1$;
(ii) $z = 0, \infty, 1$;     $w = \infty, 0, i$.

10. Let $C$ be a circle of radius $a$ and center $Q$. Points $P$, $P'$ are said to be inverses of each other with respect to $C$ if $P$ is on the segment $QP'$ or $P'$ is on $QP$ and $\overline{QP} \cdot \overline{QP'} = a^2$. $Q$ and $\infty$ are also considered as a pair of inverse points. If $C$ is a straight line, points $P$, $P'$ symmetric with respect to $C$ are called inverses of each other.

(a) Prove: $P$, $P'$ are inverses with respect to $C$, if and only if every circle through $P$, $P'$ cuts $C$ at right angles.

(b) Prove: if $P$, $P'$ are inverses with respect to $C$ and a linear fractional transformation is applied, taking $P$ to $P_1$, $P'$ to $P_1'$, $C$ to $C_1$, then $P_1$, $P_1'$ are inverses with respect to $C_1$.

[*Hint: use* (a), *noting that circles become circles and right angles become right angles under a linear fractional transformation.*]

11. (a) Let $w = f(z)$ be a linear fractional transformation mapping $|z| \leq 1$ on $|w| \leq 1$. Prove that $f(z)$ has the form (7–24).

[*Hint: let $z_0$ map on $w = 0$. By Prob.* 10(b) $1/\bar{z}_0$ *must map on $w = \infty$. The point $z = 1$ must map on a point $w = e^{i\beta}$. Take $z_1 = 1$, $z_2 = z_0$, $z_3 = 1/\bar{z}_0$ in* 9(c).]

(b) Prove that every transformation (7–24) maps $|z| \leq 1$ on $|w| \leq 1$.

12. Prove that every linear fractional transformation of $\text{Im}(z) \geq 0$ onto $\text{Im}(w) \geq 0$ has the form (7–25) and that every transformation (7–25) maps $\text{Im}(z) \geq 0$ onto $\text{Im}(w) \geq 0$.

13. Prove that every linear fractional transformation of $\text{Im}(z) \geq 0$ on $|w| \leq 1$ has form (7–26) and that every transformation (7–26) maps $\text{Im}(z) \geq 0$ onto $|w| \leq 1$.

14. Let $w = f(z)$ be analytic at $z_0$ and let $f'(z_0) = 0, \ldots, f^{(n)}(z_0) = 0$, $f^{(n+1)}(z_0) \neq 0$. Prove that angles between curves intersecting at $z_0$ are multiplied by $n + 1$ under the transformation $w = f(z)$.

*[Hint: near $z_0$, $w = w_0 + c_{n+1}(z - z_0)^{n+1} + c_{n+2}(z - z_0)^{n+2} + \cdots$, where $c_{n+1} \neq 0$. A curve starting at $z_0$ at $t = 0$ with tangent vector (complex number) $a \neq 0$ can be represented as $z = z_0 + at + \epsilon t$, $0 \leq t \leq t_1$, where $\epsilon = \epsilon(t) \to 0$ as $t \to 0+$. Show that the corresponding curve in the $w$ plane can be represented as $w = w_0 + c_{n+1}a^{n+1}t^{n+1} + \epsilon_1(t)t^{n+1}$. Show that $(w - w_0)/t^{n+1}$ has as limit, for $t \to 0+$, a tangent vector to the curve at $w_0$, and that this tangent vector has argument $\arg c_{n+1} + (n + 1)\arg a$. From this conclude that two curves in the $z$-plane forming angle $\alpha$ at $z_0$ become two curves in the $w$-plane forming angle $(n + 1)\alpha$ at $w_0$.]*

15. Prove the validity of test V.

*[Hint: let $c = a + ib$. Let $z_1$ and $z_2 = z_1 + re^{i\alpha}$ be distinct points of $D$. Then*

$$c[f(z_2) - f(z_1)] = c\int_{z_1}^{z_2} f'(z)\,dz = e^{i\alpha}\int_0^r cf'(z)\,dt,$$

*where $z = z_1 + te^{i\alpha}$ on the straight-line path of integration. Show that the real part of the last integral is positive, so that $f(z_2) \neq f(z_1)$. Cf. F. Herzog and G. Piranian, Proceedings of the American Mathematical Society, Vol. 2 (1951), pp. 625–633.]*

16. Prove the validity of test VI.

*[Hint: set $z_1 = \text{Log}(z - a)$ and show that the function $w_1 = f[z(z_1)] = g(z_1)$ is analytic and satisfies the inequality: $\text{Re}[cg'(z_1)] > 0$ in the domain: $0 < \text{Im}(z_1) < \pi$. Now apply test V.]*

## ANSWERS

7. (a) none,        (b) $\frac{1}{2}\pi + n\pi$    $(n = 0, \pm 1, \ldots)$,        (c) $\pm 1$.

9. (d) (i) $w = \dfrac{z - 1}{(1 - 2i)z - 1}$,        (ii) $w = \dfrac{i}{z}$.

## 7–3 □ APPLICATIONS OF CONFORMAL MAPPING. THE DIRICHLET PROBLEM

The following problem, known as the *Dirichlet* problem, arises in a variety of situations in fluid dynamics, electric field theory, heat conduction, and elasticity: *given a domain $D$, to find a function $u(x, y)$ harmonic in $D$ and having given values on the boundary of $D$.*

The statement is somewhat loose as to the boundary values. It will be seen immediately how it can be made more precise.

Let $D$ be a simply connected domain bounded by a simple closed curve $C$, as in Fig. 7–10. Then assignment of boundary values is achieved by giving a function $h(z)$ for $z$ on $C$ and requiring that $u = h$ on $C$. If $h$ is continuous, the natural formulation of the problem is to require that $u(x, y)$ be harmonic in $D$, continuous in $D$ plus $C$, and equal to $h$ on $C$. If $h$ is piecewise continuous, it is natural to require that $u$ be harmonic in $D$, continuous in $D$ plus $C$, except where $h$ is discontinuous, and equal to $h$ except at the points of discontinuity.

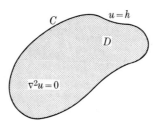

FIG. 7–10.   Dirichlet problem.

If $C$ is a circle, $|z| = R$, the problem is solved by the Poisson integral formula of Section 5–6. For example, if $R = 1$, $h$ can be written as $h(\theta)$ and

$$u(r_0, \theta_0) = \frac{1}{2\pi} \int_0^{2\pi} \frac{(1 - r_0^2)h(\theta)}{1 + r_0^2 - 2r_0 \cos (\theta_0 - \theta)} \, d\theta \qquad (7\text{--}30)$$

defines a function harmonic in $|z| < 1$. If $h(\theta)$ is continuous and we define $u(1, \theta)$ to be $h(\theta)$, then $u$ can be shown to be continuous for $|z| \leq 1$ and therefore satisfies all conditions. If $h(\theta)$ is discontinuous, the same procedure is successful and (7–30) again provides a solution.

While the formula (7–30) does provide a solution of the problem, we must also ask: is this the only solution? The answer is *yes*, when $h$ is continuous for $|z| = 1$; the answer is *no* if $h$ has discontinuities. In the latter case (7–30) provides a solution $u(x, y)$ which is bounded for $|z| < 1$, and it can be shown that this is the *only bounded solution*. With the supplementary requirement that the solution be bounded, (7–30) provides the one and only solution.

Now let $D$ be a domain bounded by $C$ as in Fig. 7–10 and let us suppose that a one-to-one conformal mapping: $z_1 = f(z)$ of $D$ onto the circular domain $|z_1| < 1$ has been found and that this mapping is also continuous and one-to-one on $D$ plus $C$, taking $C$ to $|z_1| = 1$. By assigning to each point $z_1$ on $|z_1| = 1$ the value of $h$ at the corresponding point on $C$, we obtain boundary values $h_1(z_1)$ on $|z_1| = 1$. Let $u(z_1)$ solve the Dirichlet problem for $|z_1| < 1$ with these boundary values. *Then $u[f(z)]$ is harmonic in $D$ and solves the given Dirichlet problem in $D$.* For $u(z_1)$ can be written as $\mathrm{Re}[F(z_1)]$ where $F$ is analytic and $u[f(z)] = \mathrm{Re}\{F[f(z)]\}$; i.e., $u[f(z)]$ is the real part of an analytic function in $D$. Hence $u$ is harmonic in $D$. Since continuous functions of continuous functions are continuous, $u[f(z)]$ will have the proper behavior on the boundary $C$ and hence does solve the problem.

Accordingly, conformal mapping appears as a powerful tool for solution of the Dirichlet problem. For any domain which can be mapped conformally and one-to-one on the circle $|z| < 1$, the problem is explicitly solved by (7–30). It can be shown that *every simply connected domain $D$ can be mapped in a one-to-one conformal manner on the circular domain: $|z| < 1$, provided $D$ does not consist of the entire $z$-plane. Furthermore, if $D$ is bounded by a simple closed curve $C$, the mapping can always be defined on $C$ so as to remain continuous and one-to-one.* For proofs of these theorems and of the asserted properties of the Poisson integral formula (7–30), one is referred to Kellogg's *Foundations of Potential Theory.*[*]

There now remains the question of how to map a particular simply connected domain $D$ onto a circular domain. Further information on this is given in Section 7–8 below. We shall not consider extension of the theory to multiply connected domains.

## 7–4 □ DIRICHLET PROBLEM FOR THE HALF-PLANE

Since the transformation

$$iz = \frac{z_1 - i}{z_1 + i} \qquad (7\text{–}40)$$

maps the domain $|z_1| < 1$ on the half-plane $\mathrm{Im}(z) > 0$, the Dirichlet problem for the half-plane is reducible to that for the circle as above. However, it is simpler to treat the half-plane by itself. We shall develop the equivalent of (7–30) for the half-plane. Accordingly, if a domain $D$ can be mapped on the half-plane, the Dirichlet problem for $D$ will be immediately solved.

We consider first several examples.

EXAMPLE 1.   $u(x, y)$ harmonic for $y > 0$; $u = \pi$ for $y = 0$, $x < 0$; $u = 0$ for $y = 0$, $x > 0$ as shown in Fig. 7–11. The function

$$u = \arg z = \theta, \qquad 0 \leqq \theta \leqq \pi$$

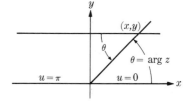

FIGURE 7–11

---

[*] New York: Springer, Berlin, 1929.

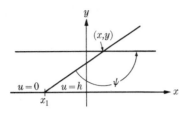

FIGURE 7–12

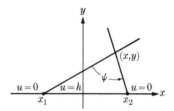

FIGURE 7–13

clearly satisfies all conditions. It is harmonic in the upper half-plane, since

$$\arg z = \theta = \operatorname{Im}(\operatorname{Log} z);$$

it is continuous on the boundary $y = 0$, except for $x = 0$ and has the correct boundary values. Furthermore $0 < u < \pi$ in the upper half-plane, so that the solution is bounded.

EXAMPLE 2. $u(x, y)$ harmonic for $y > 0$; $u = h = \text{const}$, for $y = 0$, $x > 0$; $u = 0$ for $y = 0$, $x < 0$. The solution is obtained as in Example 1:

$$u = h\left(1 - \frac{\arg z}{\pi}\right), \quad 0 \leqq \arg z \leqq \pi.$$

This function is again harmonic and has the proper boundary values.

EXAMPLE 3. $u(x, y)$ harmonic for $y > 0$; $u = h = \text{const}$, for $y = 0$, $x > x_1$; $u = 0$ for $y = 0$, $x < x_1$; see Fig. 7–12. A translation reduces this to Example 2:

$$u = h\left(1 - \frac{\arg (z - z_1)}{\pi}\right), \quad 0 \leqq \arg (z - z_1) \leqq \pi; \quad z_1 = x_1 + 0i.$$

EXAMPLE 4. $u(x, y)$ harmonic for $y > 0$; $u = h = \text{const}$, for $y = 0$, $x_1 < x < x_2$; $u = 0$ for $y = 0$, $x < x_1$ and $x > x_2$; see Fig. 7–13. The solution is obtained by subtracting two solutions of the type of Example 3:

$$u = h\left(1 - \frac{\arg (z - z_1)}{\pi}\right) - h\left(1 - \frac{\arg (z - z_2)}{\pi}\right)$$

$$= \frac{h}{\pi}[\arg (z - z_2) - \arg (z - z_1)] = \frac{h}{\pi} \arg \frac{z - z_2}{z - z_1}. \quad (7\text{–}41)$$

The result has an interesting geometric interpretation, for

$$\arg \frac{z - z_2}{z - z_1} = \psi, \quad 0 < \psi < \pi,$$

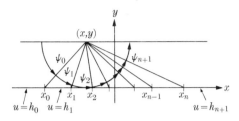

FIGURE 7–14

where $\psi$ is the angle shown in Fig. 7–13.  Accordingly

$$u = \frac{h\psi}{\pi}.$$

One can directly verify the boundary values on the figure.

*Remark.*  Examples 1, 2, and 3 can be regarded as limiting cases of Example 4.  In Example 1, $x_1 = -\infty$, $x_2 = 0$, and $h = \pi$, so that $\psi$ becomes the angle $\theta$, as shown in Fig. 7–11, and $u = \psi = \theta$.  In Example 3, $x_2 = +\infty$; the angle $\psi$ is shown in Fig. 7–12.

EXAMPLE 5.  $u(x, y)$ harmonic for $y > 0$; $u = h_0 = \text{const}$, for $y = 0$, $x < x_0$; $u = h_1$ for $y = 0$, $x_0 < x < x_1$; $u = h_2$ for $y = 0$, $x_1 < x < x_2$; $\ldots$; $u = h_n$ for $y = 0$, $x_{n-1} < x < x_n$; $u = h_{n+1}$ for $y = 0$, $x > x_n$ as in Fig. 9–49.  The solution is obtained by addition of solutions of problems like those in the previous examples:

$$u = \frac{1}{\pi}\left[ h_0 \arg(z - z_0) + h_1 \arg\frac{z - z_1}{z - z_0} + \cdots + h_n \arg\frac{z - z_n}{z - z_{n-1}}\right.$$

$$\left. + h_{n+1}\{\pi - \arg(z - z_n)\}\right]; \tag{7–42}$$

$$u = \frac{1}{\pi}[h_0\psi_0 + h_1\psi_1 + \cdots + h_{n+1}\psi_{n+1}], \quad 0 \leqq \psi_0 \leqq \pi,$$

$$0 \leqq \psi_1 \leqq \pi, \ldots \tag{7–43}$$

The angles $\psi_0, \ldots, \psi_{n+1}$ are shown in Fig. 7–14.  The sum of these angles is $\pi$; therefore $u$ is the weighted mean of the numbers $h_0, h_1, \ldots, h_{n+1}$ and hence

$$h' \leqq u \leqq h'', \tag{7–44}$$

where $h'$ is the smallest of these numbers and $h''$ is the largest.

Now let $h_0 = 0$, $h_{n+1} = 0$.  Let $z$ be fixed in the upper half-plane and let $t + 0i$ be a variable point on the $x$ axis; write

$$g(t) = \arg[z - (t + 0i)],$$

where the angle is always taken between 0 and $\pi$. Then (7–42) can be written thus:

$$u = \frac{1}{\pi} \{h_1[g(t_1) - g(t_0)] + h_2[g(t_2) - g(t_1)] + \cdots$$

$$+ h_n[g(t_n) - g(t_{n-1})]\}.$$

This formula suggests passage to the limit: $n \to \infty$; the expression suggests an integral. In fact, the expression can be interpreted (with the aid of the law of the mean) as a sum

$$u = \frac{1}{\pi} [h(t_1)g'(t_1^*) \, \Delta_1 t + \cdots + h(t_n)g'(t_n^*) \, \Delta_n t]$$

which (under appropriate assumptions) converges as $n \to \infty$ to an integral:

$$u = \frac{1}{\pi} \int_\alpha^\beta h(t)g'(t) \, dt.$$

Now

$$g(t) = \arg [z - (t + 0i)] = \arctan \frac{y}{x - t},$$

so that

$$g'(t) = \frac{y}{(x - t)^2 + y^2}.$$

We are thus led to the formula:

$$u(x, y) = \frac{1}{\pi} \int_\alpha^\beta \frac{h(t)y}{(x - t)^2 + y^2} \, dt \qquad (7\text{–}45)$$

as the expression for a harmonic function in the upper half-plane with boundary values $h(t)$ for $z = t + i0$, $\alpha < t < \beta$, and $u = 0$ otherwise on the boundary. We get complete generality by letting $\alpha = -\infty$, $\beta = +\infty$:

$$u(x, y) = \frac{1}{\pi} \int_{-\infty}^\infty \frac{h(t)y}{(x - t)^2 + y^2} \, dt. \qquad (7\text{–}46)$$

This integral is easily shown to converge, provided $h$ is piecewise continuous and bounded. *The formula (7–46) is precisely the Poisson integral formula for the half-plane.* In fact a change of variables (Prob. 6 below) transforms (7–30) into (7–46).

Just as important as the general formula (7–46) is the formula (7–42), which can be considered as the rectangular sum for approximate evaluation of the integral (7–46).

EXAMPLE 6. $u(x, y)$ harmonic in the half-strip of Fig. 7–15, with the boundary values shown. One seeks the mapping of this half-strip onto a half-plane and finds it to be given by $z_1 = \sin z$, as in Example 12 of Section 7–2. Under this mapping, $z = -\frac{1}{2}\pi$ maps on $z_1 = -1$, $z = \frac{1}{2}\pi$ on $z_1 = 1$ and the whole boundary onto the real axis of the $z_1$ plane. The new problem in the $z_1$ plane requires a function $u$ harmonic in the upper half-plane, with boundary values: $u = 2$ for $-1 < x_1 < 1$, $u = 0$ for $x_1 > 1$ and for $x_1 < 0$. This is solved as in Example 4 above by (7–41). Hence

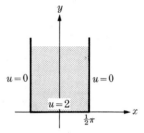

$$u = \frac{2}{\pi} \arg \frac{z_1 - 1}{z_1 + 1}$$

and, in the $z$ plane,

$$u = \frac{2}{\pi} \arg \frac{\sin z - 1}{\sin z + 1}.$$

FIGURE 7–15

To apply this formula, the simplest procedure is to use the diagram of Fig. 7–8, showing the mapping from the $z$ plane to the $z_1$ plane. For each $z$, we locate the corresponding $z_1 = \sin z$, measure the angle

$$\psi = \arg \frac{z_1 - 1}{z_1 + 1}$$

as in Fig. 7–13, and divide by $\frac{1}{2}\pi$. The answer can also be written explicitly in real form:

$$u = \frac{2}{\pi} \arctan \frac{\mathrm{Im}\left\{\dfrac{\sin z - 1}{\sin z + 1}\right\}}{\mathrm{Re}\left\{\dfrac{\sin z - 1}{\sin z + 1}\right\}}$$

$$= \frac{2}{\pi} \arctan \frac{-2 \cos x \sinh y}{\sin^2 x \cosh^2 y + \cos^2 x \sinh^2 y - 1}.$$

EXAMPLE 7. $u(x, y)$ harmonic for $|z| < 1$, $u = 1$ for $r = 1$, $\alpha < \theta < \beta$ as in Fig. 7–16; $u = 0$ on the rest of the boundary. The function

$$z_1 = e^{(1/2)(\alpha-\beta)i} \frac{z - e^{i\beta}}{z - e^{i\alpha}}$$

maps $|z| < 1$ on the half-plane $\mathrm{Im}(z_1) > 0$. The point $e^{i\alpha}$ has as image $z_1 = \infty$; the point $e^{i\beta}$ has as image $z_1 = 0$; the arc $\alpha < \theta < \beta$ corresponds to the negative real axis in the $z_1$ plane. Thus the solution is given by

$$u = \frac{1}{\pi} \arg z_1 = \frac{1}{\pi} \arg\left[ e^{(1/2)(\alpha - \beta)i} \frac{z - e^{i\beta}}{z - e^{i\alpha}} \right]. \qquad (7\text{--}47)$$

This rather clumsy formula is the formula for the circle corresponding to (7–41) for the half-plane. By use of geometry, this can be written in the much simpler form:

$$u = \frac{s}{2\pi}, \qquad (7\text{--}48)$$

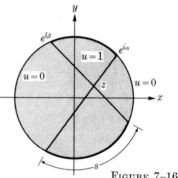

FIGURE 7–16

where $s$ is the arc length of the arc on $|z| = 1$ determined by the chords through $e^{i\alpha}$ and $z$ and through $e^{i\beta}$ and $z$; see Fig. 7–16.

This problem could also have been solved directly by the Poisson integral formula (7–30):

$$u(r_0, \theta_0) = \frac{1}{2\pi} \int_\alpha^\beta \frac{1 - r_0^2}{1 + r_0^2 - 2r_0 \cos(\theta_0 - \theta)} \, d\theta. \qquad (7\text{--}49)$$

The integration, though awkward, can be carried out with elementary functions.

## PROBLEMS

1. Solve the following boundary value problems:

   (a) $u$ harmonic and bounded in the first quadrant,

   $$\lim_{y \to 0+} u(x, y) = 1 \text{ for } 0 < x < 1, \qquad \lim_{y \to 0+} u(x, y) = 0 \text{ for } x > 1,$$

   $$\lim_{x \to 0+} u(x, y) = 1 \text{ for } 0 < y < 1, \qquad \lim_{x \to 0+} u(x, y) = 0 \text{ for } y > 1.$$

   See Fig. 7–17.

   (b) $u$ harmonic and bounded in the sector: $0 < \theta < \frac{1}{4}\pi$, with boundary values 1 on the $x$ axis and 0 on the line $y = x$, as in Fig. 7–18.

   (c) $u$ harmonic and bounded for $0 < \theta < 2\pi$, with limiting value of 1 as $z$ approaches the positive real axis from the upper half-plane and $-1$ as $z$ approaches the positive real axis from the lower half-plane.

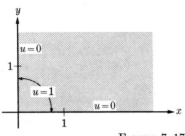

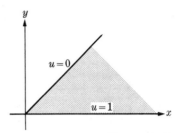

FIGURE 7–17                              FIGURE 7–18

(d) $u$ harmonic and bounded in the strip: $0 < y < 1$ with boundary values 0 for $y = 0$, $x < 0$ and for $y = 1$, $x < 0$ and boundary values 2 for $y = 0$, $x > 0$ and for $y = 1$, $x > 0$.

(e) $u$ harmonic and bounded in the domain: $0 < \theta < \pi$, $r > 1$ with boundary values of 1 on the real axis and $-1$ on the circle.

2. (a) Verify that the transformation

$$w = 2 \operatorname{Log} z - z^2$$

maps the half-plane $\operatorname{Im}(z) > 0$ in a one-to-one conformal manner on the $w$ plane minus the lines $v = 2\pi$, $u < -1$, and $v = 0$, $u < -1$.

(b) Find the electrostatic potential $U$ between two condenser plates, which are idealized as two half-planes perpendicular to the $uv$ plane along the lines $v = a$, $u < 0$, and $v = 0$, $u < 0$, if the potential difference between the plates is $U_0$; that is, solve the boundary value problem: $U(u, a) = U_0$ for $u < 0$ and $U(u, 0) = 0$ for $u < 0$, $U(u, v)$ harmonic in the remaining portion of the $uv$ plane.

3. (a) Show that the transformation $w = z^2$ maps the domain: $\operatorname{Im}(z) > 1$ in a one-to-one conformal manner on the parabolic domain

$$u < \frac{v^2}{4} - 1.$$

(b) Let a solid be idealized as an infinite cylinder perpendicular to the $uv$ plane, whose cross section in the $uv$ plane is the region $u \leq v^2$. Let this solid be in temperature equilibrium, with temperatures $T_1$ maintained on the part of the boundary surface where $v > 0$ and $T_2$ where $v < 0$. Find the temperature distribution inside the solid; that is, solve the boundary value problem: $T(u, v)$ harmonic for $u < v^2$ with boundary values $T(u, v) = T_1$ for $u = v^2$, $v > 0$, and $T(u, v) = T_2$ for $u = v^2$, $v < 0$.

4. (a) Verify that the functions (in polar coordinates)

$$r^n \cos n\theta, \qquad r^n \sin n\theta \quad (n = 0, 1, 2, \ldots)$$

are harmonic for $r < 1$ and have the boundary values $\cos n\theta$, $\sin n\theta$ for $r = 1$.

(b) Let $h(\theta)$ be continuous and have period $2\pi$ and let its Fourier series converge to $h(\theta)$ for all $\theta$:

$$h(\theta) = \tfrac{1}{2}a_0 + \sum_{n=1}^{\infty} (a_n \cos n\theta + b_n \sin n\theta),$$

$$a_n = \frac{1}{\pi} \int_{-\pi}^{\pi} h(\theta) \cos n\theta \, d\theta, \qquad b_n = \frac{1}{\pi} \int_{-\pi}^{\pi} h(\theta) \sin n\theta \, d\theta.$$

Solve the boundary value problem: $u(r, \theta)$ harmonic for $r < 1$, $\lim u(r, \theta) = h(\theta)$ as $r \to 1$.

[*Hint: use the result of* (a) *to construct the function*

$$u = \tfrac{1}{2}a_0 + \sum_{n=1}^{\infty} (a_n r^n \cos n\theta + b_n r^n \sin n\theta).$$

*Verify convergence to* $h(\theta)$ *with the aid of the remarks following Theorem 32 in Section 5–1.*]

5. (a) Verify that the function (7–42) has the limiting value $\tfrac{1}{2}(h_j + h_{j+1})$ if the point $(x, y)$ approaches the point $(x_j, 0)$ along the line $x = x_j$, $y > 0$.

(b) What is the limiting value if the approach to $(x_j, 0)$ is along a line making an angle $\alpha > 0$ with the positive $x$ direction?

(c) Discuss the limiting values of the function (7–46) as $(x, y) \to (t_1, 0)$ at a point of discontinuity $t_1$ of $h(t)$.

*Remark.* Problem 5 has an analogue in terms of the Poisson integral formula for the circle. As Problem 4 suggests, the topic is closely related to Fourier series. Actually, the properties of the Poisson integral stated in Section 7–3 above imply that, if $h(\theta)$ is piecewise continuous, then for the series obtained in Prob. 4(b)

$$\lim_{\substack{r \to 1 \\ \theta \to \theta_0}} u(r, \theta) = h(\theta_0)$$

at every point of continuity of $h(\theta)$ and

$$\lim_{r \to 1} u(r, \theta_0) = \frac{h(\theta_0+) + h(\theta_0-)}{2}$$

at each point of discontinuity of $h(\theta)$. The Fourier series for $h(\theta)$ may fail to converge to $h(\theta)$ for all $\theta$ under these assumptions, but the function $h(\theta)$ can be recovered from the series by multiplying the terms by $r^n$ and letting $r \to 1$. This process is called Poisson (or Abel) summation of the series.

6.  Show that the Poisson integral formula (7–30) is transformed into the formula (7–46) for the half-plane, if the circle $|z| < 1$ is mapped on the half-plane $\mathrm{Im}(z') > 0$ by the equation

$$z' = i\frac{1+z}{1-z}.$$

[*Hint: write (7–30) in the form*

$$u = \mathrm{Re}[f(z_0)], \qquad f(z_0) = \frac{1}{2\pi}\int_0^{2\pi}\frac{z+z_0}{z-z_0}h(z)\,d\theta,$$

*where $z = e^{i\theta}$. The change of variable must be made both for $z_0$ and for $z$:*

$$z_0' = i\frac{1+z_0}{1-z_0}, \qquad z' = i\frac{1+z}{1-z} = t + 0i.$$

*Show that $f(z_0)$ becomes*

$$\frac{1}{\pi i}\int_{-\infty}^{\infty}\left\{\frac{1}{t-z_0'} - \frac{t}{1+t^2}\right\}h_1(t)\,dt,$$

*where $h_1(t) = h[z(t)]$.*]


## ANSWERS

1. (a) $\dfrac{1}{\pi}\arg\dfrac{z^2-1}{z^2+1}$,      (b) $\dfrac{1}{\pi}(\pi - \arg z^4)$,      (c) $1 - \dfrac{\theta}{\pi}$ $(0 < \theta < 2\pi)$,

   (d) $2 - \dfrac{2}{\pi}\arg\dfrac{e^{\pi z}-1}{e^{\pi z}+1}$,   (e) $1 - \dfrac{2}{\pi}\arg\left(\dfrac{z-1}{z+1}\right)^2$.

   The argument functions are all taken between $0$ and $\pi$.

2. (b) $U = \dfrac{U_0}{\pi}\arg z$, where $z$ is the inverse of the function

   $$w = \frac{a}{2\pi}(2\,\mathrm{Log}\,z - z^2 + 1), \qquad \mathrm{Im}(z) > 0.$$

3. $T_1 + \dfrac{T_2 - T_1}{\pi}\arg(\sqrt{4w-1} - i)$; the square root is chosen to have imaginary part $>1$ and the arg is chosen between $0$ and $\pi$.

5. (b) $[\alpha h_j + (\pi - \alpha)h_{j+1}]/\pi$.

## 7–5 □ CONFORMAL MAPPING IN HYDRODYNAMICS

As pointed out in Section 5–6, the conditions

$$\text{div } \mathbf{V} = 0, \qquad \text{curl } \mathbf{V} = \mathbf{0}$$

for a two-dimensional vector field $\mathbf{V} = u\mathbf{i} - v\mathbf{j}$ are the same as the Cauchy-Riemann equations for $u$ and $v$, so that the complex function $u + iv = f(z)$ is analytic. These equations therefore describe an incompressible, irrotational, steady two-dimensional fluid motion with velocity vector $\mathbf{V}$. (See Section 5–15 of *Advanced Calculus*.)

If we restrict attention to a simply connected domain, then $f(z)$ has an indefinite integral $F(z)$ (determined up to a constant). If we write

$$F = \phi(x, y) + i\psi(x, y),$$

then

$$F'(z) = \frac{\partial \phi}{\partial x} - i \frac{\partial \phi}{\partial y} = u + iv.$$

Hence

$$\frac{\partial \phi}{\partial x} = u, \qquad \frac{\partial \phi}{\partial y} = -v$$

or

$$\text{grad } \phi = u\mathbf{i} - v\mathbf{j} = \mathbf{V}.$$

The function $\phi$ is termed the velocity potential and $F(z)$ is termed the complex velocity potential. We can write

$$\overline{F'(z)} = \frac{\partial \phi}{\partial x} + i \frac{\partial \phi}{\partial y} = u - iv.$$

Hence *the conjugate of the derivative of the complex velocity potential is the velocity vector.*

The lines $\phi(x, y) = \text{const}$ are called *equipotential lines;* they are orthogonal to the velocity vector grad $\phi$ at each point. The lines $\psi(x, y) = \text{const}$ are called *stream lines;* the velocity vector is tangent to such a line at each point, so that these stream lines can be considered as paths of actual fluid particles.

Conformal mapping can be applied to hydrodynamics problems in several ways. First of all, particular problems can be formulated as boundary value problems and solved with the aid of conformal mapping as in the preceding section. Second, starting with a known flow pattern, one can obtain a variety of others in an empirical way by simply applying different conformal transformations.

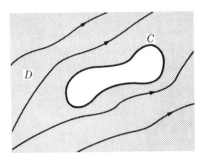

FIG. 7–19. Flow past an obstacle.          FIG. 7–20. Slit-domain.

We treat here briefly only one example of the first type. We consider the problem of flow past an obstacle, as suggested in Fig. 7–19. The domain $D$ of the flow is the exterior of a (piecewise smooth) simple closed curve $C$. Since the domain is not simply connected, we cannot be sure that there is a (single-valued) complex potential $F(z)$. It will turn out that, if we make an appropriate assumption about the flow "at $\infty$," then $F(z)$ does exist. The natural assumption is that the flow approaches a uniform flow at constant velocity at $\infty$. Hence $f(z) = F'(z)$ is analytic at $\infty$:

$$f(z) = a_0 + \frac{a_{-1}}{z} + \frac{a_{-2}}{z^2} + \cdots, \quad |z| > R,$$

$$F(z) = \text{const} + a_0 z + a_{-1} \log z - \frac{a_{-2}}{z} + \cdots, \quad |z| > R.$$

If $F(z)$ is to be single-valued, the term in $\log z$ must not be present; hence we also assume the flow to be such that $a_{-1} = 0$, so that

$$f(z) = a_0 + \frac{a_{-2}}{z^2} + \cdots, \tag{7–50}$$

$$F(z) = \text{const} + a_0 z - a_{-2} z^{-1} + \cdots.$$

The constant $a_0$ is precisely the value of $f$ at $\infty$, so that $\bar{a}_0$ is the velocity of the limiting uniform flow.

The stream function $\psi = \text{Im}[F(z)]$ is constant along $C$, since (in the absence of viscosity) the velocity vector must be tangent to $C$. It would be natural to formulate a boundary value problem for $\psi$, but it is simpler to remark that the assumption (7–50) about the behavior of $F(z)$ at $\infty$ and the condition: $\text{Im}[F(z)] = \text{const}$ on $C$ imply that $z_1 = F(z)$ *maps $D$ in a one-to-one conformal manner onto a domain $D_1$ of the $z_1$ plane*. This is established by the argument principle (Prob. 3 below). Since $\text{Im}(z_1) = y_1$ is constant on $C$, the image of $C$ must be a line segment $y_1 = \text{const}$ in the $x_1 y_1$ plane; thus $D_1$ *consists of the entire $z_1$ plane minus a slit*, as in Fig. 7–20.

Conversely, if $F(z)$ is analytic in $D$ and maps $D$ in one-to-one fashion on such a slit-domain $D_1$, then $F$ must have a pole of first order at $\infty$ and necessarily $\psi = \text{Im}[F(z)]$ is constant on $C$; thus every mapping of $D$ onto a slit-domain $D_1$ provides an appropriate complex velocity potential $F(z)$.

EXAMPLE. Let $C$ be the circle: $|z| = 1$. Then

$$z_1 = a_0 \left( z + \frac{1}{z} \right) = F(z) \quad (a_0 \text{ real})$$

maps $D$ onto a slit-domain $D_1$, the slit lying on the real axis (cf. Example 13 of Section 7–2). Hence this is an appropriate potential for the flow past the circle. The stream function is

$$\psi = a_0 y - a_0 \frac{y}{x^2 + y^2} \, ;$$

the stream lines are shown in Fig. 7–9 (Section 7–2).

It can be shown that, given $C$ and the velocity $\bar{a}_0$ at $\infty$, a mapping function $F(z)$ having the expansion (7–50) at $\infty$ exists and is uniquely determined up to an additive constant [which has no effect on the velocity vector $\overline{F'(z)}$]. A similar theorem holds for flow past several obstacles, bounded by curves $C_1, \ldots, C_n$; the complex velocity potential maps the domain of the flow onto the $z_1$ plane minus $n$ slits. For proofs one is referred to the book of Courant listed in the Bibliography.

## 7–6 □ APPLICATIONS OF CONFORMAL MAPPING IN THE THEORY OF ELASTICITY

Two-dimensional problems in the theory of elasticity are reducible to solution of the biharmonic equation

$$\frac{\partial^4 U}{\partial x^4} + 2 \frac{\partial^4 U}{\partial x^2 \, \partial y^2} + \frac{\partial^4 U}{\partial y^4} = 0$$

or, in terms of the operator $\nabla^2 = (\partial^2/\partial x^2) + (\partial^2/\partial y^2)$,

$$\nabla^4 U \equiv \nabla^2(\nabla^2 U) = 0. \tag{7–60}$$

The function $U$ is *Airy's stress function;* its second derivatives

$$\frac{\partial^2 U}{\partial x^2}, \quad \frac{\partial^2 U}{\partial x \, \partial y}, \quad \frac{\partial^2 U}{\partial y^2}$$

give components of the *stress tensor*, which describes the forces acting on an arbitrary plane cross section of the solid being studied.

Solution of (7–60) in a domain $D$ is equivalent to solution of two equations:

$$\nabla^2 U = P, \qquad \nabla^2 P = 0.$$

The solutions $P$ of the second equation are harmonic functions. Furthermore, if $U_1$, $U_2$ satisfy the first equation for given $P$, then

$$\nabla^2(U_1 - U_2) = P - P = 0;$$

hence the solutions of the first equation are of form

$$U_1 + W,$$

where $U_1$ is a particular solution and $W$ is harmonic. Now let harmonic functions $u$ and $v$ be chosen, if possible, so that

$$\frac{\partial u}{\partial x} = P = \frac{\partial v}{\partial y}.$$

Then

$$\nabla^2(xu + yv) = x\,\nabla^2 u + 2\frac{\partial u}{\partial x} + y\,\nabla^2 v + 2\frac{\partial v}{\partial y} = 4P.$$

Hence

$$U_1 = \tfrac{1}{4}(xu + yv)$$

is the desired particular solution, provided $u$ and $v$ can be found. If $D$ is simply connected, one can choose $Q$ so that $P + iQ = F(z)$ is analytic in $D$; then

$$u + iv = f(z) = \int F(z)\,dz$$

defines (up to additive constants) harmonic functions $u$ and $v$ such that $\partial u/\partial x = \partial v/\partial y = P$ and $U_1$ can be written as follows:

$$U_1 = \tfrac{1}{4}(xu + yv) = \tfrac{1}{4}\mathrm{Re}[\bar{z}f(z)].$$

Finally, the solutions $U$ of (7–60) can be written thus:

$$U = U_1 + W = \mathrm{Re}\left[\frac{\bar{z}f(z)}{4} + g(z)\right].$$

The factor of $\tfrac{1}{4}$ can be absorbed in $f(z)$ and we have the conclusion: *If $f(z)$ and $g(z)$ are analytic in domain $D$, then*

$$U = \mathrm{Re}[\bar{z}f(z) + g(z)] \qquad (7\text{–}61)$$

*is biharmonic in $D$; if $D$ is simply connected, then all biharmonic functions in $D$ can be represented in this form.*

The boundary value problems for the stress function $U$ can be formulated in terms of the analytic functions $f$ and $g$. If $D$ is mapped conformally on a second domain $D_1$, the problem is transformed into a boundary value problem for $D_1$. By mapping onto a simple domain $D_1$, such as the half-plane or unit circle, we reduce the problem to a simpler one. Hence, just as for the Dirichlet problem, conformal mapping is a powerful aid. The importance of (7–61) is that it expresses $U$ in terms of analytic functions, which *remain analytic* if a conformal change of variables is made. A biharmonic function does not in general remain biharmonic under such a transformation.

For further details on the applications to elasticity one is referred to *Mathematical Theory of Elasticity*, 2nd ed., by I. S. Sokolnikoff.*

## 7–7 □ FURTHER APPLICATIONS OF CONFORMAL MAPPING

In general, conformal mapping can be helpful in solving all boundary value problems associated with the Laplace equation or the more general *Poisson equation*

$$\frac{\partial^2 u}{\partial x^2} + \frac{\partial^2 u}{\partial y^2} = g(x, y) \tag{7–70}$$

in the plane. The crucial fact is that harmonic functions remain harmonic under conformal mapping. While the boundary values may be transformed in a complicated manner, this disadvantage is usually offset by the possibility of simplifying the domain by an appropriate mapping.

We mention here one example of the possibilities and refer to the books of Kellogg and Frank and von Mises listed in the Bibliography for further information. Let it be required to find a function $u(x, y)$ harmonic in a given domain $D$ bounded by a smooth simple closed curve $C$ and satisfying the boundary conditions: $u$ has given values $h(x, y)$ on an arc of $C$; $\partial u/\partial n = 0$ on the rest of $C$, where $\mathbf{n}$ is the normal vector to $C$. The condition $\partial u/\partial n = 0$ is equivalent to the condition that the conjugate function $v$ is constant on $C$; hence this condition is invariant under conformal mapping.

To solve the problem, we map $D$, if possible, on the *quarter-plane:* $x_1 > 0$, $y_1 > 0$, so that the arc on which $\partial u/\partial n = 0$ becomes the $y_1$ axis. The function $h(x, y)$ becomes a function $h_1(x_1)$, giving the values of $u$ for $y_1 = 0$. We now solve the boundary value problem: $u(x_1, y_1)$ harmonic in the upper half-plane; $u(x_1, 0) = h_1(x_1)$ for $x_1 > 0$ and $u(x_1, 0) = h_1(-x_1)$ for $x_1 < 0$. In other words, we *reflect* the boundary values in the line $x_1 = 0$. The function $u$ obtained is harmonic in the quarter-plane and has the correct boundary values for $x_1 > 0$. Furthermore, (7–46) shows that

---

* See Chapter 5 (New York: McGraw-Hill, 1956).

$u(x_1, y_1) = u(-x_1, y_1)$, that is, $u$ shows the same symmetry as the boundary values. This implies that $\partial u/\partial x_1 = 0$ for $x_1 = 0$, that is, $\partial u/\partial n = 0$ on the boundary of the quarter-plane. Accordingly, $u$ satisfies all conditions. If we return to the $xy$ plane, $u$ becomes a function of $x$ and $y$ which solves the given boundary value problem. This can be shown to be the only bounded solution, provided $h$ is piecewise continuous.

## PROBLEMS

1. Prove that

$$F(z) = a_0 \left( ze^{i\alpha} + \frac{1}{ze^{i\alpha}} \right) + \text{const} \quad (\alpha \text{ real})$$

maps $D: |z| > 1$ in a one-to-one conformal manner on a slit domain $D_1$ (this is the most general such map). Interpret $F$ as a complex velocity potential.

2. Show that the vector

$$\mathbf{V} = \left( 1 + \frac{y}{x^2 + y^2} - \frac{x^2 - y^2}{(x^2 + y^2)^2} \right) \mathbf{i} + \left( \frac{-x}{x^2 + y^2} - \frac{2xy}{(x^2 + y^2)^2} \right) \mathbf{j}$$

can be interpreted as the velocity of an irrotational, incompressible flow past the obstacle bounded by the circle $x^2 + y^2 = 1$. Find the complex velocity potential and the stream function, and plot several stream lines.

3. Let $w = F(z)$ be analytic in the domain $D$ outside the simple closed curve $C$ and have a pole of first order at $\infty$. Let $F(z)$ be continuous in $D$ plus $C$ and let $\text{Im}[F(z)] = \text{const}$ on $C$. Show that $F(z)$ maps $D$ in a one-to-one fashion on a slit-domain.

[*Hint: show that the argument principle of Section 6–6 here takes the form: the increase in* arg $F(z)$ *as $z$ traces $C$ in the negative direction is $2\pi$ times $(N_0 - N_\infty)$, where $N_0$ and $N_\infty$ are the numbers of zeros and poles of $F(z)$ in $D$ plus the point $z = \infty$. Show that the increase in* arg $[F(z) - w_0]$ *is $0$ for $w_0$ not on the image of $C$. Hence $N_0 - N_\infty = 0$; but $N_\infty = 1$, so that $N_0 = 1$.*]

4. Let $U(x, y)$ be biharmonic for $x^2 + y^2 < 1$. Show that $U$ can be expanded in a Taylor series in this domain, so that $U$ is *analytic* in $x$ and $y$.

5. Find the equilibrium temperature distribution $T$ in the half-strip: $0 < x < 1$, $y > 0$ if the edge $x = 0$ is maintained at a temperature $T_0$, the edge $x = 1$ is maintained at a temperature $T_1$, while the edge $y = 0$ is insulated ($\partial T/\partial n = 0$).

**ANSWERS**

2. $F(z) = z + \dfrac{1}{z} + i \log z$ (not single-valued).

3. $T_0 + x(T_1 - T_0)$.

## 7–8 □ GENERAL FORMULAS FOR ONE-TO-ONE MAPPING. SCHWARZ-CHRISTOFFEL TRANSFORMATION

The examples encountered above have indicated the importance of conformal mapping for applications. There still remains the problem of exhibiting a reasonably large class of explicit mappings to meet the needs of applications. Here we give several formulas, which help in this direction.

*Mapping onto infinite strip with slits.* Let real constants $h_1, h_2, \ldots,$ $h_n, h_{n+1}$ be chosen such that for some $m$,

$$h_1 < h_2 < \cdots < h_m; \qquad h_m > h_{m+1} > \cdots > h_{n+1}. \qquad (7\text{–}80)$$

As extreme cases one can choose $m = 1$ or $m = n + 1$. Let points $x_1, \ldots, x_n$ be chosen on the real axis such that $x_1 < x_2 < \cdots < x_n$. A bounded harmonic function $v$ in the half-plane $y > 0$, with the following boundary values for $y = 0$:

$$v = h_1 \text{ for } x < x_1, \qquad v = h_2 \text{ for } x_1 < x < x_2, \ldots,$$
$$v = h_n \text{ for } x_{n-1} < x < x_n, \qquad v = h_{n+1} \text{ for } x > x_n,$$

is provided by (7–42):

$$v = \frac{1}{\pi}\left[ h_1 \arg (z - z_1) + h_2 \arg \frac{z - z_2}{z - z_1} + \cdots + h_n \arg \frac{z - z_n}{z - z_{n-1}}\right.$$
$$\left. + h_{n+1}\{\pi - \arg (z - z_n)\} \right];$$

here $z_1 = x_1 + 0i$, $z_2 = x_2 + 0i$, ... A corresponding $f(z) = u + iv = w$ analytic in the upper half-plane is

$$f(z) = \frac{1}{\pi}\left[ h_1 \operatorname{Log} (z - z_1) + h_2 \operatorname{Log} \frac{z - z_2}{z - z_1} + \cdots + h_n \operatorname{Log} \frac{z - z_n}{z - z_{n-1}}\right.$$
$$\left. + h_{n+1}\{i\pi - \operatorname{Log} (z - z_n)\} \right] + a, \qquad (7\text{–}81)$$

where $a$ is a real constant. *When the constants $h_1, \ldots, h_{n+1}$ satisfy (7–80), this function gives a one-to-one conformal mapping of the half-plane;* for a proof, see Prob. 5 below. The image domain $D_1$ is bounded by lines $v = \text{const}$.

EXAMPLE

$$f(z) = \frac{1}{\pi}\left[\text{Log } (z+1) + 3 \text{ Log } \frac{z}{z+1} + 2(i\pi - \text{Log } z)\right]$$

$$= \frac{1}{\pi}[2\pi i + \text{Log } z - 2 \text{ Log } (z+1)]$$

maps the upper half-plane on the domain $D_1$ shown in Fig. 7–21.

In general the image domain $D_1$ lies between the lines $v = h^*$, $v = h^{**}$, where $h^*$ and $h^{**}$ are the smallest and largest of $h_1, h_2, \ldots, h_{n+1}$; the boundary of $D_1$ consists of these lines plus rays $v = $ const corresponding to the remaining $h$'s. Every such image domain $D_1$ can be obtained by appropriate choice of the numbers $x_1, \ldots, x_n, a$. For the general mapping theorem (Section 7–3) ensures existence of the map; since $v$ is bounded and has the given boundary values, the function $v$ must have the form given above, so that $f$ must have form (7–81).

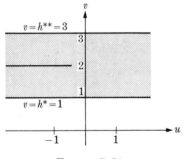

FIGURE 7–21

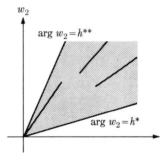

FIGURE 7–22

*Mapping onto sector with radial slits.* If $h^{**} - h^* \leq 2\pi$, so that the domain $D_1$ has width at most $2\pi$, then the function $e^w$ takes each value at most once in $D_1$. Hence $F(z) = \exp[f(z)]$ also gives a one-to-one mapping, provided (7–80) holds. The function $F(z)$ can be written as follows:

$$w_2 = F(z) = \exp[f(z)] = \frac{\exp(a + ih_{n+1})}{(z-z_1)^{k_1}(z-z_2)^{k_2}\cdots(z-z_n)^{k_n}},$$

$$k_1 = \frac{h_2 - h_1}{\pi}, \ldots, \qquad k_n = \frac{h_{n+1} - h_n}{\pi};\qquad\qquad (7\text{–}82)$$

the powers of $(z-z_1), \ldots$ are taken as *principal values*: $(z-z_1)^{k_1} = \exp[k_1 \text{ Log } (z-z_1)]$. The function $e^w$ maps $D_1$ onto a domain $D_2$ lying in the sector: $h^* < \arg w_2 < h^{**}$ and bounded by the edges of the sector and other lines and rays as suggested in Fig. 7–22; hence $w_2 = F(z)$ maps the upper half-plane on the domain $D_2$. When $h^{**} - h^* = 2\pi$, the sector has opening $2\pi$ and the boundary lines coincide.

*Schwarz-Christoffel mappings.* Another important class of mappings is obtainable from $f(z)$: namely, the mappings

$$w = G(z) = \int_{z_0}^{z} F(z)\, dz + \text{const} = \int_{z_0}^{z} e^{f(z)}\, dz + \text{const}, \quad \text{Im}(z_0) > 0,$$

or, more explicitly,

$$w = G(z) = A \int_{z_0}^{z} \frac{dz}{(z - z_1)^{k_1}(z - z_2)^{k_2} \cdots (z - z_n)^{k_n}} + B, \quad (7\text{-}83)$$

where $A$ and $B$ are complex constants. The function $w = G(z)$ defines the *Schwarz-Christoffel transformation.* Under appropriate assumptions on the constants $k_j$, $w = G(z)$ maps the upper half-plane in a one-to-one manner onto a domain bounded by straight lines or line segments, and it can be shown that every one-to-one mapping of the half-plane onto such a domain is representable in the form (7–83). This includes, in particular, every mapping onto the interior of a polygon.

The function $G(z)$ satisfies the boundary conditions:

$$\arg G'(z) = h_1 \text{ for } y = 0, \quad x < x_1,$$
$$\arg G'(z) = h_2 \text{ for } y = 0, \quad x_1 < x < x_2, \ldots,$$

for

$$G'(z) = e^{f(z)} = e^{u+iv}, \quad \arg G'(z) = v = \text{Im}[f(z)].$$

The quantity $\arg G'(z)$ measures the amount by which directions are rotated in going from the $z$ plane to the $w$ plane (Sections 2–4 and 7–1). Hence along the boundary the amount of rotation is piecewise constant; accordingly, each interval $x < x_1$, $x_1 < x < x_2$, ... must be mapped on a *straight line* by $w = G(z)$. The numbers $h_1$, $h_2$, ... give the angles from the direction of the positive real axis to these lines, as suggested in Fig. 7–23 for the case of a convex polygonal domain; the numbers

$$k_1\pi = h_2 - h_1,$$
$$k_2\pi = h_3 - h_2, \ldots,$$
$$k_n\pi = h_{n+1} - h_n$$

are successive *exterior angles* of the polygon; the $(n + 1)$-st exterior angle is $h_1 + 2\pi - h_{n+1}$. It can happen that $h_{n+1} = h_1 + 2\pi$, in which case the polygon has only $n$ vertices; otherwise, for a proper convex poly-

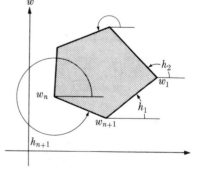

FIGURE 7–23

gon, $h_{n+1} < h_1 + 2\pi$. Since

$$k_1\pi + \cdots + k_n\pi = (h_2 - h_1) + \cdots + (h_{n+1} - h_n) = h_{n+1} - h_1,$$

the two cases are as follows:

$$k_1 + \cdots + k_n = 2 \quad (n \text{ vertices}),$$
$$k_1 + \cdots + k_n < 2 \quad (n + 1 \text{ vertices}).$$

The vertices $w_1, \ldots, w_n$ of the polygon are the images of $z_1, \ldots, z_n$. The $(n + 1)$-st vertex, if present, is the image of $z = \infty$. We note that, for a convex polygon, $0 < k_1\pi < \pi, 0 < k_2\pi < \pi, \ldots$, so that the $k$'s are between 0 and 1. Given any set of $k$'s such that

$$k_1 + k_2 + \cdots + k_n \leqq 2,$$
$$0 < k_1 < 1, \ldots, \quad 0 < k_n < 1,$$

the corresponding function $w = G(z)$ determines a one-to-one mapping of the upper half-plane onto the interior of a convex polygon with exterior angles $k_1\pi, k_2\pi, \ldots$ Conversely, given a polygon with vertices $w_1, \ldots, w_{n+1}$, there exists a one-to-one mapping $w = G(z)$ of the upper half-plane onto the interior of the polygon. Determination of the points $z_1, \ldots, z_n$ and the constants $A$ and $B$ is in general a difficult problem in implicit equations; for special cases, as illustrated in the problems below, the constants can all be determined.

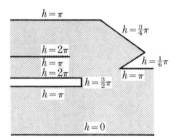

Figure 7–24

As mentioned above, the image domain can also be bounded by infinite lines. Such a case is suggested in Fig. 7–24, on which the values of the $h$'s are shown. The boundary of the domain can be regarded as a polygon, some of whose vertices are at $\infty$. In the example shown, there are 10 vertices in all. As the example shows, some of the sides can overlap, so that arg $G'(z)$ has values differing by $\pm\pi$ on opposite "edges" of the side.

*Remark.* Let a simply connected domain $D$ of the $w$ plane be given and let it be required to map the half-plane $y > 0$ of the $z$ plane in a one-to-one conformal manner on $D$. It follows from the general mapping theorem of Section 7–3 that such a mapping can be found, provided $D$ is not the finite $w$ plane. In fact, infinitely many such mappings can be provided. Let $w = f(z)$ be one such mapping and let $z = g(z_1)$ be a linear fractional transformation [cf. (7–25)] of the half-plane $\text{Im}(z_1) > 0$ on the half-plane $\text{Im}(z) > 0$. Then $w = f[g(z_1)] = h(z_1)$ maps $\text{Im}(z_1) > 0$ on $D$; that is, $w = h(z)$ maps $\text{Im}(z) > 0$ on $D$. For every choice of the mapping $g$ of half-plane on half-plane, we get a new mapping $h$ of half-plane on $D$. It can be shown that *all* mappings of the half-plane on the given domain $D$ are obtainable from a single mapping $f$ by compounding in this way with a linear fractional transformation $g$ of half-plane on half-plane.

One can single out a particular mapping $f$ by imposing additional conditions. For example, one can require that three specified points $z_1$, $z_2$, $z_3$ on the real axis correspond to three specified points $w_1$, $w_2$, $w_3$ on the boundary of $D$, provided the cyclic order of the triples matches the corresponding positive directions on the boundaries. The justification for this rule is given by the fact that one can map the half-plane onto itself to take three given points on the real axis to three given points on the real axis, provided the cyclic orders match (cf. Prob. 9 following Section 7–2).

The points $z_1, \ldots, z_n$, $\infty$ play special roles in the transformations (7–81), (7–82), (7–83). In seeking a transformation of one of these types onto a given domain, one can assume three of the points at convenient positions, provided the cyclic order chosen agrees with the sense-preserving property of the transformation. It will be found most convenient to always make $\infty$ a special point, so that $h_{n+1} \neq h_1$ and, for (7–83), $h_{n+1} \neq h_1 + 2\pi$. The other two special points can be chosen, for example, as 0 and 1.

*Maps onto circle with teeth.* As a final example of a class of explicit one-to-one conformal mappings, we mention functions $w = H(z)$ having the following form:

$$H(z) = z + \sum_{s=1}^{n} k_s z_s \left[ 1 - \left( 1 - \frac{z}{z_s} \right)^{\alpha_s} \right]. \qquad (7\text{–}84)$$

Here the numbers $k_s$ and $\alpha_s$ are real and $k_s > 0$, $0 < \alpha_s < 1$ for $s = 1$, $\ldots, n$; the numbers $z_1, \ldots, z_n$ represent distinct points on the circle $|z| = 1$; the principal value of the $\alpha_s$ power is used. The function $H(z)$ is then analytic for $|z| < 1$ and is moreover one-to-one in this domain (Prob. 6 below). The image domain is approximately the region $|w| < 1$ plus $n$ sharp "teeth" projecting from it; the points of the teeth are the images of the points $z_1, \ldots, z_n$. The smaller each $\alpha_s$, the sharper the corresponding tooth. Further properties of these functions and other mapping classes are described in a paper by P. Erdös, F. Herzog, and G. Piranian, *Pacific Coast Journal of Mathematics*, Vol. 1 (1951), pp. 75–82.

## PROBLEMS

1. Verify that the following functions define one-to-one conformal mappings of the upper half-plane and determine the image domains:

   (a) $w = 2 \operatorname{Log} (z + 1) - \operatorname{Log} z$

   (b) $w = \operatorname{Log} \dfrac{z - 1}{z} + 2 \operatorname{Log} \dfrac{z - 2}{z - 1} + 3 \operatorname{Log} \dfrac{z - 3}{z - 2} - 2 \operatorname{Log} (z - 3)$

   (c) $w = \sqrt{\dfrac{(z - 2)(z - 3)}{z(z - 1)}}$ (principal value).

2. Determine a one-to-one conformal transformation of the half-plane $\operatorname{Im}(z) > 0$ onto each of the following domains:

   (a) the domain bounded by the lines $v = 0$, $v = 2$ and the ray $v = 1$, $0 \leq u < \infty$

      [*Hint: seek a transformation of form (7–81), with $z_1 = 0$, $z_2 = 1$, $h_1 = 0$, $h_2 = 1$, $h_3 = 2$.*]

   (b) the domain bounded by the lines $v = 0$, $v = 2$ and the rays: $v = 1$, $-\infty < u \leq -1$; $v = 1$, $1 \leq u < \infty$

      [*Hint: use (7–81) with $z_1 = -1$, $z_2 = 0$, $z_3 = p > 0$, $h_1 = 0$, $h_2 = 1$, $h_3 = 2$, $h_4 = 1$ and determine $p$ so that the mapping is correct.*]

   (c) the first quadrant of the $w$ plane minus the segment from

      $$w = 0 \text{ to } w = \exp\left(i\frac{\pi}{4}\right).$$

      [*Hint: first apply the transformation $w_1 = \operatorname{Log} w$ and then map the half-plane on the resulting domain in the $w_1$ plane.*]

3. Show that each of the following transformations of the upper half-plane can be regarded as a special case of the Schwarz-Christoffel transformation:

   (a) $w = \sqrt{z}$
   (b) $w = \sin^{-1} z$, $-\frac{1}{2}\pi < \operatorname{Re}(w) < \frac{1}{2}\pi$
   (c) the transformations of form (7–81)
   (d) the transformations of form (7–82).

4. With the aid of the Schwarz-Christoffel transformation, determine a one-to-one conformal transformation of the half-plane $\operatorname{Im}(z) > 0$ on the $w$ plane minus the lines $v = 2\pi$, $u < -1$ and $v = 0$, $u < -1$ [cf. Prob. 2(a) following Section 7–4].

5. Prove that, if (7–80) holds, then (7–81) defines a one-to-one conformal transformation of the half-plane $\operatorname{Im}(z) > 0$.

[*Hint: prove that each non-constant term $g$ of $f = -\Sigma k_j \, \text{Log} \, (z - z_j) + \text{const}$ satisfies the inequality:* $\text{Re}[i(z - z_m)g'(z)] > 0$ *in the half-plane.* *Then apply test VI of Section 7–1.*]

6. Let $w = u + iv = H(z)$ be defined by (7–84), under the conditions described above. Show that $H(z)$ is analytic and one-to-one for $|z| < 1$.

[*Hint: show that each term $h$ of $H(z)$ satisfies the condition:* $\text{Re}[h'(z)] > 0$ *for* $|z| < 1$. *Now apply test V of Section 7–1.*]

## ANSWERS

1. (a) The domain bounded by the lines $v = \pm\pi$ and the ray $v = 0$, $\log 4 \leq u < \infty$;
   (b) the domain bounded by the lines $v = \pi$, $v = -2\pi$ and the rays: $v = -\pi$, $1.89 \leq u < \infty$; $v = 0$, $1.28 \leq u < \infty$; $v = 0$, $-\infty < u \leq -3.17$;
   (c) the upper half of the $w$ plane minus the portions of the imaginary axis between $0$ and $0.27i$ and between $3.7i$ and $\infty$.

2. (a) $\dfrac{1}{\pi}\left[\text{Log}\,\dfrac{z-1}{z} + 2\pi i - 2\,\text{Log}\,(z-1) - \log 4\right]$;

   (b) $\dfrac{1}{\pi}\left[\text{Log}\,\dfrac{z}{z+1} + 2\,\text{Log}\,\dfrac{z-5.1}{z} + \pi i - \text{Log}\,(z-5.1) - 0.03\right]$;

   (c) $(1+i)z^{-1/2}(z-1)^{1/4}$.

# 8 □ *Analytic Continuation and Riemann Surfaces*

## 8–1 □ ANALYTIC CONTINUATION

The multiple-valued functions, such as $\log z$, $\sin^{-1} z$, have been awkward to deal with, since they are not functions in the ordinary sense. We have been forced to select "branches" in an arbitrary way in order to use these as analytic functions. There is a more natural point of view, to be described here, on the basis of which $\log z$, $\sin^{-1} z$, all other inverse functions, and their combinations with each other and with elementary functions become "analytic functions," in the proper sense of that term.

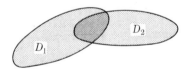

FIG. 8–1.   Direct analytic continuation.

Let $f_1(z)$ be defined and analytic in a domain $D_1$; let $f_2(z)$ be analytic in domain $D_2$, and let $D_2$ overlap $D_1$ as in Fig. 8–1. If $f_2(z) \equiv f_1(z)$ in the common part of $D_1$ and $D_2$, then $f_2(z)$ is said to be a *direct analytic continuation* of $f_1(z)$. We also say that $f_1(z)$ has been continued analytically from $D_1$ to the domain $D_2$.

Given $f_1(z)$ in $D_1$ and given $D_2$ overlapping $D_1$, it may or may not be possible to continue $f_1(z)$ to $D_2$; however, *if continuation is possible, it can be done in only one way.* For if $f_2(z)$ and $f_2^*(z)$ are both analytic in $D_2$ and both coincide with $f_1(z)$ in the common part, then $f_2(z) - f_2^*(z) \equiv 0$ in the common part; hence, by Theorem 43 of Section 6–2, $f_2(z) \equiv f_2^*(z)$ in $D_2$.

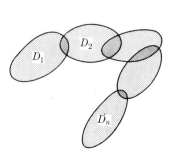

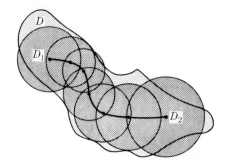

Fig. 8-2. Indirect analytic continuation.

Figure 8-3

Having continued $f_1(z)$ from $D_1$ to $D_2$, we can now try to continue $f_2(z)$ from $D_2$ to a new domain $D_3$, and so on. By repeating this a finite number of times, we finally reach a function $f_n(z)$, analytic in $D_n$, as suggested in Fig. 8-2. We call $f_n(z)$ an *indirect analytic continuation* of $f_1(z)$ and say that $f_1(z)$ has been continued analytically to $D_n$, via the domains $D_2$, $D_3$, $\ldots$, $D_{n-1}$. We can no longer assert that the function $f_n(z)$ is uniquely determined by $f_1(z)$; for it may be possible to continue $f_1(z)$ to $D_n$ via a second chain of domains and the results in $D_n$ need not agree. This is illustrated by continuations of Log $z$ going around the origin in different directions. In particular, it can happen that $D_n$ overlaps $D_1$, and yet $f_n$ is different from $f_1$ in the common part. However, if $f_1$ can be continued to $D_n$ via $D_2$, $D_3$, $\ldots$, $D_{n-1}$, then the result obtained in $D_n$ is the same for all such continuations *via the same chain* $D_2$, $D_3$, $\ldots$, $D_{n-1}$. The result in $D_2$ is unique as above, hence the result in $D_3$ is unique, etc.

A fundamental method for analytic continuation is that of power series. Let $f_1(z)$ itself be defined by a power series, so that $D_1$ is bounded by a circle; we assume the radius to be finite, for otherwise the question is without interest. Let $z_1$ be the center of the circle and let $z_2$ be a second point of $D_1$. By Theorem 38 (Section 5-4), $f_1(z)$ can be expanded in a Taylor series about $z_2$; this series defines an analytic function $f_2(z)$ in a circular domain $D_2$. $D_2$ may reach only to the boundary of $D_1$ or it may extend farther; in the latter case, $f_2(z)$ is a direct analytic continuation of $f_1(z)$. By repeating the process in $D_2$, we get new continuations $f_3(z)$ and so on.

In particular, let $f(z)$ be analytic in a noncircular domain $D$ and let $f_1(z)$ be the sum of the Taylor series of $f(z)$ about a point $z_1$ of $D$. If $f_2(z)$ is a second such Taylor series, about a point $z_2$ of $D$, then $f_1(z)$ can be continued to $f_2(z)$ by power series expansions of $f(z)$; that is, a chain of circular domains in $D$, connecting the domains $D_1$ and $D_2$, can be found, as suggested in Fig. 8-3. The Taylor series expansions of $f(z)$ about the centers of these circles provide the desired continuation. Thus $f(z)$ can be regarded as the result of continuation of one power series $f_1(z)$ along chains of circular domains in $D$. This suggests thinking of $f(z)$ *as a collection of power series, all related by analytic continuation.*

This point of view can be generalized, and is the clue to understanding the multiple-valued function. Let $f_1(z)$ be defined by a power series in a circular domain $D_1$. We now consider *all* power series $f(z)$ obtainable from $f_1(z)$ by power series continuation, direct and indirect. This, in general, vast collection of power series is precisely what we mean by an *analytic function* in the broad sense.

For example, $\log z$ is regarded as the same as all power series

$$\log |z_0| + i \arg z_0 + \sum_{n=1}^{\infty} (-1)^{n-1} \frac{(z - z_0)^n}{n z_0^n}, \quad z_0 \neq 0.$$

For given $z_0$, there are infinitely many series, but any two are analytic continuations of each other.

Another reason for considering all power series related by analytic continuation as part of the same analytic function is that any functional property of one series will be shared by all the others. Thus, if $f_1(z)$ satisfies the algebraic relation

$$[f_1(z)]^2 + 2f_1(z) + 3 = 0,$$

then every analytic continuation of $f_1(z)$ satisfies the same relation: Let

$$g_1(z) = [f_1(z)]^2 + 2f_1(z) + 3.$$

Then $g_1(z)$ is an analytic function of $z$ in $D_1$ and can be continued wherever $f_1(z)$ can be continued; in particular, the continuation of $g_1(z)$ to $D_n(z)$ on a particular chain is precisely

$$g_n(z) = [f_n(z)]^2 + 2f_n(z) + 3,$$

where $f_n(z)$ is the continuation of $f_1(z)$ on this chain. But $g_1(z) \equiv 0$ in $D_1$; hence, by the uniqueness property, all continuations of $g_1(z)$ are identically 0; that is,

$$[f_n(z)]^2 + 2f_n(z) + 3 = 0.$$

This reasoning extends to identities of great variety, and to differential equations. Thus, since one series of $\log z$ satisfies the condition

$$\frac{dw}{dz} - \frac{1}{z} = 0,$$

this condition must be satisfied by all the series.

The identification of "analytic function" with class of power series has certain defects. Thus, if a branch of a function has a pole at $z_0$, we would somehow like to include this in the description of the function; this can be done simply by adjoining the Laurent series about $z_0$. Similarly, one can adjoin series about $z_0 = \infty$, if a branch of the function has a pole or is analytic at $z_0 = \infty$. A more complicated difficulty arises with a function such as $w = \sqrt{z}$. Here no series expansion covers the point $z = 0$, at which we wish to assign $w$ the value 0. If we permit series of form

$$\sum_{n=-N}^{\infty} a_n(z - z_0)^{np/q}, \tag{8-10}$$

where $p$ and $q$ are integers without common factor, then this defect can be remedied. We say that the function has an *algebraic branch point of order* $q - 1$ at $z_0$; when $N = 0$, the series gives the value $a_0$ to the function.

For a more complete definition of branch points and further information on analytic continuation, the reader is referred to Chapter 6 of *Complex Analysis* by L. V. Ahlfors.

## 8-2 □ RIEMANN SURFACES

While the general definition of analytic function just given does simplify the description of multiple-valued functions such as $\log z$, the multiple-valued nature still remains. For each $z_0$, there may be many different series in powers of $z - z_0$ which are all part of the same function.

In order to make the function single-valued, one introduces the *Riemann surface* associated with the function. This can be thought of as being constructed as follows: to each power series forming part of the function, one associates a circle whose radius is the radius of convergence. The circle need no longer be placed in the $z$ plane and is to be regarded as an object by itself. If two such series are analytic continuations of each other, we merge the two circles along the common part for which the two series have the same sum. If the circles are represented as pieces of paper in space, the merger can be accomplished by pasting together. If this is done for all the series which make up the function, one obtains a surface which is in general quite complicated. For $\log z$ it is precisely the surface of Fig. 4-2. One now uses the original $z$ values within each circle to measure distances and angles within the circle; in other words, we flatten the surface onto the $z$ plane, so that the circles fall back on their original positions and the original $z$ coordinates are recovered. Many circles may have the same center $z_0$, but they are to be regarded as distinct unless the corresponding series are identical. This ideal surface is the Riemann surface of the function. Each point of the surface lies in one of the circles and the value of the function at the point is the sum of the series associated with that circle; this value is the same for any two circles containing the same point. Hence the *function is single-valued on the surface.*

For $w = \sqrt{z}$, there are two series for each $z$ other than the origin, hence the surface has two layers or "sheets" above the $z$ plane. At the origin there is only one series, of form (8–10); thus the origin corresponds to one point of the surface. A similar statement holds at $\infty$. If one traces a simple closed path $C$ around the origin in the $z$ plane, there is a corresponding path in the surface; we need only select a chain of power series, whose centers are on $C$, and which form successive analytic continuations. In this way, each point of $C$ is associated with a point on the surface. However, in tracing $C$ once from $z_1$ to $z_1$, the corresponding analytic continuation will not return to its initial value, but to the negative of that value. *The corresponding path on the Riemann surface is not closed.* In order to obtain a closed path, it is necessary to go around the origin twice. This is typical of a branch point of order 1.

Riemann surfaces have proved to be of inestimable value, especially in the study of algebraic functions. There is a large literature on the subject. We refer to the books of Knopp, Hurwitz and Courant, Springer, Ahlfors, and Bieberbach in the Bibliography for further background and references to other sources.

## PROBLEMS

1. (a) Prove Theorem A of Section 3–4.
   (b) Prove Theorem B of Section 3–4.

2. Represent the following analytic functions (in the broad sense) as collections of power series:

   (a) $w = \dfrac{1}{z}$

   (b) $w = \dfrac{1}{z(z - 1)}$

   (c) $w = z^{1/2}$

   (d) $w = \log z + e^{z}$.

3. Which of the following pairs of functions form analytic continuations?

   (a) $f_1(z) = \displaystyle\sum_{n=0}^{\infty} z^n, \quad |z| < 1$ and $f_2(z) = \dfrac{1}{1 - z}$ for $\mathrm{Re}(z) > \tfrac{1}{2}$

   (b) $f_1(z) = \mathrm{Log}\, z, \quad f_2(z) = \log|z| + i \arg z, \quad 0 < \arg z < 2\pi$

   (c) $f_1(z) = \displaystyle\sum_{n=0}^{\infty} (-1)^n (z - 1)^n, \quad |z - 1| < 1$ and

   $f_2(z) = \displaystyle\sum_{n=0}^{\infty} (-1)^n \dfrac{(z - 2)^n}{2^n}, \quad |z - 2| < 2.$

4. Analyze the Riemann surfaces of the following functions:

(a) $w = \sqrt[3]{z}$      (b) $w = \log \dfrac{z-1}{z+1}$.

It will be found helpful to plot, for (a), $\mathrm{Re}[f(z)]$ and, for (b), $\arg[f(z)]$ as a function of $x$ and $y$; cf. Section 4–1 above. The Riemann surface is obtainable from this surface by flattening it onto the $z$ plane, while retaining the separate identities of the sheets.

## ANSWERS

2. (a) $\displaystyle\sum_{n=0}^{\infty} (-1)^n \frac{(z-z_0)^n}{z_0^{n+1}}$ plus series: $w = \dfrac{1}{z}$ at $0$ and $\infty$ ;

(b) $\displaystyle\sum_{n=0}^{\infty} (-1)^n \left[ \frac{1}{(z_0-1)^{n+1}} - \frac{1}{z_0^{n+1}} \right] (z-z_0)^n, \quad -\frac{1}{z} - \sum_{n=0}^{\infty} z^n$ at $0$,

$\dfrac{1}{z-1} - \displaystyle\sum_{n=0}^{\infty} (-1)^n (z-1)^n$ at $1$, $\displaystyle\sum_{n=2}^{\infty} \frac{1}{z^n}$ at $\infty$ ;

(c) $z_0^{1/2} \left[ 1 + \dfrac{1}{2} \dfrac{z-z_0}{z_0} - \dfrac{1}{2^2 2!} \dfrac{(z-z_0)^2}{z_0^2} + \dfrac{1\cdot 3}{2^3 3!} \dfrac{(z-z_0)^3}{z_0^3} + \cdots \right]$,

where $z_0^{1/2} = |z_0|^{1/2} \exp\left(\tfrac{1}{2}i \arg z_0\right)$, plus series: $w = z^{1/2}$ at $0$ and $\infty$ ;

(d) $\displaystyle\sum_{n=0}^{\infty} \frac{e^{z_0}}{n!} (z-z_0)^n + \log|z_0| + i \arg z_0 + \sum_{n=1}^{\infty} (-1)^{n+1} \frac{(z-z_0)^n}{n z_0^n}$,

no series at $0$ or $\infty$.

3 (a) and (b) are analytic continuations.

# 9 □ Analytic Functions
# of Several Complex Variables

## 9–1 □ INTRODUCTION

By a complex function of $n$ complex variables $z_1, \ldots, z_n$, we mean a function

$$w = F(z_1, \ldots, z_n),$$

where a complex value $w$ is assigned to each $n$-tuple $(z_1, \ldots, z_n)$ of a given set of such $n$-tuples. For example,

$$w = z_1^2 - z_2^2 + z_1 e^{iz_2} \tag{9–10}$$

defines a function $w = F(z_1, z_2)$ for all $(z_1, z_2)$. Similarly,

$$w = \frac{z_1}{z_1^2 + z_2^2} \tag{9–11}$$

is defined for all $(z_1, z_2)$ except where $z_1^2 + z_2^2 = 0$; that is, except where $z_1 = \pm iz_2$.

For a function $F(z_1, z_2)$ each of the independent variables $z_1, z_2$ varies over a complex plane. Hence a *four*-dimensional space would be required to represent all possible pairs $(z_1, z_2)$. We can write

$$z_1 = x_1 + iy_1, \qquad z_2 = x_2 + iy_2$$

and use $(x_1, y_1, x_2, y_2)$ as real coordinates in this four-dimensional space. In general, a function $F(z_1, \ldots, z_n)$ is defined in a set in the space of all $(z_1, \ldots, z_n)$, which can be regarded as the space of all $2n$-tuples $(x_1, y_1, x_2, y_2, \ldots, x_n, y_n)$ of real numbers. As for one complex variable, we shall normally assume that $F$ is defined in a *domain* in this $2n$-dimensional space (see the footnote in Section 2–1).

The dependent variable $w$ varies in a complex plane, which can be represented as usual as the $uv$-plane, $w = u + iv$.

A complex function $w = F(z_1, \ldots, z_n)$ is said to be *analytic* in a domain $D$ in the space of all $(z_1, \ldots, z_n)$ if $F$ is defined and continuous in $D$ and the partial derivatives $\partial F/\partial z_j$ $(j = 1, \ldots, n)$ are also defined and continuous in $D$. (The definitions of continuity and partial derivatives are, in form, identical to the familiar ones.) It follows that, for each point $(z_1^0, \ldots, z_n^0)$ in $D$, $F(z_1, z_2^0, \ldots, z_n^0)$ is an analytic function of $z_1$ in a neighborhood of $z_1^0$; that is, $F$ is analytic in each variable separately. We can now apply all the theory of analytic functions of one variable and obtain a power series expansion

$$\sum c_{k_1 k_2 \cdots k_n}(z_1 - z_1^0)^{k_1} \cdots (z_n - z_n^0)^{k_n}, \tag{9-12}$$

an analog of the Cauchy integral formula, and a host of other conclusions about zeros, singularities, and integrals.

One might thus be led to expect that the theory of analytic functions of $n$ complex variables $(n \geq 2)$ is simply a natural extension of the theory of analytic functions of one complex variable. However, this is not the case at all. The region of convergence of a power series (9-12) is, in general, far more complicated than the circular region obtained for one variable. The zeros of $F(z_1, \ldots, z_n)$ are *not isolated* for $n \geq 2$, but form certain "varieties," having complicated structure in general. Most remarkable are the theorems on analytic continuation, of which the following is a sample:

**Theorem.**    *If $F(z_1, z_2)$ is analytic for $a < |z_1|^2 + |z_2|^2 < b$, then $F$ can be continued analytically to the domain $|z_1|^2 + |z_2|^2 < b$.*

Thus a function analytic in the "spherical shell": $a < x_1^2 + y_1^2 + x_2^2 + y_2^2 < b$ in 4-dimensional space, can always be continued analytically to the spherical domain: $x_1^2 + y_1^2 + x_2^2 + y_2^2 < b$.

In this chapter we shall explore both the expected and the unexpected properties of functions of several complex variables. The subject, though relatively new, has a rapidly growing literature. References are given at the end of the book.

## 9-2 □ BASIC DEFINITIONS

We shall denote by $K_n$ the set of all $n$-tuples $(z_1, \ldots, z_n)$ of complex numbers; here $n$ is an integer, $n \geq 1$. We call $K_n$ the *complex $n$-dimensional space*. The distance $d$ between two points $(z_1', \ldots, z_n')$, $(z_1'', \ldots, z_n'')$ of $K_n$ is defined by the equation

$$d = \{|z_1' - z_1''|^2 + \cdots + |z_n' - z_n''|^2\}^{1/2}. \tag{9-20}$$

If we write $z_k = x_k + iy_k$, $k = 1, \ldots, n$, then $K_n$ can also be regarded as a *real 2n-dimensional space*, with coordinates $(x_1, y_1, \ldots, x_n, y_n)$ and distance given by the usual formula.

In terms of the distance $d$, one can define the concept of neighborhood of radius $\epsilon$, open set, and domain (see the footnote in Section 2–1). We can then also define limits and continuity for complex-valued functions $w = f(z_1, \ldots, z_n)$ defined in a domain (or more general set), and the discussion of Sections 2–1, 2–2, and 2–3 can be repeated with no essential change, except for the concept of point at infinity in $K_n$ (which will not be discussed here). In particular, each polynomial such as $w = 1 + 2z_1 + 3z_2 + 5z_1^2 + 10z_1z_2 + 11z_2^2 + 8z_1^3$ is continuous everywhere. Also the series

$$\sum_{n=1}^{\infty} \frac{(z_1 + z_2)^n}{n}$$

converges absolutely for $|z_1 + z_2| < 1$; it converges uniformly for $|z_1 + z_2| \leqq r$, for each $r < 1$, and hence defines a continuous function for $|z_1 + z_2| < 1$.

Let $w = f(z_1, z_2)$ be a complex function defined in a domain $D$ of $K_2$. For each point $(z_1^0, z_2^0)$ of $D$, there is then an $\epsilon$-neighborhood,

$$|z_1 - z_1^0|^2 + |z_2 - z_2^0|^2 < \epsilon^2$$

of $(z_1^0, z_2^0)$, lying in $D$. In particular, for $z_2 = z_2^0$, $f(z_1, z_2^0)$ is defined for $|z_1 - z_1^0| < \epsilon$. Thus $f(z_1, z_2^0)$ is a complex function of $z_1$, defined in a neighborhood of $z_1^0$. We can hence define the partial derivative $\partial f/\partial z_1$ at $(z_1^0, z_2^0)$ as

$$\frac{\partial f}{\partial z_1}\bigg|_{(z_1^0,\, z_2^0)} = \lim_{h \to 0} \frac{f(z_1^0 + h, z_2^0) - f(z_1^0, z_2^0)}{h}. \tag{9–21}$$

The partial derivative $\partial f/\partial z_2$ is defined similarly. We call $f(z_1, z_2)$ *analytic* (or *holomorphic*) in $D$ if

(a) $f$ is continuous in $D$,

(b) the partial derivatives $\partial f/\partial z_1$, $\partial f/\partial z_2$ exist and are continuous in $D$.

It follows that for each fixed $z_2 = z_2^0$, $f$ must be an analytic function of $z_1$ in a neighborhood of $z_1^0$, where $(z_1^0, z_2^0)$ is any point of $D$.

As for functions of one complex variable, the definition of analyticity given here is a "practical" one, and we can require less. It is, in fact, sufficient to require that the partial derivatives $\partial f/\partial z_1$, $\partial f/\partial z_2$ exist in $D$; properties (a) and (b) then follow from theorems of Osgood and Hartogs.*

---

* See S. Bochner and W. T. Martin, *Several Complex Variables*, Princeton: Princeton University Press, 1948, pp. 139–141.

The definition has been given only for $n = 2$ but it can be given for arbitrary $n$ in exactly the same way.

The following are examples of analytic functions:

$$w = z_1 e^{z_2} + \sin(2z_1 - z_2^2), \quad \text{all } (z_1, z_2), \tag{9-22}$$

$$w = \frac{z_1^2 + z_2^2}{1 - z_1 z_2 z_3}, \quad z_1 z_2 z_3 \neq 1, \tag{9-23}$$

$$w = \sum_{n=1}^{\infty} \frac{(z_1 + z_2)^n}{n^2}, \quad |z_1 + z_2| < 1, \tag{9-24}$$

$$w = \oint_{|\zeta|=1} \frac{e^{\zeta}}{(\zeta - z_1)(\zeta - z_2)} \, d\zeta, \quad |z_1| < 1, |z_2| < 1. \tag{9-25}$$

The discussion of these examples is left to the exercises (Problem 2 below).

Since a circular domain is so common for analytic functions of one complex variable, one might expect spherical domains to be typical for analytic functions of several complex variables. However, it turns out that another type of domain, the polycylindrical domain, is more natural. By a *polycylindrical domain* (or, briefly, *polycylinder*) in $K_n$ we mean a domain described by inequalities

$$|z_k - a_k| < b_k \quad (k = 1, \dots, n), \tag{9-26}$$

where $a_k$ is complex and $b_k$ is real, $0 < b_k \leqq \infty$. We verify easily that (9-26) does describe a domain $D$ [see Problem 1(e) below]. The *boundary* of $D$ is described by the analogous inequalities

$$|z_k - a_k| \leqq b_k \quad (k = 1, \dots, n), \tag{9-27}$$

whereby *at least one equality* must hold. Thus for $n = 2$, the boundary consists of those $(z_1, z_2)$ for which

$$|z_1 - a_1| = b_1, \qquad |z_2 - a_2| \leqq b_2 \tag{9-28a}$$

and those for which

$$|z_1 - a_1| \leqq b_1, \qquad |z_2 - a_2| = b_2. \tag{9-28b}$$

In (9-26) each coordinate, $z_1, \dots, z_n$ varies in a circular domain. This leads to a generalization: By a *generalized polycylindrical domain* (or, briefly, *generalized polycylinder*) in $K_n$, we mean a domain $D$ in $K_n$, consisting of all $(z_1, \dots, z_n)$ for which $z_1$ is in $D_1, \dots, z_n$ is in $D_n$, where $D_1, \dots, D_n$ are given domains in the $z_1$-plane, $\dots, z_n$-plane respectively.

For example, $D$ could be described by the inequalities

$$0 < \operatorname{Re} z_k < 1, \qquad 0 < \operatorname{Im} z_k < 1 \quad (k = 1, \ldots, n).$$

The resulting domain is a $2n$-dimensional "hypercube."

A set in $K_n$ described by inequalities (9–27), where $0 < b_k < \infty$ for $k = 1, \ldots, n$, will be called a *closed polycylinder*.


## PROBLEMS

1. Verify that each of the following sets in $K_2$ is a domain and find its boundary:

   (a) all $(z_1, z_2)$ for which $|z_1|^2 + |z_2|^2 < 1$
   (b) all $(z_1, z_2)$ for which $|z_1| + |z_2| < 1$
   (c) all $(z_1, z_2)$ except $(0, 0)$
   (d) all $(z_1, z_2)$ except the points for which $z_1 z_2 = 0$
   (e) the polycylinder $|z_1 - a_1| < b_1$, $|z_2 - a_2| < b_2$, where $0 < b_1 \leqq \infty$, $0 < b_2 \leqq \infty$
   (f) the generalized polycylinder: $1 < |z_1| < 2$, $1 < |z_2 - i| < 2$
   (g) the generalized polycylinder: $z_1$ in $D_1$, $z_2$ in $D_2$, where $D_k$ is a domain in the $z_k$-plane for $k = 1, 2$.

2. Verify that each of the following equations defines an analytic function:

   (a) Eq. (9–22)          (b) Eq. (9–23)
   (c) Eq. (9–24)          (d) Eq. (9–25)

3. Prove: If $D$ is a domain in $K_2$, then for every point $(z_1^0, z_2^0)$ of $D$ one can choose a polycylinder neighborhood of $(z_1^0, z_2^0)$ in $D$; that is, a polycylinder $D_1$: $|z_1 - z_1^0| < \epsilon_1$, $|z_2 - z_2^0| < \epsilon_2$ contained in $D$.

4. Prove: If $E$ is an open set in $K_2$, then $E$ contains at least one point $(z_1, z_2)$ for which $z_1 z_2 \neq 0$.

5. Prove: If $D$ is a domain in $K_2$ and $D_1$ consists of those points of $D$ not on the coordinate planes $z_1 = 0$, $z_2 = 0$, then $D_1$ is a domain.

6. Prove: If $D$ is a domain in $K_2$, $w = f(z_1, z_2)$ is continuous in $D$, and the set of values of $w$ forms an open set $E$ in the $w$-plane, then $E$ is connected and is hence a domain in the $w$-plane.

[*Hint: show that each pair of points $w'$, $w''$ in $E$ can be joined by a path in $E$. Since one can write $w' = f(z_1', z_2')$, $w'' = f(z_1'', z_2'')$, the desired path is obtained as the image of a path from $(z_1', z_2')$ to $(z_1'', z_2'').$*]

## 9-3 □ CAUCHY INTEGRAL FORMULA.  POWER SERIES EXPANSION

For most of the theory to follow, the discussion will be restricted to $K_2$ (functions of two complex variables); where the extension to $K_n$ is not evident, remarks will be made.

**Theorem 51.** *Let $f(z_1, z_2)$ be analytic in the generalized polycylindrical domain $D$: $z_1$ in $D_1$, $z_2$ in $D_2$, where $D_1$, $D_2$ are domains in the $z_1$-, $z_2$-planes respectively.  Let $C_1$, $C_2$ be piecewise smooth simple closed curves in $D_1$, $D_2$ respectively, whose interiors are also in $D_1$, $D_2$.  Then*

$$f(z_1, z_2) = \frac{1}{(2\pi i)^2} \oint_{C_1} \oint_{C_2} \frac{f(\zeta_1, \zeta_2)}{(\zeta_1 - z_1)(\zeta_2 - z_2)} \, d\zeta_2 \, d\zeta_1 \quad (9\text{-}30)$$

*for each $(z_1, z_2)$ of the generalized polycylindrical domain $D_0$: $z_1$ inside $C_1$, $z_2$ inside $C_2$.*

*Proof.* For each fixed $z_2$ in $D_2$, $f(z_1, z_2)$ is analytic in $z_1$ for $z_1$ in $D_1$. Hence, for $z_1$ inside $C_1$,

$$f(z_1, z_2) = \frac{1}{2\pi i} \oint_{C_1} \frac{f(\zeta_1, z_2)}{\zeta_1 - z_1} \, d\zeta_1$$

by the usual Cauchy integral formula.  For each fixed $\zeta_1$ on $C_1$, $f(\zeta_1, z_2)$ is analytic in $z_2$ for $z_2$ in $D_2$.  Hence, for $z_2$ inside $C_2$,

$$f(\zeta_1, z_2) = \frac{1}{2\pi i} \oint_{C_2} \frac{f(\zeta_1, \zeta_2)}{\zeta_2 - z_2} \, d\zeta_2.$$

Combining the last two expressions, we obtain (9-30).

*Remark.* The integral formula (9-30) expresses the values of the analytic function $f$ for $(z_1, z_2)$ in the *four*-dimensional domain $D_0$, in terms of the values of $f$ at the points $(\zeta_1, \zeta_2)$, where $\zeta_1$ is on $C_1$ and $\zeta_2$ on $C_2$, so that $(\zeta_1, \zeta_2)$ varies on a *two*-dimensional set.  For example, if $C_1$ is the circle $|z_1| = 1$, $C_2$ the circle $|z_2| = 1$, then (9-30) can be written as a *double* integral:

$$f(z_1, z_2) = \frac{1}{(2\pi)^2} \int_0^{2\pi} \int_0^{2\pi} \frac{f(e^{i\theta_1}, e^{i\theta_2}) e^{i\theta_1} e^{i\theta_2}}{(e^{i\theta_1} - z_1)(e^{i\theta_2} - z_2)} \, d\theta_1 \, d\theta_2.$$

The whole boundary of $D_0$ is three dimensional, but the values of $f$ inside $D_0$ are determined by its values on a two-dimensional portion of the boundary.  The whole boundary is given as in (9-28a), (9-28b) as the set of $(z_1, z_2)$ for which $|z_1| \leqq 1$, $|z_2| = 1$, plus the set of $(z_1, z_2)$ for which

$|z_1| = 1$, $|z_2| \leqq 1$; our integral uses only the values for which $|z_1| = 1$, $|z_2| = 1$.

**Theorem 52.** *Under the hypotheses of Theorem 51, $f$ has partial derivatives of all orders at each point of $D$, and for $(z_1, z_2)$ in $D_0$*

$$\frac{\partial^{k+l}f}{\partial z_1^k \, \partial z_2^l} = \frac{k!l!}{(2\pi i)^2} \oint_{C_1} \oint_{C_2} \frac{f(\zeta_1, \zeta_2)}{(\zeta_1 - z_1)^{k+1}(\zeta_2 - z_2)^{l+1}} \, d\zeta_2 \, d\zeta_1. \quad (9\text{–}31)$$

*Proof.* For $(z_1, z_2)$ in $D_0$, (9–30) is valid. The integrand has first partial derivatives with respect to $z_1, z_2$:

$$\frac{f(\zeta_1, \zeta_2)}{(\zeta_1 - z_1)^2(\zeta_2 - z_2)}, \qquad \frac{f(\zeta_1, \zeta_2)}{(\zeta_1 - z_1)(\zeta_2 - z_2)^2},$$

which are continuous with respect to $\zeta_1, \zeta_2, z_1, z_2$. Hence Leibnitz's rule is applicable (see Problem 9, following Section 5–6) and one can differentiate under the integral sign to find $\partial f/\partial z_1$, $\partial f/\partial z_2$. For example,

$$\frac{\partial f}{\partial z_1} = \frac{1}{(2\pi i)^2} \oint_{C_1} \oint_{C_2} \frac{f(\zeta_1, \zeta_2)}{(\zeta_1 - z_1)^2(\zeta_2 - z_2)} \, d\zeta_2 \, d\zeta_1.$$

Repetition of the process gives the general formula (9–31). Thus the partial derivatives exist at each point $(z_1, z_2)$ in $D_0$. An arbitrary point $(z_1, z_2)$ in $D$ can be enclosed in a polycylinder $|z_1 - a_1| < b_1, |z_2 - a_2| < b_2$ in $D$ (Problem 3, following Section 9–2), and hence the partial derivatives exist everywhere in $D$.

*Remark* 1. The argument just given shows that, if $f(z_1, z_2)$ is analytic in a domain $D$, then $f$ has partial derivatives of all orders in $D$. Furthermore, since the integrand in (9–31) is continuous in $(\zeta_1, \zeta_2, z_1, z_2)$, we conclude that all the partial derivatives of $f$ are continuous in $D$. Thus all these derivatives are analytic in $D$.

*Remark* 2. The method of proof of Theorem 52 shows that a function $f(z_1, z_2)$ defined by an integral:

$$f(z_1, z_2) = \int_C \phi(z_1, z_2, \zeta) \, d\zeta,$$

is analytic in a domain $D$ in $K_2$, provided $\phi$, $\partial\phi/\partial z_1$, and $\partial\phi/\partial z_2$ are defined and continuous for $(z_1, z_2)$ in $D$ and $\zeta$ on the piecewise smooth path $C$ in the $\zeta$-plane. For then the Leibnitz rule can be applied as above to show existence and continuity of $\partial f/\partial z_1$, $\partial f/\partial z_2$ in $D$. Similar remarks apply to functions defined by multiple integrals.

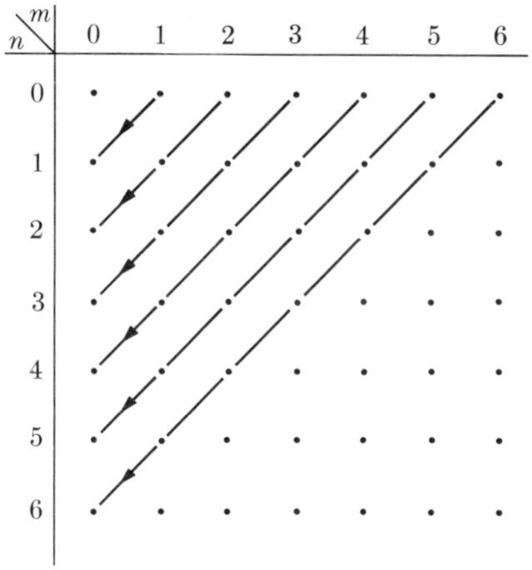

FIG. 9–1. Arrangement of pairs $(m, n)$ to reduce double series to simple series.

**Theorem 53.** *Let $f(z_1, z_2)$ be analytic in a domain $D$ and let $(z_1^0, z_2^0)$ be a point of $D$. Then $f$ can be expanded in an absolutely convergent power series:*

$$f(z_1, z_2) = \sum_{m,n=0}^{\infty} c_{mn}(z_1 - z_1^0)^m (z_2 - z_2^0)^n, \tag{9-32}$$

*in a neighborhood of $(z_1^0, z_2^0)$. The series (9–32) is the Taylor series of $f$; that is,*

$$c_{mn} = \frac{1}{m!\,n!} \frac{\partial^{m+n} f}{\partial z_1^m \partial z_2^n}(z_1^0, z_2^0). \tag{9-33}$$

*Remark 3.* The series (9–32) is a *double* series because of the double index $m, n$. We can, however, arrange the terms to form a simple series, for example,

$$c_{00} + c_{10}(z_1 - z_1^0) + c_{01}(z_2 - z_2^0) + c_{20}(z_1 - z_1^0)^2$$
$$+ c_{11}(z_1 - z_1^0)(z_2 - z_2^0) + c_{02}(z_2 - z_2^0)^2 + c_{30}(z_1 - z_1^0)^3 + \cdots$$

We are thus sweeping out all the combinations $(m, n)$ by following diagonals of the corresponding array (see Fig. 9–1). Another simple method is to go around the sides of squares of increasing size, that is, to choose the successive pairs $(m, n)$ as follows: $(0, 0)$, $(1, 0)$, $(1, 1)$, $(0, 1)$, $(2, 0)$, $(2, 1)$, $(2, 2)$, $(1, 2)$, $(0, 2)$, $(3, 0)$, . . . The statement in the theorem that the series is absolutely convergent means that, in at least one arrangement as a simple series, one has an absolutely convergent series. However, once we know this holds for one such arrangement, we know that it holds for every arrangement as a simple series, and that the sum is the same for all arrangements (see *Advanced Calculus*, p. 333).

The concept of rearrangement can be broadened to include formation of the "iterated series" (like an iterated integral)

$$\sum_{m=0}^{\infty} \left[ \sum_{n=0}^{\infty} c_{mn}(z_1 - z_1^0)^m (z_2 - z_2^0)^n \right].$$

Again, if the original series is absolutely convergent for some arrangement as a simple series, then for each $m$, the series in brackets is absolutely convergent and we can sum with respect to $m$ to obtain an absolutely convergent series whose sum is the same as that of the original series.*

A double series $\sum \phi_{mn}(z_1, z_2)$ will be termed *M-uniformly convergent* in a set $E$ in $K_2$, if in $E$ one has $|\phi_{mn}(z_1, z_2)| \leq M_{mn}$ for appropriate constants $M_{mn}$, where the series $\sum M_{mn}$ converges in one (and hence in every) arrangement as a simple series. Thus the series $\sum \phi_{mn}(z_1, z_2)$ is uniformly convergent by the Weierstrass $M$-test for every arrangement as a simple series.

*Proof of Theorem 53.* For simplicity we take $z_1^0 = 0$, $z_2^0 = 0$. The general case is treated in a similar fashion. We can choose $R_1 > 0$, $R_2 > 0$, so small that $f(z_1, z_2)$ is analytic for $|z_1| < R_1$, $|z_2| < R_2$; we choose $r_1, r_2$ so that $0 < r_1 < R_1$, $0 < r_2 < R_2$. By the Cauchy integral formula (9–30), we have

$$f(z_1, z_2) = \frac{1}{(2\pi i)^2} \oint_{C_1} \oint_{C_2} \frac{f(\zeta_1, \zeta_2)}{(\zeta_1 - z_1)(\zeta_2 - z_2)} \, d\zeta_2 \, d\zeta_1,$$

where $C_1, C_2$ are circles $|\zeta_1| = r_1$, $|\zeta_2| = r_2$, and $|z_1| < r_1$, $|z_2| < r_2$. Hence we have the absolutely convergent series expansions

$$\frac{1}{\zeta_1 - z_1} = \frac{1}{\zeta_1(1 - (z_1/\zeta_1))} = \sum_{m=0}^{\infty} \frac{z_1^m}{\zeta_1^{m+1}}, \qquad \frac{1}{\zeta_2 - z_2} = \sum_{n=0}^{\infty} \frac{z_2^n}{\zeta_2^{n+1}}.$$

If we multiply, we obtain the expansion

$$\frac{1}{\zeta_1 - z_1} \frac{1}{\zeta_2 - z_2} = \sum_{m,n=0}^{\infty} \frac{z_1^m z_2^n}{\zeta_1^{m+1} \zeta_2^{n+1}},$$

which is again absolutely convergent for any arrangement (see *Advanced Calculus*, pp. 333–335). Furthermore, for fixed $z_1, z_2$, the series, in any

---

* See K. Knopp, *Theory and Application of Infinite Series*, London: Blackie and Sons, 1928, pp. 136–145.

arrangement, is $M$-uniformly convergent for $\zeta_1$ on $C_1$, $\zeta_2$ on $C_2$. For we can apply the $M$-test, with the aid of the corresponding arrangement of the convergent series of constants

$$\sum_{m,n=0}^{\infty} \frac{|z_1|^m}{r_1^{m+1}} \frac{|z_2|^n}{r_2^{n+1}} = \sum_{m=0}^{\infty} \frac{|z_1|^m}{r_1^{m+1}} \sum_{n=0}^{\infty} \frac{|z_2|^n}{r_2^{n+1}}.$$

Since $f(\zeta_1, \zeta_2)$ is continuous, the series remains uniformly convergent after multiplication by $f(\zeta_1, \zeta_2)$. Hence, we can integrate term by term:

$$f(z_1, z_2) = \frac{1}{(2\pi i)^2} \oint_{C_1} \oint_{C_2} f(\zeta_1, \zeta_2) \left( \frac{1}{\zeta_1 - z_1} \frac{1}{\zeta_2 - z_2} \right) d\zeta_2 \, d\zeta_1$$

$$= \frac{1}{(2\pi i)^2} \oint_{C_1} \oint_{C_2} f(\zeta_1, \zeta_2) \sum \frac{z_1^m z_2^n}{\zeta_1^{m+1} \zeta_2^{n+1}} \, d\zeta_2 \, d\zeta_1$$

$$= \sum_{m,n=0}^{\infty} c_{mn} z_1^m z_2^n, \tag{9-34}$$

$$c_{mn} = \frac{1}{(2\pi i)^2} \oint_{C_1} \oint_{C_2} \frac{f(\zeta_1, \zeta_2)}{\zeta_1^{m+1} \zeta_2^{n+1}} \, d\zeta_2 \, d\zeta_1.$$

The function $f(\zeta_1, \zeta_2)$ is continuous on the bounded closed set $|\zeta_1| = r_1$, $|\zeta_2| = r_2$, and therefore $|f(\zeta_1, \zeta_2)| \leq M$ for some constant $M$. We conclude that

$$|c_{mn}| \leq \frac{1}{4\pi^2} \int_0^{2\pi} \int_0^{2\pi} \frac{M}{r_1^{m+1} r_2^{n+1}} r_2 \, d\theta_2 \, r_1 \, d\theta_1 = \frac{M}{r_1^m r_2^n}.$$

Hence the series $\sum c_{mn} z_1^m z_2^n$, in any arrangement, is absolutely convergent for $|z_1| < r_1$, $|z_2| < r_2$. For each term is less than or equal to the corresponding term of the convergent series

$$\sum M \left| \frac{z_1}{r_1} \right|^m \left| \frac{z_2}{r_2} \right|^n = M \sum_{m=0}^{\infty} \left| \frac{z_1}{r_1} \right|^m \sum_{n=0}^{\infty} \left| \frac{z_2}{r_2} \right|^n.$$

The expression (9–33) for the coefficients (with $z_1^0 = 0$, $z_2^0 = 0$) follows at once from (9–34) and (9–31).

*Remark 3.* From the proof of Theorem 53, we see that the representation (9–32) is valid in each polycylinder $|z_1 - z_1^0| < r_1$, $|z_2 - z_2^0| < r_2$ contained in $D$. However, in general, there is no unique pair of radii $r_1, r_2$, both of which are as large as possible. For example, if $f = (1 - z_1 z_2)^{-1}$, then

$$f = \sum_{n=0}^{\infty} z_1^n z_2^n, \qquad |z_1| \, |z_2| < 1.$$

Hence this representation is valid for $|z_1| < 10$, $|z_2| < 1/10$, or for $|z_1| < 100$, $|z_2| < 1/100$, and so on.

## PROBLEMS

1. Let $w = u + iv$ be defined and continuous in a domain $D$ in $K_2$ and let $u$, $v$ have continuous first partial derivatives with respect to $x_1$, $y_1$, $x_2$, $y_2$ ($z_1 = x_1 + iy_1$, $z_2 = x_2 + iy_2$).

   (a) Show that $f$ is analytic if and only if the Cauchy-Riemann equations hold in $D$:

   $$\frac{\partial u}{\partial x_k} = \frac{\partial v}{\partial y_k}, \qquad \frac{\partial u}{\partial y_k} = -\frac{\partial v}{\partial x_k} \quad (k = 1, 2).$$

   (b) Show that, if $f$ is analytic in $D$, then

   $$\frac{\partial^2 u}{\partial x_k \, \partial x_l} + \frac{\partial^2 u}{\partial y_k \, \partial y_l} = 0, \qquad \frac{\partial^2 u}{\partial x_k \, \partial y_l} - \frac{\partial^2 u}{\partial x_l \, \partial y_k} = 0$$

   for $k = 1, 2$, $l = 1, 2$.

2. Evaluate the integrals:

   (a) $\displaystyle\oint_{|\zeta_2|=1} \oint_{|\zeta_1|=2} \frac{e^{\zeta_1} \sin(\zeta_1 + \zeta_2)}{(\zeta_1 - 1)\zeta_2} \, d\zeta_1 \, d\zeta_2$

   (b) $\displaystyle\oint_{|\zeta_2|=1} \oint_{|\zeta_1|=1} \frac{1}{(3 + \zeta_1^2 + \zeta_2^2)\zeta_1\zeta_2} \, d\zeta_1 \, d\zeta_2$

   (c) $\displaystyle\oint_{|\zeta_2|=2} \oint_{|\zeta_1|=1} \frac{e^{\zeta_1\zeta_2}}{\zeta_1^3(\zeta_2 - 1)^3} \, d\zeta_1 \, d\zeta_2.$

3. Expand each of the following functions in a Taylor series $\sum c_{mn} z_1^m z_2^n$ about $(0, 0)$ and describe pairs $r_1$, $r_2$ such that the series converges to the function for $|z_1| < r_1$, $|z_1| < r_2$:

   (a) $z_1 z_2 e^{z_1 + z_2}$　　　　(b) $\dfrac{z_2}{1 - z_1 + z_2}$　　　　(c) $\text{Log}\,(1 + z_1 z_2)$.

4. Verify that each of the following is an analytic function of $z_1$, $z_2$ in the domain given:

   (a) $\displaystyle\int_0^1 e^{-z_1 t^2} \sin z_2 t \, dt$　(t real),　　all $(z_1, z_2)$

   (b) $\displaystyle\int_0^1 \sin t^2 \, \frac{z_2}{(z_1 - t)^2 + z_2^2} \, dt$,　　$|z_1| > 2$, $|z_2| < 1$.

**ANSWERS**

2. (a) $(2\pi i)^2 e \sin 1$,        (b) $(2\pi i)^2/3$,        (c) $-2\pi^2$.

3. (a) $c_{mn} = [(m - 1)!(n - 1)!]^{-1}$, with $c_{m0} = 0$, $c_{n0} = 0$; $r_1 = \infty$, $r_2 = \infty$;

   (b) $c_{mn} = \begin{pmatrix} m + n - 1 \\ n - 1 \end{pmatrix}$, with $c_{m0} = 0$; $r_1 + r_2 = 1$ except for $z_2 = 0$,

   when $r_1 = \infty$;

   (c) $c_{mn} = 0$ except for $c_{nn} = (-1)^n/n$ for $n = 1, 2, \ldots$; $r_1 r_2 = 1$ except
   for $z_1 = 0$, $r_2 = \infty$ and $r_1 = \infty$, $z_2 = 0$.

## 9-4 □ CONVERGENCE REGION FOR POWER SERIES

We have seen that each analytic function of two variables is represented
by a power series in a neighborhood of each point of analyticity. We now
ask whether every power series $\sum c_{mn}(z_1 - z_1^0)^m (z_2 - z_2^0)^n$, converging at
more than one point, represents an analytic function and, more important,
in what sort of domain. Throughout we shall take $z_1^0 = 0$, $z_2^0 = 0$ and
consider the series

$$\sum c_{mn} z_1^m z_2^n. \tag{9-40}$$

The substitution of $z_1 - z_1^0$ for $z_1$ and $z_2 - z_2^0$ for $z_2$ gives the general
case.

Mainly, we shall be interested in the absolute convergence of (9-40),
that is, in the convergence of the series

$$\sum |c_{mn}| |z_1|^m |z_2|^n. \tag{9-41}$$

Since its terms are all positive or zero, if this series converges for one
arrangement as a simple series, it converges for all such arrangements and
hence so does (9-40), with the same sum for all arrangements (see *Advanced
Calculus*, pp. 333-334). We also note that the convergence of (9-41)
depends only on the pair of real numbers $(|z_1|, |z_2|)$ and hence can be
recorded in a $|z_1|, |z_2|$ plane. We thus obtain a convergence set as shown
in Fig. 9-2; the series (9-40) is absolutely convergent for all $(z_1, z_2)$
corresponding to points of the convergence set of Fig. 9-2.

**Theorem 54.** *Let the series* (9-40) *converge* (*for some arrangement as a
simple series*) *for* $z_1 = a_1$, $z_2 = a_2$, *where* $a_1 \neq 0$, $a_2 \neq 0$. *Then the
series converges absolutely for each* $(z_1, z_2)$ *such that* $|z_1| < |a_1|$, $|z_2| < |a_2|$.

*Proof.* Since the series $\sum c_{mn} a_1^m a_2^n$ (for some arrangement as a simple
series) is convergent, the $N$th term approaches zero as $N$ becomes infinite,
and accordingly the terms are bounded. Thus

$$|c_{mn} a_1^m a_2^n| < M = \text{const} \quad \text{for } m = 0, 1, 2, \ldots, \quad n = 0, 1, 2, \ldots$$

(cf. the proof of Theorem 31 in Section 5–1). Now for $|z_1| < |a_1|$, $|z_2| < |a_2|$,

$$\left| c_{mn} z_1^m z_2^n \right| = \left| c_{mn} a_1^m a_2^n \right| \left| \frac{z_1}{a_1} \right|^m \left| \frac{z_2}{a_2} \right|^n \leqq M \left| \frac{z_1}{a_1} \right|^m \left| \frac{z_2}{a_2} \right|^n.$$

Since $|z_1/a_1| < 1$, $|z_2/a_2| < 1$, the series

$$\sum_{m,n=0}^{\infty} M \left| \frac{z_1}{a_1} \right|^m \left| \frac{z_2}{a_2} \right|^n = M \sum_{m=0}^{\infty} \left| \frac{z_1}{a_1} \right|^m \sum_{n=0}^{\infty} \left| \frac{z_2}{a_2} \right|^n$$

converges and hence the series (9–40) converges absolutely.

*Remarks.* If the series (9–40) converges for $z_1 = a_1 \neq 0$ and $z_2 = 0$, then the same reasoning shows that the series (9–40) converges absolutely for $|z_1| < |a_1|$, $z_2 = 0$.

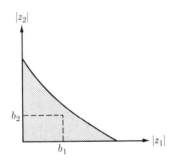

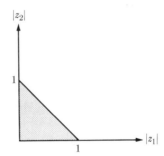

FIG. 9–2. Absolute-convergence diagram for series $\sum c_{mn} z_1^m z_2^n$.

FIG. 9–3. Absolute-convergence diagram for series of Example 1.

Theorem 54 shows that the convergence diagram of Fig. 9–2 has a special property: If $(b_1, b_2)$ is a convergence point of the diagram, then the rectangle $0 \leqq |z_1| \leqq b_1$, $0 \leqq |z_2| \leqq b_2$ is included in the diagram, as suggested in Fig. 9–2.

EXAMPLE 1. $1 + z_1 + z_2 + z_1^2 + 2z_1 z_2 + z_2^2 + z_1^3 + 3z_1^2 z_2 + 3z_1 z_2^2 + z_2^3 + z_1^4 + \cdots$, so that the terms could be grouped to give $\sum (z_1 + z_2)^n$. We test for absolute convergence. The series $1 + |z_1| + |z_2| + |z_1^2| + \cdots$ has only positive terms, and therefore its convergence and sum are unaffected by grouping (see *Advanced Calculus*, p. 332). Hence it is the same as the series $\sum (|z_1| + |z_2|)^n$, which converges for $|z_1| + |z_2| < 1$ and diverges otherwise. Thus our given series converges absolutely for $|z_1| + |z_2| < 1$, as in Fig. 9–3. We remark that the inequality $|z_1| + |z_2| < 1$ describes a domain $D$ in $K_2$, whose boundary has equation $|z_1| + |z_2| = 1$. [See Problem 1(b), following Section 9–3.]

If the point $(z_1^0, z_2^0)$ is not in $D$ or on its boundary, then the series diverges at $(z_1^0, z_2^0)$ for *every* arrangement. For $|z_1^0| + |z_2^0| = k$ must be greater than 1. We choose $c$ so that $1 < c < k$. If the series converges at $(z_1^0, z_2^0)$ for some arrangement, then by Theorem 54 it must converge absolutely for $|z_1| < |z_1^0|$, $|z_2| < |z_2^0|$ (or, as in the remark, for $|z_1| < |z_1^0|$, $z_2 = 0$ if, for example, $z_2^0 = 0$). In particular, it would converge absolutely at $(z_1^0/c, z_2^0/c)$. Since $(|z_1^0|/c) + (|z_2^0|/c) > 1$, this is impossible. Hence the series diverges for $|z_1| + |z_2| > 1$. On the boundary $|z_1| + |z_2| = 1$, the analysis is more complicated (see Problem 3 below).

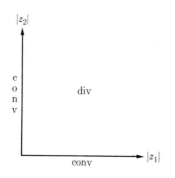
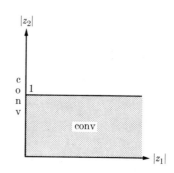

FIG. 9–4.  Absolute-convergence diagram for series of Example 2.

FIG. 9–5.  Absolute-convergence diagram for series of Example 3.

EXAMPLE 2.  $\sum_{n=0}^{\infty} n! z_1 z_2^n + \sum_{n=0}^{\infty} n! z_2 z_1^n$; that is, $\sum c_{mn} z_1^m z_2^n$, where $c_{mn} = 0$ except for $c_{1n} = n!$, $c_{m1} = m!$. For $z_1 = 0$ the series converges absolutely for all $z_2$; for $z_2 = 0$ the series converges absolutely for all $z_1$. For $z_1 \neq 0$, $z_2 \neq 0$, $n! z_1 z_2^n$ approaches $\infty$ as $n$ approaches $\infty$, so that there is no possibility of convergence. Hence, in this example the set of convergence (and absolute convergence) consists of the points $(z_1, 0)$ and the points $(0, z_2)$; they do not form a domain in $K_2$ (Problem 4, following Section 9–2). The absolute convergence diagram is shown in Fig. 9–4.

EXAMPLE 3.  $\sum_{n=0}^{\infty} z_1 z_2^n$. This series converges absolutely for $z_1 \neq 0$, $|z_2| < 1$, and for $z_1 = 0$, $z_2$ arbitrary. The diagram is shown in Fig. 9–5. [See Problem 1(a) below.]

By an *interior point* of a set $E$ in $K_2$ we mean a point $(z_1^0, z_2^0)$ which has a neighborhood lying in $E$. Thus a set $E$ is a domain precisely when $E$ is connected and consists solely of interior points. By the *interior* of a set $E$ we mean the set of all interior points of $E$; the interior may be empty.

By a *Reinhardt domain* in $K_2$ with *center* $(z_1^0, z_2^0)$ we mean a domain $D$ such that, for each point $(z_1', z_2')$ in $D$, all $(z_1, z_2)$ for which

$$|z_1 - z_1^0| = |z_1' - z_1^0|, \qquad |z_2 - z_2^0| = |z_2' - z_2^0|$$

are in $D$. Thus whether or not $(z_1, z_2)$ is in $D$ depends only on the pair $(|z_1 - z_1^0|, |z_2 - z_2^0|)$. If, for each $(z_1', z_2')$ in $D$, all $(z_1, z_2)$ for which

$$|z_1 - z_1^0| \leqq |z_1' - z_1^0|, \qquad |z_2 - z_2^0| \leqq |z_2' - z_2^0|$$

are in $D$, then $D$ is called a *complete Reinhardt domain* with center $(z_1^0, z_2^0)$.

**Theorem 55.** *Let $E$ denote the set of $(z_1, z_2)$ for which the series (9–40) converges; let $E^i$ be the interior of $E$ and let $E^i$ be nonempty. Then $E^i$ is a complete Reinhardt domain with center $(0, 0)$. The series (9–40) converges absolutely in $E^i$ and converges M-uniformly on each closed polycylinder $|z_1| \leqq r_1$, $|z_2| \leqq r_2$ contained in $E^i$.*

*Proof.* Since $E^i$ is not empty, $E^i$ is an open set and must contain some points $(z_1, z_2)$ not on the coordinate planes $z_1 = 0$, $z_2 = 0$ (Problem 4, following Section 9–2). Let $(a_1, a_2)$ be such a point, so that $a_1 \neq 0$, $a_2 \neq 0$. By Theorem 54, all points $(z_1, z_2)$ for which $|z_1| < |a_1|$, $|z_2| < a_2$ are in $E$; since these points form an open set, they are all in $E^i$. In particular, the origin $(0, 0)$ is in $E^i$, as are all points $(ta_1, ta_2)$ for $0 \leqq t \leqq 1$. Thus each point $(a_1, a_2)$ in $E^i$ with $a_1 \neq 0$, $a_2 \neq 0$ can be joined to the origin by a straight line $z_1 = ta_1$, $z = ta_2$ lying in $E^i$. If, for example, a point $(a_1, 0)$ is in $E^i$, with $a_1 \neq 0$, then it has a neighborhood $|z_1 - a_1|^2 + |z_2|^2 < \epsilon^2$ in $E^i$; such a neighborhood contains a point $(a_1', a_2')$ in $E^i$ with $a_1' \neq 0$, $a_2' \neq 0$, for example, the point $(a_1, \frac{1}{2}\epsilon)$. We can join $(a_1, 0)$ to $(a_1, \frac{1}{2}\epsilon)$ by the line segment $z_1 = a_1$, $z_2 = \frac{1}{2}\epsilon t$, $0 \leqq t \leqq 1$ in $E^i$ and then join $(a_1, \frac{1}{2}\epsilon)$ to $(0, 0)$, as above, by a line segment in $E^i$. Thus every point of $E^i$ can be joined to $(0, 0)$ by a broken line in $E^i$ and $E^i$ is connected. Thus $E^i$ is a domain.

Now let $(z_1', z_2')$ be a point of $E^i$, $z_1' \neq 0$, $z_2' \neq 0$. Then each point $(z_1'(1 + \epsilon), z_2'(1 + \epsilon))$ is also in $E^i$ for $\epsilon > 0$ sufficiently small. By Theorem 54, every point $(z_1, z_2)$ for which

$$|z_1| < |z'|(1 + \epsilon), \qquad |z_2| < |z_2'|(1 + \epsilon)$$

is in $E$ and, since these inequalities describe an open set, in $E^i$. In particular, the points $(z_1, z_2)$ for which $|z_1| \leqq |z_1'|$, $|z_2| \leqq |z_2'|$ are in $E^i$. The reasoning is easily extended to the points $(z_1', 0)$ and $(0, z_2')$ (Problem 4 below). We conclude that $E^i$ is a complete Reinhardt domain. The same reasoning and Theorem 54 show that the series (9–40) converges absolutely in $E^i$. If the closed polycylinder $|z_1| \leqq r_1$, $|z_2| \leqq r_2$ is in $E^i$, then the series (9–40) converges $M$-uniformly in the closed polycylinder by the Weierstrass $M$-test, with series $\sum M_n$ given by $\sum |c_{mn}| r_1^m r_2^n$ in some arrangement as a simple series.

**Theorem 56.** *Under the hypotheses of Theorem 55, the sum of the series (9–40) is an analytic function* $f(z_1, z_2)$ *in* $E^i$ *and (9–40) is its Taylor series.*

*Proof.* By Theorem 55, the series converges $M$-uniformly in each closed polycylinder $|z_1| \leq r_1$, $|z_2| \leq r_2$ in $E^i$. Hence the sum $f$ is continuous on each such region. Since every point of $E^i$ can be included in the interior of such a polycylinder, $f$ is continuous everywhere in $E^i$.

We now consider the series obtained by differentiating (9–40) term by term with respect to $z_1$, that is

$$\sum c_{mn} m z_1^{m-1} z_2^n. \tag{9–42}$$

As in the proof of Theorem 34 in Section 5–11, for each fixed $b > 1$, $m < kb^m$ for some constant $k$, $m = 0, 1, 2, \ldots$ Hence

$$m|c_{mn}| \, |z_1|^m \, |z_2|^n \leq k|c_{mn}| \, |bz_1|^m \, |z_2|^n.$$

We thus conclude that the series $\sum c_{mn} m z_1^m z_2^n$ converges absolutely for $(bz_1, z_2)$ in $E^i$. Since $b$ is an arbitrary number greater than 1, we conclude that the series converges absolutely for every $(z_1, z_2)$ in $E^i$. Accordingly, the series (9–42) also converges absolutely in $E^i$. If we denote its sum by $g_1(z_1, z_2)$, then $g_1(z_1, z_2)$ is continuous in $E^i$.

Now the series (9–40) is absolutely convergent in $E^i$ for every arrangement as a simple series. In particular, we can group terms according to powers of $z_1$ and write

$$f(z_1, z_2) = \sum_{m=0}^{\infty} h_m(z_2) z_1^m, \qquad h_m(z_2) = \sum_{n=0}^{\infty} c_{mn} z_2^n.$$

For each fixed $(z_1^0, z_2^0)$ in $E^i$, the series (9–40) converges in a polycylinder $|z_1| < |z_1^0| + \epsilon$, $|z_2| < |z_2^0| + \epsilon$, for $\epsilon$ sufficiently small and positive. Accordingly, we can write

$$f(z_1, z_2^0) = \sum_{m=0}^{\infty} h_m(z_2^0) z_1^m, \qquad |z_1| < |z_1^0| + \epsilon.$$

Thus $f(z_1, z_2^0)$ is an analytic function of $z_1$ with the power series shown, and its derivative is obtained by differentiating term by term:

$$\frac{\partial f}{\partial z_1} = \sum_{m=1}^{\infty} m h_m(z_2^0) z_1^{m-1}. \tag{9–43}$$

But the series for $g_1(z_1, z_2^0)$ can also be grouped as a power series in $z_1$ to give the right-hand side of (9–43). We conclude that $\partial f / \partial z_1 = g_1(z_1, z_2)$ at every $(z_1, z_2)$ in $E^i$. Since $g_1$ is continuous in $E^i$, $\partial f / \partial z_1$ is continuous in $E^i$. In the same way, $\partial f / \partial z_2$ is continuous in $E^i$. Thus $f$ is an analytic

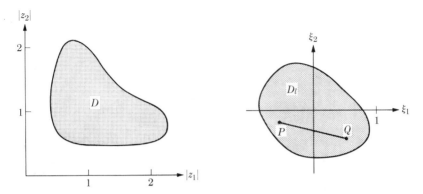

FIG. 9–6.   Logarithmic image and logarithmic convexity.

function in $E^i$. By the same reasoning, $g_1(z_1, z_2) = \partial f/\partial z_1$ and $g_2(z_1, z_2) = \partial f/\partial z_2$ are analytic in $E^i$. Accordingly, all partial derivatives $\partial^{k+l}f/\partial^k z_1\,\partial^l z_2$ are analytic in $E^i$, and these derivatives are obtained from the series (9–40) by differentiating term by term. In particular,

$$\frac{\partial^{k+l}f}{\partial^k z_1\,\partial^l z_2}\bigg|_{(0,0)} = k!\,l!\,c_{kl},$$

so that (9–40) is indeed the Taylor series of $f$.

*Logarithmic convexity.* Let $D$ be a Reinhardt domain in $K_2$ with center $(0, 0)$. To each $(z_1, z_2)$ in $D$ with $z_1 \neq 0$, $z_2 \neq 0$, we assign the pair of *real* numbers $(\xi_1, \xi_2)$, where $\xi_1 = \log|z_1|$, $\xi_2 = \log|z_2|$. The points $(\xi_1, \xi_2)$ obtained then form a set $D_l$ in the $\xi_1\xi_2$-plane, which we call the *logarithmic image* of $D$. The set $D_l$ is a domain (Problem 5 below). We can obtain the logarithmic image in two stages, first by forming the set of values of $(|z_1|, |z_2|)$, as in the absolute convergence diagram, and then by setting $\xi_1 = \log|z_1|$, $\xi_2 = \log|z_2|$, that is, introducing a logarithmic scale on both axes. The process is illustrated in Fig. 9–6. We call $D$ *logarithmically convex* if the domain $D_l$ is *convex*, that is, if each pair of points $P, Q$ in $D_l$ can be joined by a line segment $PQ$ in $D_l$, as in Fig. 9–6.

**Theorem 57.** *Under the hypotheses of Theorem 55, the set $E^i$ is a logarithmically convex Reinhardt domain.*

*Proof.* Since $E^i$ is nonempty, we know it contains points $(z_1, z_2)$, not on the coordinate planes $z_1 = 0$, $z_2 = 0$. Thus $E_l^i$ is also nonempty. Let $(\xi_1', \xi_2')$, $(\xi_1'', \xi_2'')$ be two points in $E_l^i$. An arbitrary third point $(\xi_1, \xi_2)$ on the line segment joining the two points is given by

$$\xi_1 = (1 - t)\xi_1' + t\xi_1'', \quad \xi_2 = (1 - t)\xi_2' + t\xi_2'', \quad 0 \leqq t \leqq 1. \quad (9\text{--}44)$$

We can write

$$\xi_1' = \log|z_1'|, \quad \xi_2' = \log|z_2'|, \quad \xi_1'' = \log|z_1''|, \quad \xi_2'' = \log|z_2''|,$$

where $(z_1', z_2')$ and $(z_1'', z_2'')$ are points of $E^i$. We wish to show that each pair $\xi_1, \xi_2$ satisfying (9–44) can be similarly represented in terms of a point of $E^i$. We assert that if we set $z_1 = e^{\xi_1}$, $z_2 = e^{\xi_2}$ (so that $z_1, z_2$ are real and positive), then $(z_1, z_2)$ is in $E^i$, so that $(\xi_1, \xi_2) = (\log|z_1|, \log|z_2|)$ is in $E_l^i$. To justify our assertion we must first show that (9–40) converges absolutely at $(z_1, z_2)$ and then show that it converges absolutely in a neighborhood of $(z_1, z_2)$.

Now the general term of (9–40) at $(z_1, z_2)$ has absolute value

$$
\begin{aligned}
|c_{mn}z_1^m z_2^n| &= |c_{mn}|e^{m\xi_1}e^{n\xi_2} = |c_{mn}|e^{m\xi_1+n\xi_2} \\
&= |c_{mn}|e^{(1-t)(m\xi_1'+n\xi_2')+t(m\xi_1''+n\xi_2'')} \\
&= |c_{mn}|(|z_1'|^m |z_2'|^n)^{1-t}(|z_1''|^m |z_2''|^n)^t \\
&= (|c_{mn}| |z_1'|^m |z_2'|^n)^{1-t} (|c_{mn}| |z_1''|^m |z_2''|^n)^t.
\end{aligned}
$$

For $a \geq 0$, $b \geq 0$, $0 \leq t \leq 1$, the inequality $a^{1-t}b^t \leq a + b$ is valid (Problem 6 below). Hence,

$$|c_{mn}z_1^m z_2^n| \leq |c_{mn}| |z_1'|^m |z_2'|^n + |c_{mn}| |z_1''|^m |z_2''|^n.$$

Since both series $\sum c_{mn}z_1'^m z_2'^n$, $\sum c_{mn}z_1''^m z_2''^n$ converge absolutely, we conclude that the series $\sum c_{mn}z_1^m z_2^n$ also converges absolutely. This shows that $(z_1, z_2) = (e^{\xi_1}, e^{\xi_2})$ is in $E$.

To show that $(e^{\xi_1}, e^{\xi_2})$ is in $E^i$, we note that, since $E_l^i$ is a domain, we can choose $\epsilon$ so small and positive that the points $(\xi_1' + \epsilon, \xi_2' + \epsilon)$, $(\xi_1'' + \epsilon, \xi_2'' + \epsilon)$ are in $E_l^i$. Hence, by the previous proof, all points

$$(z_1^*, z_2^*) = (e^{\xi_1^*}, e^{\xi_2^*})$$

are in $E$, where

$$\xi_1^* = (1 - t)(\xi_1' + \epsilon) + t(\xi_1'' + \epsilon) = (1 - t)\xi_1' + t\xi_1'' + \epsilon = \xi_1 + \epsilon,$$
$$\xi_2^* = (1 - t)(\xi_2' + \epsilon) + t(\xi_2'' + \epsilon) = \xi_2 + \epsilon,$$

so that $|z_1^*| = e^\epsilon e^{\xi_1}$, $|z_2^*| = e^\epsilon e^{\xi_2}$. By Theorem 54 the series (9–40) converges absolutely for $|z_1| < e^\epsilon e^{\xi_1}$, $|z_2| < e^\epsilon e^{\xi_2}$, so that $(e^{\xi_1}, e^{\xi_2})$ is interior to $E$, that is, in $E^i$.

*Remark.* Theorems 54 through 57 sharply restrict the set of absolute convergence of the series (9–40) or, correspondingly, the absolute convergence diagram. It can be shown that the boundary of the absolute

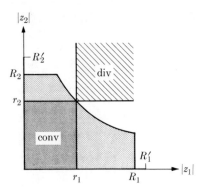

FIG. 9–7.   Properties of absolute convergence diagram.

convergence diagram is typically as suggested in Fig. 9–7; that is, it is formed of two line segments on which $|z_2| = R_2$ and $|z_1| = R_1$ respectively, and a continuous curve joining them, plus possibly extra intervals $R_1 \leq |z_1| \leq R_1'$, $|z_2| = 0$ and $R_2 \leq |z_2| \leq R_2'$, $|z_1| = 0$. Thus the convergence set in the coordinate planes may extend beyond the limits expected from the part of $E$ not in those planes. It can be shown further that every logarithmically convex complete Reinhardt domain with center $(0, 0)$ is the set $E^i$ for some power series (9–40). For further discussion one is referred to *Functions of Several Complex Variables*, by W. Kaplan* and to *Mehrere Komplexe Veraenderliche*, by H. Behnke and P. Thullen.†

## PROBLEMS

1. Describe, with the aid of a figure, the absolute convergence diagram for each of the following series:

   (a) $\displaystyle\sum_{n=0}^{\infty} z_1 z_2^n$ (Example 3 above)   (b) $\displaystyle\sum_{m,n=0}^{\infty} \frac{z_1^m z_2^n}{n!}$

   (c) $\displaystyle\sum_{m,n=1}^{\infty} (m + n) z_1^m z_2^n$   (d) $\displaystyle\sum_{n=1}^{\infty} z_1^{5n} z_2^{3n}$.

2. Describe, with the aid of a figure, the logarithmic image of each of the absolute convergence regions of Problem 1 (see Answers to Problem 1 below).

3. Show that the series of Example 1 in Section 9–4, in the order given, is conditionally convergent for $z_2 = -z_1$, where $|z_1| = \frac{1}{2}$.

---

* Ann Arbor: Ann Arbor Publishers, 1964.
† Berlin: Springer, 1934.

4. Let $E^i$ be defined as in Theorem 55, and let $(z_1', 0)$ be a point of $E^i$, $z_1' \neq 0$. Show that $\epsilon$ can be chosen, $\epsilon > 0$, so that all points $(z_1, z_2)$ for which $|z_1| < |z_1'|(1 + \epsilon)$, $|z_2| < \epsilon$ are in $E^i$.

5. Let $D_l$ be the logarithmic image of a Reinhardt domain $D$ in $K_2$ with center $(0, 0)$. Show that $D_l$ is a domain in the $\xi_1\xi_2$-plane.

[Hint: apply the result of Problem 6, following Section 9–2.]

6. Prove: If $a$, $b$, $t$ are real numbers such that $a \geq 0, b \geq 0, 0 \leq t \leq 1$, then $a^{1-t}b^t \leq a + b$.

7. Let a series (9–40) be given. Prove: To each $r_1 > 0$, there exists a number $r_2$, $0 \leq r_2 \leq \infty$, such that the series (9–40) converges absolutely for $|z_1| < r_1$, $|z_2| < r_2$ and diverges for $|z_1| > r_1$, $|z_2| > r_2$ (see Fig. 9–7).

[Hint: show that the real numbers $r_2'$ for which the series (9–40) converges absolutely for $|z_1| < r_1$, $|z_2| < r_2'$ form an interval of form $0 \leq r_2' \leq r_2$ for some $r_2$, $0 \leq r_2 \leq \infty$. If $r_2 < \infty$, show, with the aid of Theorem 54, that the series cannot converge for any $(z_1, z_2)$ for which $|z_1| > r_1$, $|z_2| > r_2$. The numbers $r_1, r_2$ are called associated radii of convergence.]

8. Let $r_1, r_2$ and $\rho_1, \rho_2$ be two pairs of associated radii of convergence (Problem 7) for the series (9–40) and let $r_1 < \rho_1$. Prove that $r_2 \geq \rho_2$.

## ANSWERS

1. (a) For $z_1 \neq 0$, $|z_2| < 1$; for $z_1 = 0$, $|z_2| < \infty$;
   (b) $|z_1| < 1$, $|z_2| < \infty$;
   (c) for $z_1 \neq 0$ and $z_2 \neq 0$, $|z_1| < 1$ and $|z_2| < 1$; for $z_1 = 0$, $|z_2| < \infty$; and for $z_2 = 0$, $|z_1| < \infty$;
   (d) for $z_1 \neq 0$ and $z_2 \neq 0$, $|z_1|^5|z_2|^3 < 1$; for $z_1 = 0$, $|z_2| < \infty$; for $z_2 = 0$, $|z_1| < \infty$.

2. (a) $\xi_2 < 0$,          (b) $\xi_1 < 0$,
   (c) $\xi_1 < 0$, $\xi_2 < 0$,          (d) $5\xi_1 + 3\xi_2 < 0$.

## 9–5 □ LAURENT EXPANSION

The Laurent expansion for a function $f(z)$ of one complex variable represents $f(z)$ in an annulus $R' < |z - z_0| < R''$. For a function $f(z_1, z_2)$ of two variables, we obtain a similar expression for a domain

$$R_1' < |z_1 - z_1^0| < R_1'', \qquad R_2' < |z_2 - z_2^0| < R_2'',$$

which can be considered to be a generalization of an annulus. However, we can go further and show that such an expansion is available in a Reinhardt domain with center $(z_1^0, z_2^0)$. A Reinhardt domain $D$ can also be considered as a generalization of an annulus. For whether or not $(z_1, z_2)$ is in $D$ is determined solely by the values of $|z_1 - z_1^0|$, $|z_2 - z_2^0|$, just as for one variable, where $z$ is in the annulus with center $z_0$ according to the value of $|z - z_0|$.

For simplicity, we take the center $(z_1^0, z_2^0)$, as before, to be the origin $(0, 0)$ in $K_2$.

**Theorem 58.** *Let $f(z_1, z_2)$ be analytic in the domain $D$ defined by the inequalities $R_1' < |z_1| < R_1''$, $R_2' < |z_2| < R_2''$, where $0 \leq R_1' < R_1'' \leq \infty$, $0 \leq R_2' < R_2'' \leq \infty$. Then in $D$, $f(z_1, z_2)$ can be represented by an absolutely convergent series:*

$$f(z_1, z_2) = \sum_{m,n=-\infty}^{\infty} c_{mn} z_1^m z_2^n. \tag{9–50}$$

*The coefficients are uniquely determined by $f(z_1, z_2)$. The series converges M-uniformly on each region $r_1' \leq |z_1| \leq r_1''$, $r_2' \leq |z_2| \leq r_2''$, where $R_1' < r_1' < r_1'' < R_1''$, $R_2' < r_2' < r_2'' < R_2''$.*

*Remark.* The discussion of double series in Remark 3 in Section 9–3 can be extended to the series of form (9–50), in which the indices $m$, $n$ vary from $-\infty$ to $+\infty$. In particular, the series can be arranged as a simple series in many ways (Problem 3 below).

*Proof.* Let $r_1'$, $r_1''$, $r_2'$, $r_2''$ be chosen as described and let $(z_1, z_2)$ be such that $r_1' < |z_1| < r_1''$, $r_2' < |z_2| < r_2''$. For $z_2$ fixed, $f(\zeta_1, z_2)$ is analytic in $\zeta_1$ in the annulus $R_1' < |\zeta_1| < R_1''$. Hence by the Cauchy integral formula for the annular region (see Section 5–3 above),

$$f(z_1, z_2) = \frac{1}{2\pi i} \oint_{|\zeta_1|=r_1''} \frac{f(\zeta_1, z_2)}{\zeta_1 - z_1} d\zeta_1 - \frac{1}{2\pi i} \oint_{|\zeta_1|=r_1'} \frac{f(\zeta_1, z_2)}{\zeta_1 - z_1} d\zeta_1. \tag{9–51}$$

Now for fixed $\zeta_1$, $R_1' < |\zeta_1| < R_2''$, $f(\zeta_1, \zeta_2)$ is analytic in $\zeta_2$ in the annulus $R_2' < |\zeta_2| < R_2''$. Hence, in the same way,

$$f(\zeta_1, z_2) = \frac{1}{2\pi i} \oint_{|\zeta_2|=r_2''} \frac{f(\zeta_1, \zeta_2)}{\zeta_2 - z_2} d\zeta_2 - \frac{1}{2\pi i} \oint_{|\zeta_2|=r_2'} \frac{f(\zeta_1, \zeta_2)}{\zeta_2 - z_2} d\zeta_2. \tag{9–52}$$

If we combine (9–51) and (9–52), we obtain a representation of $f$ as a sum of four terms:

$$f(z_1, z_2) = \frac{1}{(2\pi i)^2} \oint_{|\zeta_1|=r_1''} \oint_{|\zeta_2|=r_2''} \frac{f(\zeta_1, \zeta_2)}{(\zeta_1 - z_1)(\zeta_2 - z_2)} \, d\zeta_2 \, d\zeta_1$$

$$+ \frac{(-1)}{(2\pi i)^2} \oint_{|\zeta_1|=r_1''} \oint_{|\zeta_2|=r_2'} \cdots$$

In the first term we can write

$$\frac{1}{(\zeta_1 - z_1)(\zeta_2 - z_2)} = \frac{1}{\zeta_1 \zeta_2 (1 - z_1/\zeta_1)(1 - z_2/\zeta_2)}$$

$$= \sum_{m,n=0}^{\infty} \frac{z_1^m z_2^n}{\zeta_1^{m+1} \zeta_2^{n+1}},$$

where the series converges absolutely, since $|z_1|/|\zeta_1| = |z_1|/r_1'' < 1$, $|z_2|/|\zeta_2| = |z_2|/r_2'' < 1$. The convergence is $M$-uniform for $(z_1, z_2)$ fixed and $|\zeta_1| = r_1''$, $|\zeta_2| = r_2''$, since the general term is, in absolute value, equal to $|z_1|^m |z_2|^n r_1''^{-m-1} r_2''^{-n-1}$.

In the second term we can write

$$\frac{1}{(\zeta_1 - z_1)(\zeta_2 - z_2)} = \frac{-1}{\zeta_1 z_2 (1 - z_1/\zeta_1)(1 - \zeta_2/z_2)}$$

$$= - \sum_{m,n=0}^{\infty} \frac{z_1^m z_2^{-n-1}}{\zeta_1^{m+1} \zeta_2^{-n}},$$

where again the series converges absolutely and $M$-uniformly, since

$$|z_1|/|\zeta_1| = |z_1|/r_1'' < 1, \qquad |\zeta_2|/|z_2| = r_2'/|z_2| < 1.$$

The remaining two terms are analyzed in the same way.

The four series remain $M$-uniformly convergent after multiplication of each term by $f(\zeta_1, \zeta_2)$, a continuous function, and hence can be integrated term by term. The integration yields the expansion (9–50), where

$$c_{mn} = \frac{1}{(2\pi i)^2} \oint_{|\zeta_1|=r_1} \oint_{|\zeta_2|=r_2} \frac{f(\zeta_1, \zeta_2)}{\zeta_1^{m+1} \zeta_2^{n+1}} \, d\zeta_2 \, d\zeta_1 \qquad (9\text{–}53)$$

and $r_1, r_2$ can be chosen as any values such that $R_1' < r_1 < R_1''$, $R_2' < r_2 < R_2''$. As in the proof of Theorem 53, we obtain an estimate

$$|c_{mn}| \le \frac{M}{r_1^m r_2^n},$$

from which we can show that the integrated series is also absolutely and $M$-uniformly convergent as stated in the theorem.

*Uniqueness of coefficients.* Let $f(z_1, z_2)$ be represented as an absolutely convergent series (9–50) in the given region. We can write this series as a sum of four series, with corresponding $m, n$ values:

$$m \geqq 0, \quad n \geqq 0; \qquad m \geqq 0, \quad n < 0;$$

$$m < 0, \quad n \geqq 0; \qquad m < 0, \quad n < 0.$$

Each of the four series is also absolutely convergent (as subseries of an absolutely convergent series). The first is a power series in $z_1, z_2$, convergent for $R_1' < |z_1| < R_1''$, $R_2' < |z_2| < R_2''$. Hence, by Theorem 55, the series converges absolutely and $M$-uniformly in each region $|z_1| \leqq r_1 < R_1''$, $|z_2| \leqq r_2 < R_2''$. The second series can be regarded as a power series in $z_1$ and $z_2^{-1}$, and is hence $M$-uniformly convergent in each region $|z_1| \leqq r_1 < R_1''$, $|z_2| \geqq r_2 > R_2'$. Similar statements apply to the other two series. We conclude that the combined series (9–50) is $M$-uniformly convergent for $|z_1| = r_1$, $|z_2| = r_2$, where $R_1' < r_1 < R_1''$, $R_2' < r_2 < R_2''$. It remains $M$-uniformly convergent if every term is divided by $z_1^{p+1} z_2^{q+1}$, where $p$ and $q$ are fixed integers. Hence,

$$\oint_{|z_1|=r_1} \oint_{|z_2|=r_2} \frac{f(z_1, z_2)}{z_1^{p+1} z_2^{q+1}} \, dz_2 \, dz_1 = \sum_{m,n=-\infty}^{\infty} \oint \oint \frac{c_{mn} z_1^m z_2^n}{z_1^{p+1} z_2^{q+1}} \, dz_2 \, dz_1.$$

But each term on the right is 0 except for $m = p$, $n = q$, when it reduces to $c_{pq}(2\pi i)^2$. Thus the coefficients $c_{mn}$ are given by (9–53) and are uniquely determined by $f(z_1, z_2)$.

*Remark* 1. If $f(z_1, z_2)$ is analytic in a domain $D$ of form $|z_1| < R_1''$, $R_2' < |z_2| < R_2''$, then Theorem 58 is applicable with $R_1' = 0$. However, in (9–53) $f(\zeta_1, \zeta_2)$ is analytic in $\zeta_1$, for fixed $\zeta_2$, for $|\zeta_1| \leqq r_1$, so that $c_{mn} = 0$ for $m < 0$ and (9–50) can be written

$$f(z) = \sum_{m=0,\, n=-\infty}^{\infty} c_{mn} z_1^m z_2^n.$$

If the domain is of form $|z_1| < R_1''$, $|z_2| < R_2''$, then $c_{mn} = 0$ for $m < 0$ and for $n < 0$, and we obtain the Taylor series expansion of Theorem 53.

**Theorem 59.** *Let $f(z_1, z_2)$ be analytic in $D$, a Reinhardt domain with center $(0, 0)$. Then $f$ can be represented in $D$ by an absolutely convergent series (9–50), $M$-uniformly convergent in each closed region $r_1' \leqq |z_1| \leqq r_1''$, $r_2' \leqq |z_2| \leqq r_2''$ contained in $D$.*

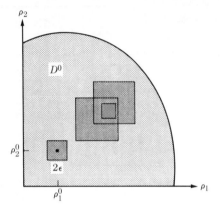

FIG. 9–8.  Uniqueness of Laurent expansion in a Reinhardt domain.

*Proof.*  To each point $(z_1, z_2)$ in $D$ with $z_1 \neq 0$, $z_2 \neq 0$, we associate the point $(\rho_1, \rho_2)$ in the $\rho_1\rho_2$-plane, where $\rho_1 = |z_1|$, $\rho_2 = |z_2|$.  The points $(\rho_1, \rho_2)$ obtained form a set $D^0$ in the first quadrant of the $\rho_1\rho_2$-plane.  Since $D$ is a Reinhardt domain with center $(0, 0)$, if $(\rho_1^0, \rho_2^0)$ is a point of $D^0$, then all points $(z_1, z_2)$ such that $|z_1| = \rho_1^0$, $|z_2| = \rho_2^0$ are in $D$.  Since $D$ is a domain, we can show that $D^0$ is a domain (Problem 4 below).  For each point $(\rho_1^0, \rho_2^0)$ in $D^0$, we can thus choose a square neighborhood

$$D_\epsilon^0 : \quad \rho_1^0 - \epsilon < \rho_1 < \rho_1^0 + \epsilon, \quad \rho_2^0 - \epsilon < \rho_2 < \rho_2^0 + \epsilon$$

of side $2\epsilon$ in $D^0$, as in Fig. 9–8.  Hence the corresponding domain $D_\epsilon$: $\rho_1^0 - \epsilon < |z_1| < \rho_1^0 + \epsilon$, $\rho_2^0 - \epsilon < |z_2| < \rho_2^0 + \epsilon$ is contained in $D$.  Therefore $f(z_1, z_2)$ can be represented by an absolutely convergent series of form (9–50) in $D_\epsilon$.  If two different square neighborhoods of the type of $D_\epsilon^0$ overlap, then a smaller square can be chosen, contained in both squares, as suggested in Fig. 9–8.  The expansions for each of the large squares must coincide with the expansion for the smaller square by the uniqueness of the Laurent coefficients.  Hence the expansions for the overlapping squares must coincide.  Since $D$ is a domain, we conclude that only one expansion holds for all squares $D_\epsilon^0$; that is, one expansion (9–50) represents $f(z_1, z_2)$ in all of $D$, except perhaps the points of $D$ on the coordinate planes (see Problem 5 below).  If $(z_1^0, 0)$ is a point of $D$ on the coordinate plane $z_2 = 0$, then we can choose a domain

$$D_\epsilon : |z_1^0| - \epsilon < |z_1| < |z_1^0| + \epsilon, \qquad |z_2| < \epsilon$$

or, if $z_1^0 = 0$, a domain $D_\epsilon$: $|z_1| < \epsilon$, $|z_2| < \epsilon$ in which $f$ is analytic and hence can be represented by a series (9–50).  Since each of the domains

$D_\epsilon$ contains points where $z_1 \neq 0$, $z_2 \neq 0$, the same series (9–50) as above must be obtained. Therefore $f$ is represented by one absolutely convergent series in all of $D$. The $M$-uniform convergence now follows from Theorem 58.

*Remark* 2. By Remark 1 above, if $D$ contains points $(z_1, 0)$ and points $(0, z_2)$, then in (9–50) $c_{mn} = 0$ for $m < 0$ or $n < 0$, so that (9–50) becomes an ordinary power series (9–40).

## PROBLEMS

1. Expand $f(z_1, z_2) = e^{1/z_2}/(z_1^2 - z_1)$ in a Laurent series for $0 < |z_1| < 1$, $0 < |z_2| < \infty$.

2. Expand $f(z_1, z_2) = 1/(1 - z_1 - 2z_2)$ in a Laurent series for $|z_1| > 2$, $|z_2| < \frac{1}{2}$.

3. Describe several ways of arranging the series (9–50) as a simple series.

4. Show that, if $D$ is a domain in $K_2$, then the equations $\rho_1 = |z_1|$, $\rho_2 = |z_2|$ for $(z_1, z_2)$ in $D$, $z_1 \neq 0$, $z_2 \neq 0$, transform $D$ onto a domain $D^0$ in the $\rho_1\rho_2$-plane.

5. Complete the proof of Theorem 59 by showing that one expansion (9–50) is valid in $D_1 = D$ minus the points on the coordinate planes.

[*Hint: the proof in the text provides such an expansion in each domain $D_\epsilon$. Choose one fixed $D_\epsilon$ and let $D^*$ be the set of all points of $D_1$ in a neighborhood of which one has the same expansion as in the chosen $D_\epsilon$. Show that $D^*$ is an open set, and also that the points of $D_1$ not in $D^*$ form an open set. Now use the fact that $D_1$ is a domain (Problem 5, following Section 9–2).*]

## ANSWERS

1. $c_{mn} = 1/(-n)!$ for $m \geqq -1$, $n \leqq 0$, $c_{mn} = 0$ otherwise.

2. $c_{mn} = -\dbinom{-m-1}{n}(-2)^n$ for $m = -1, -2, \ldots, n = 0, 1, \ldots, -m-1$,
   $c_{mn} = 0$ otherwise.

## 9–6  □  ANALYTIC CONTINUATION

The concepts of Section 8–1 find immediate extension to analytic functions of several variables. Thus $f_2(z_1, z_2)$ is a *direct analytic continuation* of $f_1(z_1, z_2)$ if $f_1$ is given in domain $D_1$, $f_2$ in domain $D_2$, where $D_1$ and $D_2$ overlap, and $f_1 \equiv f_2$ in the common part of $D_1$, $D_2$. The continuation is also *unique;* that is, if $f_3$ is another function analytic in $D_2$, and $f_3, f_2$ are both analytic continuations of $f_1$, then $f_3 \equiv f_2$ in $D_2$. For $f_2 - f_3 \equiv 0$

in a domain contained in $D_2$, so that $f_2 - f_3 \equiv 0$ in all of $D_2$, as follows from the following theorem:

**Theorem 60.** *Let $f(z_1, z_2)$ be analytic in domain $D$. Let $D_1$ be a domain contained in $D$ and let $f(z_1, z_2) \equiv 0$ in $D_1$. Then $f(z_1, z_2) \equiv 0$ in $D$.*

*Proof.* We first note that for analytic functions of two variables, it is not true that the zeros are isolated as for functions of one variable (see Section 9–7 below). Hence we cannot reason as in the proof of Theorem 43 of Section 6–2.

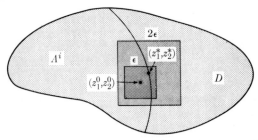

FIG. 9–9.    Proof of uniqueness of analytic continuation.

We let $A$ be the set of points in $D$ at which $f = 0$, let $A^i$ be the interior of $A$. Since $D_1$ is a domain, $D_1$ is contained in $A^i$ and $A^i$ is nonempty. We assert that $A^i$ coincides with $D$. If we suppose the contrary, then at least one boundary point $(z_1^*, z_2^*)$ of $A^i$ must lie in $D$ (see Problem 2 below and Fig. 9–9). We choose $\epsilon > 0$ so small that the polycylinder $D^*$: $|z_1 - z_1^*| < \epsilon$, $|z_2 - z_2^*| < \epsilon$ is in $D$. Since $(z_1^*, z_2^*)$ is a boundary point of $A^i$, we can find $(z_1^0, z_2^0)$ in $A^i$ such that $|z_1^0 - z_1^*| < \frac{1}{2}\epsilon$, $|z_2^0 - z_2^*| < \frac{1}{2}\epsilon$. The polycylinder $D^0$: $|z_1 - z_1^0| < \frac{1}{2}\epsilon$, $|z_2 - z_2^0| < \frac{1}{2}\epsilon$ is contained in $D^*$, hence in $D$. Now $f(z_1, z_2)$ is analytic in $D^0$ and hence by Theorem 53, $f$ can be expanded in $D^0$ in a Taylor series about $(z_1^0, z_2^0)$. Since $f \equiv 0$ in a neighborhood of $(z_1^0, z_2^0)$, all derivatives of $f$ are 0 at $(z_1^0, z_2^0)$, so that the Taylor series reduces identically to 0. Thus $f \equiv 0$ in $D^0$. But $(z_1^*, z_2^*)$ is interior to $D^0$. Hence $f \equiv 0$ in a neighborhood of $(z_1^*, z_2^*)$, and $(z_1^*, z_2^*)$ is in $A^i$. This is a contradiction, since $(z_1^*, z_2^*)$ was chosen as a boundary point of $A^i$. Thus $A^i = D$ and the theorem is proved.

We could now go on to discuss indirect analytic continuation as in Section 8–1. However, of much greater interest is a group of theorems which assert that, for certain domains $D$ in $K_2$, *a function $f(z_1, z_2)$ analytic in $D$ can always be continued to a well-determined larger domain $D'$.* We give one example of this assertion in Theorem 61 below.

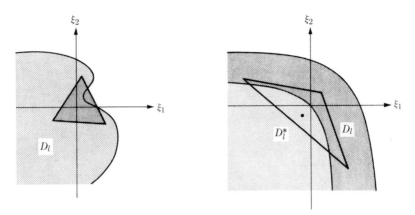

FIG. 9–10. Formation of convex hull.     FIG. 9–11.   Sets $D_l$ and $D_l^*$ for Example 1.

*Envelope of holomorphy.* Let $D$ be a Reinhardt domain with center $(0, 0)$ and let $D$ meet both coordinate planes $z_2 = 0$, $z_1 = 0$. In general, $D$ is neither logarithmically convex nor complete. We wish to add as few points as necessary to $D$ to make it have these two properties. To this end we form the set $H(D)$, called the *envelope of holomorphy of* $D$, as follows:

We first form $D_l$, the logarithmic image of $D$, as in Section 9–4 above; $D_l$ consists of all points $(\xi_1, \xi_2)$, where $\xi_1 = \log |z_1|$, $\xi_2 = \log |z_2|$ $(z_1 \neq 0, z_2 \neq 0)$, and $(z_1, z_2)$ is in $D$.

Next we form $D_l^*$, the *convex hull* of $D_l$. This is formed by adjoining to $D_l$ all the points (inside or on the sides) of each triangle whose vertices are in $D_l$ (as suggested in Fig. 9–10). Now let $D^*$ be the set of points in $K_2$ formed of the *inverse logarithmic image* of $D_l^*$; that is, $D^*$ consists of all $(z_1, z_2)$, such that $(\xi_1, \xi_2)$ is in $D_l^*$, where $\xi_1 = \log |z_1|$, $\xi_2 = \log |z_2|$.

Finally, let $D^{**}$ be formed from $D^*$ by "completion," as follows: We adjoin to $D^*$ all points $(z_1, z_2)$ such that $|z_1| < |z_1^*|$, $|z_2| < |z_2^*|$ for some $(z_1^*, z_2^*)$ in $D^*$. The resulting set $D^{**}$ is the envelope of holomorphy $H(D)$.

EXAMPLE 1.    Let $D$ be the domain $a < |z_1|^2 + |z_2|^2 < b$, where $0 < a < b < \infty$. The sets $D_l$ and $D_l^*$ are shown in Fig. 9–11. The set $D_l$ is described by the inequalities $a < e^{2\xi_1} + e^{2\xi_2} < b$; its boundary consists of the two curves $e^{2\xi_1} + e^{2\xi_2} = a$, $e^{2\xi_1} + e^{2\xi_2} = b$. On both of these,

$$\frac{d\xi_2}{d\xi_1} = -e^{2\xi_1 - 2\xi_2}, \qquad \frac{d^2\xi_2}{d\xi_1^2} = -e^{2(\xi_1 - \xi_2)}(1 + e^{2(\xi_1 - \xi_2)}),$$

so that each curve has negative slope and is concave downward.    As

$\xi_1 \to -\infty$, $\xi_2 \to \frac{1}{2}\log a$ or $\frac{1}{2}\log b$; as $\xi_2 \to -\infty$, $\xi_1 \to \frac{1}{2}\log a$ or $\frac{1}{2}\log b$. To obtain $D_l^*$, we simply fill in the triangles as required. Every point below the curve $e^{2\xi_1} + e^{2\xi_2} = b$ lies in a triangle whose vertices are in $D_l$, as suggested in Fig. 9–11. Since the curve $e^{2\xi_1} + e^{2\xi_2} = b$ is concave downward, these are the only points in $D_l^*$, and $D_l^*$ is clearly *convex;* that is, each pair of points in $D_l^*$ can be joined by a line segment in $D_l^*$.

The set $D^*$ now consists of all points $(z_1, z_2)$ such that $z_1 z_2 \neq 0$ and $|z_1|^2 + |z_2|^2 < b$. Finally, we complete $D^*$ by adding the points whose coordinates have absolute values less, respectively, than those of some point in $D^*$. We need only adjoin the points on the coordinate planes $(z_1, 0)$, $(z_2, 0)$ for which $|z_1|^2 < b$, $|z_2|^2 < b$, respectively. Thus $H(D)$ consists of the points of the four-dimensional spherical region $|z_1|^2 + |z_2|^2 < b$. This is clearly a logarithmically convex complete Reinhardt domain. In Theorem 61 we prove that the example is typical of the general case:

**Theorem 61.** *Let $D$ be a Reinhardt domain with center $(0, 0)$, and let $D$ meet both coordinate planes $z_1 = 0$, $z_2 = 0$. Let $H(D)$, the envelope of holomorphy of $D$, be constructed as above. Then $H(D)$ is a logarithmically convex complete Reinhardt domain. If $f(z_1, z_2)$ is analytic in $D$, then $f$ can be continued analytically to $H(D)$.*

*Proof.* The points of $D$ which are not in the coordinate planes form a domain (Problem 5, following Section 9–2). Also, $D_l$, the logarithmic image of $D$, is a domain in the $\xi_1 \xi_2$-plane (see Problem 5, following Section 9–4). The set $D_l^*$ can be shown to be a convex domain (see Problem 3 below).

The set $D^*$ consists of the points $(z_1, z_2)$ for which $(\xi_1, \xi_2) = (\log |z_1|, \log |z_2|)$ is in $D_l^*$. We remark that, since $D_l^*$ contains $D_l$, $D^*$ contains all points of $D$ not on the coordinate planes. Also, from the fact that $D_l^*$ is a domain, it follows that $D^*$ is a domain (Problem 5 below). By its definition, $D^*$ is a Reinhardt domain.

Next, $D^{**} = H(D)$ is obtained by adjoining to $D^*$ all $(z_1, z_2)$ for which $|z_1| < |z_1^*|$, $|z_2| < |z_2^*|$ for some $(z_1^*, z_2^*)$ in $D^*$. We note that $H(D)$ then includes all of $D$, even the points on the coordinate planes. For if $(z_1^0, 0)$, for example, is in $D$, $z_1^0 \neq 0$, then we can find a polycylinder neighborhood of $(z_1^0, 0)$ in $D$: $|z_1 - z_1^0| < \epsilon$, $|z_2| < \epsilon$. The point $(z_1^0 + \frac{1}{2}\epsilon z_1^0/|z_1^0|, \frac{1}{2}\epsilon)$ is in $D$ and not on a coordinate plane, hence it is also in $D^*$. Therefore all points $(z_1, z_2)$, such that $|z_1| < |z_1^0 + \frac{1}{2}\epsilon z_1^0/|z_1^0|| = |z_1^0| + \frac{1}{2}\epsilon$, $|z_2| < \frac{1}{2}\epsilon$, are in $D^{**}$; in particular, $(z_1^0, 0)$ is in $D^{**}$. A similar argument applies to points $(0, z_2^0)$ or $(0, 0)$ in $D$.

Since $D^*$ is a domain, $D^{**}$ is also a domain (Problem 6 below). From its definition, $D^{**}$ must thus be a complete Reinhardt domain and we further assert that $D^{**}$ is logarithmically convex. To prove this, we form $D_l^{**}$, the logarithmic image of $D^{**}$. By the definition of $D^{**}$ (and the fact that $\log x$ increases with $x$ for $x > 0$), $D_l^{**}$ can be obtained from $D_l^*$ by adjoining to $D_l^*$ all points $(\xi_1, \xi_2)$ for which $\xi_1 < \xi_1^*$, $\xi_2 < \xi_2^*$, for some point $(\xi_1^*, \xi_2^*)$ in $D_l^*$. We must now show that $D_l^{**}$ is convex. To this end we let $(\xi_1', \xi_2')$ $(\xi_1', \xi_2'')$ be two points of $D_l^{**}$. Then by the construction of $D_l^{**}$ we can choose points $(\xi_1^{*\prime}, \xi_2^{*\prime})$, $(\xi_1^{*\prime\prime}, \xi_2^{*\prime\prime})$ in $D_l^*$ for which $\xi_1' < \xi_1^{*\prime}$, $\xi_2' < \xi_2^{*\prime}$, $\xi_1'' < \xi_1^{*\prime\prime}$, $\xi_2'' < \xi_2^{*\prime\prime}$. An arbitrary point $(\xi_1, \xi_2)$ on the line segment joining $(\xi_1', \xi_2')$ to $(\xi_1'', \xi_2'')$ can be represented thus:

$$\xi_1 = t\xi_1' + (1 - t)\xi_1'', \qquad \xi_2 = t\xi_2' + (1 - t)\xi_2'',$$

where $0 \leqq t \leqq 1$. Now

$$\xi_1 = t\xi_1' + (1 - t)\xi_1'' < t\xi_1^{*\prime} + (1 - t)\xi_1^{*\prime\prime} = \xi_1^*,$$

$$\xi_2 = t\xi_2' + (1 - t)\xi_2'' < t\xi_2^{*\prime} + (1 - t)\xi_2^{*\prime\prime} = \xi_2^*$$

and, since $D_l^*$ is convex, $(\xi_1^*, \xi_2^*)$ is in $D_l^*$. Hence by our construction, $(\xi_1, \xi_2)$ is in $D_l^{**}$. Thus $D_l^{**}$ is convex.

To complete the proof of the theorem, we must show that $f(z_1, z_2)$, given as an analytic function in $D$, can be continued analytically to $H(D)$. By Theorem 59, $f$ can be represented in $D$ as the sum of a power series (9–50). By our assumptions about $D$ and Remark 2 in Section 9–5, the series contains no terms in negative powers of $z_1$ or $z_2$. By Theorems 55, 56, and 57, the series converges in a set $E$ whose interior $E^i$ is a logarithmically convex complete Reinhardt domain and $g(z_1, z_2)$, the sum of the series, is analytic in $E^i$. The set $E^i$ must include $D$. We assert that $E^i$ also includes $D^{*\cdot} = H(D)$. Indeed, the logarithmic image $E_l^i$ of $E^i$ includes $D_l$, and $E_l^i$ is convex; therefore $E_l^i$ includes all of $D_l^*$ and $E^i$ includes all of $D^*$. Since $E^i$ is a complete Reinhardt domain, it also includes all of $D^{**} = H(D)$. Thus $g(z_1, z_2)$ is analytic in $D^{**}$, and $g(z_1, z_2) \equiv f(z_1, z_2)$ in $D$. Accordingly, $g(z_1, z_2)$ forms a direct analytic continuation of $f(z_1, z_2)$ to $H(D)$.

EXAMPLE 2. $D$ is a polycylinder: $|z_1| < a$, $|z_2| < b$. Then $D = H(D)$, so that Theorem 61 tells us nothing new. [See Problem 1(a) below.]

EXAMPLE 3. $D$ is the set of all $(z_1, z_2)$ for which $(|z_1|, |z_2|)$ is in the shaded set (including the boundary segments $AO$ and $OB$ except for $A$ and $B$) in Fig. 9–12. The set $D_l$ is shown in Fig. 9–13, as is the set $D_l^*$; the latter consists of all points $(\xi_1, \xi_2)$ for which $\xi_1 < 0$. Thus $D^*$ consists of all $(z_1, z_2)$ for which $z_1 \neq 0$, $z_2 \neq 0$ and $|z_1| < 1$, $|z_2| < 1$. Finally, $D^{**} = H(D)$ is the polycylinder $|z_1| < 1$, $|z_2| < 1$.

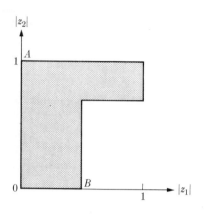
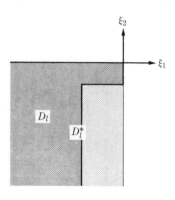

FIG. 9–12. Absolute-value diagram for Example 3.    FIG. 9–13.    Sets $D_l$ and $D_l^*$ for Example 3.

**Corollary of Theorem 61.** *An analytic function of* $n \geq 2$ *variables has no isolated nonremovable singularities.*

*Proof for* $n = 2$. Let $f(z_1, z_2)$ have an isolated singularity, which we can assume to be at $(0, 0)$. Then $f$ is analytic in a domain $D: 0 < |z_1|^2 + |z_2|^2 < \epsilon^2$ for some $\epsilon > 0$. Hence $f$ can be continued analytically to $H(D)$, which we find, as in Example 1, to be the domain $|z_1|^2 + |z_2|^2 < \epsilon^2$. Thus the singularity at $(0, 0)$ is removable.

For further discussion of analytic continuation, one is referred to the books mentioned at the end of Section 9–4.

## PROBLEMS

1. Describe the envelope of holomorphy for each of the following domains in $K_2$:

    (a) a polycylinder $|z_1| < a$, $|z_2| < b$    (b) $1 < |z_1| + |z_2| < 2$

    (c) $|z_2| - 1 < |z_1| < 1$    (d) $|z_2|(|z_1| - 1) < 1$.

2. Prove: If $B$ is an open subset of a domain $D$ in $K_2$ and $B$ does not coincide with $D$, then at least one boundary point of $B$ lies in $D$.

[*Hint: let $E$ denote the set of all points in $D$ which are not in $B$. Show that if no boundary point of $B$ lies in $D$, then $D$ would be formed of two disjoint nonempty open sets $B$ and $E$ and hence would not be a domain.*]

3. The set $D_l^*$ (the convex hull of $D_l$) is obtained from the domain $D_l$ in the $\xi_1 \xi_2$-plane by adjoining to $D_l$ all the points of each triangle whose vertices are in $D_l$. Show that $D_l^*$ is convex and that $D_l^*$ is a domain.

[*Hint: to prove that $D_l^*$ is convex, let $P'$, $P''$ be points of $D_l$, so that $P'$ is contained in a triangle $A'B'C'$, $P''$ in a triangle $A''B''C''$, all 6 vertices being in $D_l$. Show by geometry that every point of the segment $P'P''$ is contained in a triangle whose vertices are chosen from $A'$, $B'$, $C'$, $A''$, $B''$, $C''$.*]

4. The convex hull $D_l^*$ (see Problem 3) can also be defined as the set of all points which are common to all convex sets containing $D_l$. Show that this definition is equivalent to the one of Problem 3.

   *Remark.* For sets in a space of more than two dimensions, the definition of Problem 3 must be modified by replacing the triangle by the appropriate generalization—in three dimensions, this would be the tetrahedron.

5. Let $D_l^*$ be a domain in the $\xi_1\xi_2$-plane and let $D^*$ be the inverse logarithmic image of $D_l^*$; that is, $D^*$ is the set of all $(z_1, z_2)$ such that $(\log|z_1|, \log|z_2|)$ is in $D_l^*$. Show that $D^*$ is a Reinhardt domain with center $(0, 0)$.

[*Hint: the fact that $D^*$ is an open set follows from the continuity of the transformation $\xi_1 = \log|z_1|$, $\xi_2 = \log|z_2|$. To prove $D^*$ is connected, let $(z_1', z_2')$, $(z_1'', z_2'')$ be points of $D$ and let $\xi_1' = \log|z_1'|, \ldots$ Join $(z_1', z_2')$ to $(|z_1'|, |z_2'|)$ in $K_2$ by the path $z_1 = e^{-\omega_1' t}z_1'$, $z_2 = e^{-\omega_2' t}z_2'$, where $z_1' = |z_1'|e^{i\omega_1}$, $z_2' = |z_2'|e^{i\omega_2}$, and similarly join $(z_1'', z_2'')$ to $(|z_1''|, |z_2''|)$. Now join $(|z_1'|, |z_2'|)$ to $(|z_1''|, |z_2''|)$ by a path $z_1 = z_1(t) = e^{\xi_1(t)}$, $z_2 = z_2(t) = e^{\xi_2(t)}$, where $\xi_1 = \xi_1(t)$, $\xi_2 = \xi_2(t)$ is a path from $(\xi_1', \xi_2')$ to $(\xi_1'', \xi_2'')$ in $D_l^*$.*]

6. Let $D^*$ be a Reinhardt domain in $K_2$ with center $(0, 0)$ and let $D^{**}$ consist of $D^*$ plus all $(z_1, z_2)$ such that $|z_1| < |z_1^*|$, $|z_2| < |z_2^*|$ for some $(z_1^*, z_2^*)$ in $D^*$. Show that $D^{**}$ is a complete Reinhardt domain.

[*Hint: show that $D^{**}$ could also be defined simply as all $(z_1, z_2)$, such that $|z_1| < |z_1^*|$, $|z_2| < |z_2^*|$ for some $(z_1^*, z_2^*)$ in $D^*$, and hence $D^*$ is an open set. To show that $D^{**}$ is connected, join each point of $D^{**}$ to $(0, 0)$.*]

## ANSWERS

1. (a) same polycylinder,               (b) $|z_1| + |z_2| < 2$,
   (c) $|z_1| < 1$, $|z_2| < 2$,         (d) $K_2$.

## 9–7 □ ZEROS OF ANALYTIC FUNCTIONS

By a *zero* of $f(z_1, z_2)$ we mean a point $(z_1^0, z_2^0)$ such that $f(z_1^0, z_2^0) = 0$. An analytic function $f(z_1, z_2)$ can have no *isolated* zeros. For each zero of $f$ is a singularity of $1/f = g$. By the Corollary of Theorem 61, if $f$ had an isolated zero $(z_1^0, z_2^0)$, then $g = 1/f$ would have a removable singularity at $(z_1^0, z_2^0)$, so that $g$ would have a finite limit as $(z_1, z_2) \to (z_1^0, z_2^0)$. This is a contradiction, because $f \cdot g = 1$ and $\lim f = 0$ as $(z_1, z_2) \to (z_1^0, z_2^0)$.

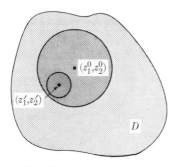
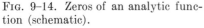
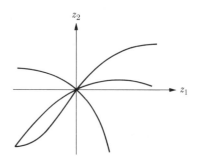

FIG. 9–14. Zeros of an analytic function (schematic).

FIG. 9–15. Typical locus $f(z_1, z_2) = 0$ near a particular zero [only real pairs $(z_1, z_2)$ are shown].

Although the zeros of $f$ are not isolated, we know from Theorem 60 that $f$ cannot be identically zero in any neighborhood (unless $f$ is identically 0 everywhere). From this it follows that, if $f$ is analytic in $D$, $f \not\equiv 0$, and $f(z_1^0, z_2^0) = 0$, then every neighborhood of $(z_1^0, z_2^0)$ contains a neighborhood of some point $(z_1', z_2')$ in which $f \neq 0$. (The relationship between the neighborhoods is suggested in Fig. 9–14.) For since $f \not\equiv 0$ in the given neighborhood of $(z_1^0, z_2^0)$, $f(z_1', z_2') \neq 0$ for some point $(z_1', z_2')$ in the neighborhood. Hence by continuity there is a neighborhood of $(z_1', z_2')$ in which $f \neq 0$.

Thus the zeros of an analytic function are relatively sparse. The following theorems provide more details on the set of zeros.

**Theorem 62** (Weierstrass preparation theorem). *Let $f(z_1, z_2)$ be analytic for $|z_1| < a$, $|z_2| < b$, let $f(0, 0) = 0$, but $f(0, z_2) \not\equiv 0$. Then there is a polycylinder $|z_1| < \delta$, $|z_2| < r$ in which $f$ can be represented as follows:*

$$f = g(z_1, z_2)(z_2^m + p_1(z_1)z_2^{m-1} + \cdots + p_m(z_1)), \qquad (9\text{--}70)$$

*where $g$ is analytic, $g(z_1, z_2) \neq 0$, $p_\alpha(z_1)$ is analytic in $z_1$ for $|z_1| < \delta$ and $p_\alpha(0) = 0$ $(\alpha = 1, \ldots, m)$.*

*Remark 1.* Since $g(z_1, z_2) \neq 0$, $f = 0$ precisely where the second factor is 0, in the polycylinder $|z_1| < \delta$, $|z_2| < r$:

$$z_2^m + p_1(z_1)z_2^{m-1} + \cdots + p_m(z_1) = 0. \qquad (9\text{--}71)$$

Thus for each $z_1$, $z_2$ must satisfy an algebraic equation of degree $m$; accordingly, for each $z_1$, $z_2$ has $m$ values (some possibly coinciding). For $z_1 = 0$, $z_2 = 0$ ($m$ times). If all quantities were real, the locus $f = 0$ near $(0, 0)$ would appear as it does in Fig. 9–15 (for which $m = 3$). Equation (9–71) is called a *pseudoalgebraic* equation; the left-hand side is called a *pseudopolynomial* [polynomial in one variable, with coefficients analytic in the other(s)].

*Proof of Theorem 62.* Since $f(0, z_2)$ is an analytic function of $z_2$ for $|z_2| < b$, not identically 0, with $f(0, 0) = 0$, we can choose $r$ so small (and less than $b$) that $f(0, z_2) \neq 0$ for $0 < |z_2| \leqq r$. In particular, $f(0, z_2) \neq 0$ for $|z_2| = r$. It follows by continuity that, for $\delta$ sufficiently small (and less than $a$), $f(z_1, z_2) \neq 0$ for $|z_2| = r$, $|z_1| < \delta$ (Problem 4 below). For each fixed $z_1$, $|z_1| < \delta$, $f(z_1, z_2)$ (as a function of $z_2$) has $N_0$ zeros inside the circle $|z_2| = r$ and none on the circumference; $N_0$ is given by the argument principle (Section 6–6) as follows:

$$N_0 = \frac{1}{2\pi i} \oint_{|z_2|=r} \frac{1}{f(z_1, z_2)} \frac{\partial f}{\partial z_2} (z_1, z_2) \, dz_2. \qquad (9\text{--}72)$$

For $z_1 = 0$, $N_0$ has a certain value $m$. As $z_1$ varies, the integrand on the right-hand side of (9–72) varies continuously, so that $N_0$ also varies continuously. But $N_0$ is an integer; hence $N_0$ is constant, $N_0 = m$.

Now for each $z_1$, let the zeros of $f$ (repeated if necessary) be denoted by $\eta_1, \ldots, \eta_m$ (all of which depend on $z_1$). Now let

$$F(z_1, z_2) = (z_2 - \eta_1)(z_2 - \eta_2) \cdots (z_2 - \eta_m)$$

$$= z_2^m + p_1(z_1)z_2^{m-1} + \cdots + p_m(z_1);$$

that is, $F$ is (for each fixed $z_1$) the polynomial whose zeros coincide with those of $f$ for $|z_2| < r$. Since $f(0, z_2) = 0$ only for $z_2 = 0$, it follows that $p_\alpha(0) = 0$ for $\alpha = 1, \ldots, m$.

We now write

$$S_k(z_1) = \eta_1^k + \cdots + \eta_m^k \quad (k = 1, \ldots, m).$$

It is known from algebra* that the $p_\alpha(z_1)$ can be expressed as polynomials in terms of $S_1, \ldots, S_m$. For example, for $m = 2$,

$$p_1 = -(\eta_1 + \eta_2) = -S_1,$$

$$p_2 = \eta_1 \eta_2 = \tfrac{1}{2}[(\eta_1 + \eta_2)^2 - (\eta_1^2 + \eta_2^2)] = \tfrac{1}{2}S_1^2 - \tfrac{1}{2}S_2.$$

Hence to show that $p_1(z_1), \ldots, p_m(z_1)$ are analytic in $z_1$, we need only

---

* See L. E. Dickson, *First Course in the Theory of Equations*, New York: John Wiley and Sons, 1922, pp. 145–147.

show that $S_1, \ldots, S_m$ are analytic in $z_1$. But by residues,

$$S_k(z_1) = \frac{1}{2\pi i} \oint_{|z_2|=r} \frac{z_2^k}{f(z_1, z_2)} \frac{\partial f}{\partial z_2} \, dz_2$$

(Problem 5 below) and thus $S_k$ is given by an expression

$$S_k(z_1) = \oint_C \phi(z_1, z_2) \, dz_2, \qquad |z_1| < \delta,$$

where $\phi$ is analytic in $z_1, z_2$. Accordingly, as in Remark 2 in Section 9–3 (or Problem 9, following Section 5–6), $S_k(z_1)$ is analytic. Hence $p_\alpha(z_1)$ is analytic in $z_1$ for $\alpha = 1, \ldots, m$. Therefore, the pseudopolynomial $F = z_2^m + p_1 z_2^{m-1} + \cdots + p_m$ is analytic in $(z_1, z_2)$.

Now for each $z_1$, the zeros of $F$ (as a function of $z_2$) coincide with the zeros of $f$ (as a function of $z_2$) for $|z_2| \leqq r$. Hence for each $z_1$,

$$g(z_1, z_2) = \frac{f(z_1, z_2)}{F(z_1, z_2)}, \qquad |z_1| < \delta, |z_2| < r$$

has only removable singularities and can be considered as an analytic function of $z_2$, with $g(z_1, z_2) \neq 0$. For $|z_2| = r$, $|z_1| < \delta$, $F(z_1, z_2) \neq 0$; hence $1/F$ is an analytic function of $(z_1, z_2)$ for these points, and so is $g(z_1, z_2)$. In particular, for fixed $z_1$.

$$g(z_1, z_2) = \frac{1}{2\pi i} \oint_{|\zeta_2|=r} \frac{g(z_1, \zeta_2)}{\zeta_2 - z_2} \, d\zeta_2. \tag{9–73}$$

By Remark 2 in Section 9–3, the right-hand side of (9–73) defines an analytic function of $(z_1, z_2)$ for $|z_1| < \delta$, $|z_2| < r$. Hence $g(z_1, z_2)$ is analytic in this polycylinder and $g(z_1, z_2) \neq 0$. Finally,

$$\begin{aligned} f(z_1, z_2) &= g(z_1, z_2)F(z_1, z_2) \\ &= g(z_1, z_2)(z_2^m + p_1(z_1)z_2^{m-1} + \cdots + p_m(z_1)), \end{aligned}$$

as asserted.

**Theorem 63.** *Let $f(z_1, z_2)$ be an analytic function of $(z_1, z_2)$ in a domain $D$ in $K_2$. Let $(0, 0)$ be in $D$; let $f(0, 0) = 0$, $f(z_1, z_2) \not\equiv 0$. Then in a suitable polycylinder $|z_1| < \delta$, $|z_2| < r$, $f$ can be represented as follows:*

$$f(z_1, z_2) = z_1^n g(z_1, z_2)(z_2^m + p_1(z_1)z_2^{m-1} + \cdots + p_m(z_1)), \tag{9–74}$$

*where $g(z_1, z_2) \neq 0$, $n$ and $m$ are integers, $n \geqq 0$, $m \geqq 0$, and $p_1(z_1), \ldots, p_m(z_1)$ are analytic in $z_1$ and equal $0$ for $z_1 = 0$.*

*Remark* 2.   In contrast to Theorem 62, it is not assumed here that $f(0, z_2) \not\equiv 0$.

*Proof.* If $f(0, z_2) \not\equiv 0$, the conclusion follows from the previous theorem with $n = 0$. If $f(0, z_2) \equiv 0$, then we expand $f$ in a power series about $(0, 0)$ and collect terms in powers of $z_2$:

$$f = z_1(c_{10} + c_{11}z_2 + \cdots) + z_1^2(c_{20} + c_{21}z_2 + \cdots) + \cdots.$$

The coefficient of $z_1$ may be identically 0, as may that of $z_1^2, \ldots$, but, since $f$ is not identically 0, it follows from Theorem 60 that at least one coefficient is not identically 0, so that we can write

$$f = z_1^n(c_{n0} + c_{n1}z_2 + \cdots) + z_1^{n+1}(c_{n+1,0} + \cdots) + \cdots = z_1^n f_1(z_1, z_2),$$

where $f_1(0, z_2) = c_{n0} + c_{n1}z_2 + \cdots \not\equiv 0$. If $f_1(0, 0) = c_{n0} \neq 0$, then $f_1(z_1, z_2) \neq 0$ in some polycylinder neighborhood of $(0, 0)$ and we obtain the representation (9–74) with $f_1 = g$, $m = 0$. If $f_1(0, 0) = 0$, then the previous theorem is applicable to $f_1(z_1, z_2)$, and we again obtain the representation (9–74).

*Remark* 3.   Theorem 63 shows that, in general, the locus $f = 0$ has the structure suggested in Fig. 9–15, where in addition $f$ may be 0, of multiplicity $n$, along the $z_2$-"axis" (where $z_1 = 0$).

*Remark* 4.   Theorem 63 does not generalize to functions of more than two complex variables. For example, $f(z_1, z_2, z_3) = z_2z_3 + z_1z_3 + z_1z_2$ has a zero at $(0, 0, 0)$, but the analog of the Weierstrass preparation theorem is not applicable, since $f(z_1, 0, 0) \equiv 0$, $f(0, z_2, 0) \equiv 0$, $f(0, 0, z_3) \equiv 0$. Also no power of $z_1$, $z_2$, or $z_3$ can be factored out. However, the substitution

$$\zeta_1 = z_1, \qquad \zeta_2 = z_1 + z_2, \qquad \zeta_3 = z_1 + z_3$$

converts $f$ to the function $g(\zeta_1, \zeta_2, \zeta_3) = \zeta_2\zeta_3 - \zeta_1^2$, and $g(\zeta_1, 0, 0) = -\zeta_1^2 \not\equiv 0$. One can now apply the analog of the Weierstrass preparation theorem to $g(\zeta_1, \zeta_2, \zeta_3)$. In fact, $g$ already has the form

$$\zeta_1^m + p_1(\zeta_2, \zeta_3)\zeta_1^{m-1} + \cdots + p_m(\zeta_2, \zeta_3)$$

of a pseudopolynomial. One can verify that a similar procedure is applicable to every analytic function $f(z_1, \ldots, z_n)$; that is, if $f(0, \ldots, 0) = 0$ and $f(z_1, \ldots, z_n) \not\equiv 0$, then a suitable one-to-one linear transformation converts $f$ to a function $g$ to which the analog of the preparation theorem is applicable. The linear transformation can be regarded as a mere change of coordinate axes in $K_n$. Thus, again the diagram of Fig. 9–15 is suggestive of the appearance of the locus $f = 0$ near a particular zero.

*Remark* 5. The factorization of a general function $f(z_1, \ldots, z_n)$ near a zero can be carried further; in particular, a pseudopolynomial may be factorable, as for example,

$$z_1^2 + (2z_2 + z_3)z_1 + z_2^2 + z_2z_3 = (z_1 + z_2)(z_1 + z_2 + z_3).$$

The function $f$ is always representable as a product of a finite number of "primes" $f_1, \ldots, f_k$; that is, analytic functions $f_l$, each of which has a zero at $(0, 0, \ldots, 0)$ and each of which cannot be factored further into a product of two functions with a zero at $(0, \ldots, 0)$.*

## 9–8 □ SINGULARITIES OF ANALYTIC FUNCTIONS

We have already seen that there cannot be any nonremovable isolated singularities of an analytic function of two (or more) variables. In general, we are led to consider as singularity of an analytic function $f(z_1, z_2)$ any point $(z_1^0, z_2^0)$ which is on the boundary of the domain $D$ in which $f$ is analytic. We call the singularity *removable* if there is a function $g(z_1, z_2)$, analytic at $(z_1^0, z_2^0)$, and such that $f \equiv g$ in some neighborhood of $(z_1^0, z_2^0)$, wherever $f$ is defined (see Fig. 9–16). For example,

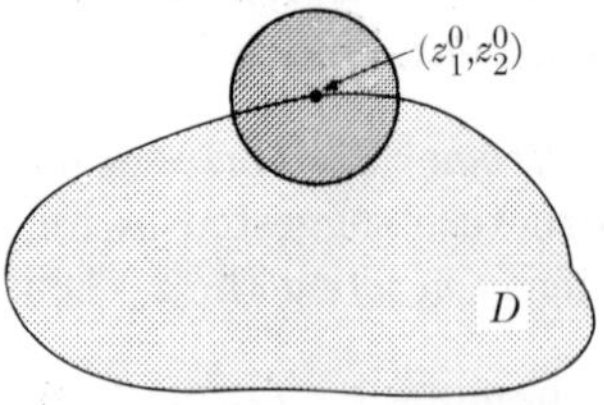

$$f = \frac{z_1^2 - z_2^2}{z_1 - z_2}$$

FIG. 9–16. Removable singularities (schematic).

is analytic in the domain consisting of all $(z_1, z_2)$ for which $z_1 \neq z_2$. Hence every point at which $z_1 = z_2$ is a singularity of $f$: $(1, 1)$, $(1 + i, 1 + i)$, and so on. However, each of these singularities is removable, since $f$ coincides in $D$ with the analytic function $g = z_1 + z_2$. As for functions of one variable, we usually tacitly eliminate the removable singularities by redefining the function properly at each such singular point. At a pole $z_0$ of a function $f(z)$ of one complex variable, one has a representation $f = g/h$, where $g$ and $h$ are analytic at $z_0$ and $h = 0$ at $z_0$; every function $f$ so representable has a pole or a removable singularity at $z_0$. For functions of two variables, the situation is more complicated. For example, $f = (z_1 + z_2)/(z_1 - z_2)$ might be considered to have a singularity analogous to a pole at each point where the denominator is zero. For example, at the point $(1, 1)$, $1/f$ has a zero (after removing the singularity). However,

---

* For a discussion see Chapter 2 of *Functions of Several Complex Variables* by W. Kaplan, Ann Arbor: Ann Arbor Publishers, 1964.

at $(0, 0)$ both numerator and denominator are 0. This example suggests a general definition.

The singularity $(z_1^0, z_2^0)$ of the analytic function $f(z_1, z_2)$ is said to be *nonessential* if there exist functions $g(z_1, z_2)$, $h(z_1, z_2)$ with the following properties:

(a) $g$ and $h$ are defined and analytic in a neighborhood of $(z_1^0, z_2^0)$;

(b) $h$ has a zero at $(z_1^0, z_2^0)$ and $h(z_1, z_2) \not\equiv 0$;

(c) $g$ and $h$ have no common analytic factor $p(z_1, z_2)$ with a zero at $(z_1^0, z_2^0)$; that is, we cannot write $g = p(z_1, z_2)G(z_1, z_2)$, $h = p(z_1, z_2)H(z_1, z_2)$, where $G$ and $H$ are analytic at $(z_1^0, z_2^0)$;

(d) $f = g/h$ wherever $h \neq 0$.

There are then two cases:

*Case I.* $g(z_1^0, z_2^0) \neq 0$, so that $1/f$ has a zero at $(z_1^0, z_2^0)$. Here $(z_1^0, z_2^0)$ is called a *pole* of $f$, or a *nonessential singularity of first kind*.

*Case II.* $g(z_1^0, z_2^0) = 0$. Here $(z_1^0, z_2^0)$ is called a *point of indeterminacy* of $f$ or a *nonessential singularity of second kind*.

A nonessential singularity cannot be removed (Problem 7 below). A singularity of $f$ which is neither removable nor nonessential is called an *essential* singularity.

**Theorem 64.** *Let $f(z_1, z_2)$ be analytic for $|z_1| < r_1$, $|z_2| < r_2$ except on a set $E$ which is contained in the polycylinder $|z_1| < r_1'$, $|z_2| < r_2$, where $r_1' < r_1$, and let $E$ meet each plane $z_2 = $ const in a finite set. Let $f(z_1, z_2)$ be bounded. Then $f$ has a direct analytic continuation to all of the polycylinder $|z_1| < r_1$, $|z_2| < r_2$, so that every point of $E$ is a removable singularity of $f$.*

*Remark 1.* This theorem can be considered as a generalization of Riemann's theorem for functions of one variable (Problem 12, following Section 6–3).

*Proof of Theorem 64.* For fixed $z_2$, $|z_2| < r_2$, $f$ is analytic in $z_1$ for $|z_1| < r_1$ except for a finite set of points, contained in the circular domain $|z_1| < r_1'$ (Fig. 9–16). Since $f$ is bounded, all these singularities are removable, by Riemann's theorem. In particular,

$$f(z_1, z_2) = \frac{1}{2\pi i} \oint_{|\zeta_1| = \rho_1} \frac{f(\zeta_1, z_2)}{\zeta_1 - z_1} d\zeta_1, \qquad |z_1| < \rho_1,$$

where $r_1' < \rho_1 < r_1$. As in Remark 2 in Section 9–3, the right-hand side defines an analytic function $g$ of $(z_1, z_2)$ for $|z_1| < \rho_1$, $|z_2| < r_2$ and $f = g$ except on $E$. Hence $g$ provides the desired analytic continuation.

EXAMPLE. Let $f(z_1, z_2)$ be analytic and bounded for $|z_1| < 2$, $|z_2| < 1$ except at the points where $z_1^2 + z_1 z_2 + z_2^2 = 0$. The set $E$, therefore, consists of the points $(z_1, z_2)$ for which $z_1 = z_2[(-1 \pm \sqrt{3}i)/2]$, $|z_1| < 2$, $|z_2| < 1$. Thus $E$ meets each plane $z_2 = $ const in a set consisting of two points lying in the domain $|z_1| < 1$ (since $|z_2| < 1$, $|(1 \pm \sqrt{3}i)/2| = 1$). Accordingly the singularities are removable.

*Remark 2.* As Theorem 64 illustrates, the study of singularities, especially removable singularities, is closely related to the topic of analytic continuation. In particular, Theorem 61 can be interpreted as stating that certain singularities are removable.


**PROBLEMS**

1. Factor in accordance with the Weierstrass preparation theorem, verifying that all hypotheses are satisfied:

   (a) $f = z_2^2 e^{z_1 z_2} + z_2 \sin z_1 + 1 - \cos z_1$

   (b) $f = z_2^3 + z_2^2(1 + 2z_1 + \sin z_1) + z_2(z_1 + z_1^2 + \sin z_1 + 2z_1 \sin z_1)$
   $\quad + (z_1 + z_1^2) \sin z_1$.

2. Show that $f = z_1^2 + z_2^3$ is prime at $(0, 0)$.

   [*Hint: assume $f = g \cdot h$, where $g$ and $h$ both have a zero at $(0, 0)$. Use power series to show there is a contradiction.*]

3. Classify all singularities:

   (a) $w = \dfrac{\sin z_1 - \sin z_2}{z_1 - z_2}$ \qquad (b) $w = \dfrac{z_1^2 + z_2^2 - 1}{z_1^2 - 3z_2^2}$.

4. Let $f(z_1, z_2)$ be analytic for $|z_1| < a$, $|z_2| < b$, and $f(0, z_2) \neq 0$ for $|z_2| = r < b$. Show that there exists a $\delta > 0$, such that $f(z_1, z_2) \neq 0$ for $|z_1| < \delta$, $|z_2| = r$.

   [*Hint: assume the contrary. Show that this implies existence of a sequence $(z_1^{(n)}, z_2^{(n)})$, such that $|z_1^{(n)}| < 1/n$, $|z_2^{(n)}| = r$ and $f(z_1^{(n)}, z_2^{(n)}) = 0$. As in the proof of Theorem 47 in Section 6–6, the sequence $z_2^{(n)}$ has a convergent subsequence with limit $z_2^0$. Show that $f(0, z_2^0) = 0$, $|z_2^0| = r$ and that this gives a contradiction.*]

5. Let $f(z)$ be analytic inside and on a simple closed smooth curve $C$ in the $z$-plane. Let $f \neq 0$ on $C$; let $f$ have zeros at $z_1, \ldots, z_m$ inside $C$,

repeated according to multiplicity.  Show by residues that

$$z_1^k + \cdots + z_m^k = \frac{1}{2\pi i} \oint_C \frac{z^k f'(z)}{f(z)}\, dz, \quad (k = 1, 2, \ldots).$$

6. (a) Prove: If $f(z_1, z_2)$ is analytic for all $(z_1, z_2)$ and is bounded, then $f \equiv$ const.

   [*Hint: apply Liouville's theorem, given in Problem 8, following Section 5–4.*]

   (b) Prove: If $f(z_1, z_2)$ is analytic for $|z_1| + |z_2| > 1$ and $f$ is bounded, then $f \equiv$ const (so that all singularities are removable).

   [*Hint: apply Liouville's theorem to show that $f = f(z_1, 0)$ for $|z_1| > 1$, $f = f(0, z_2)$ for $|z_2| > 1$ and hence $f =$ const for $|z_1| > 1$, $|z_2| > 1$. Now apply Theorem 60.*]

7. Let $f$ have a nonessential singularity as defined in the text, so that $f = g/h$.
   (a) Show that $g \not\equiv 0$.
   (b) Show that the singularity cannot be removable.

   [*Hint: use part (c) of the definition.*]

## ANSWERS

1. (a) $e^{z_1 z_2}[z_2^2 + (e^{-z_1 z_2} \sin z_1)z_2 + e^{-z_1 z_2}(1 - \cos z_1)]$,
   (b) $(1 + z_1 + z_2)(z_2^2 + (z_1 + \sin z_1)z_2 + z_1 \sin z_1)$.

3. (a) Singularities where $z_1 = z_2$, removable,
   (b) singularities where $z_1^2 - 3z_2^2 = 0$, nonessential of first kind, except at $(\pm\frac{1}{2}\sqrt{3}, \pm\frac{1}{2})$ of second kind.

# Bibliography

**I. References for functions of one complex variable** (Chapters 1-8)

AHLFORS, L. V., *Complex Analysis*. New York: McGraw-Hill, 1953.

BEHNKE, H. and SOMMER, F., *Theorie der analytischen Funktionen einer komplexen Veränderlichen*, 2nd ed. Berlin: Springer, 1962.

BIEBERBACH, L., *Lehrbuch der Funktionentheorie* (2 vols.), 4th ed. Leipzig: B. G. Teubner, 1934.

CHURCHILL, R. V., *Complex Variables and Applications*, 2nd ed. New York: McGraw-Hill, 1960.

COURANT, R., *Dirichlet's Principle, Conformal Mapping and Minimal Surfaces*. New York: Interscience, 1950.

FRANK, P. and v. MISES, R., *Die Differentialgleichungen der Mechanik und Physik*. Vol. 1, 2nd ed. Braunschweig: Vieweg, 1930. Vol. 2, 2nd ed. Braunschweig: Vieweg, 1935.

GOURSAT, E., *A Course in Mathematical Analysis*, Vol. 2, Part 1 (transl. by E. R. Hedrick and O. Dunkel). New York: Ginn and Co., 1916.

HILLE, E., *Analytic Function Theory*, Vol. 1. Blaisdell: New York, 1959. Vol. 2. Blaisdell: New York, 1963.

HURWITZ, A. and COURANT, R., *Funktionentheorie*, 4th ed. Berlin: Springer, 1964.

KAPLAN, W., *Advanced Calculus*. Reading, Mass.: Addison-Wesley, 1952.

KELLOGG, O. D., *Foundations of Potential Theory*. Berlin: Springer, 1929.

KNOPP, K., *Theory and Application of Infinite Series* (transl. by Miss R. C. Young). Glasgow: Blackie and Sons, 1928.

KNOPP, K., *Theory of Functions*, 2 vols. (transl. by F. Bagemihl). New York: Dover, 1945.

KOBER, H., *Dictionary of Conformal Representation*. New York: Dover, 1952.

NEHARI, Z., *Conformal Mapping*. New York: McGraw-Hill, 1952.

NEHARI, Z., *Introduction to Complex Analysis*. Boston: Allyn and Bacon, 1961.

NEVANLINNA, R., *Eindeutige Analytische Funktionen*, 2nd ed. Berlin: Springer, 1953.

OSGOOD, W. F., *Lehrbuch der Funktionentheorie*, Vol. 1, 3rd ed. Leipzig: B. G. Teubner, 1920.

PICARD, E., *Traité d'Analyse*, Vol. 2, 3rd ed. Paris: Gauthier-Villars, 1922.

SPRINGER, G., *Introduction to Riemann Surfaces*. Reading, Mass.: Addison-Wesley, 1957.

TITCHMARSH, E. C., *The Theory of Functions*, 2nd ed. Oxford: Oxford University Press, 1939.

WHITTAKER, E. T., and WATSON, G. N., *A Course of Modern Analysis*, 4th ed. Cambridge: Cambridge University Press, 1950.

## II. References for functions of several complex variables (Chapter 9)

BEHNKE, H. and THULLEN, P., *Theorie der Funktionen mehrerer komplexer Veränderlichen*. Berlin: Springer, 1934. (Reprinted by Chelsea Publishing Co., New York).

BOCHNER, S. and MARTIN, W. T., *Several Complex Variables*. Princeton: Princeton University Press, 1948.

GUNNING, R. C. and ROSSI, H., *Analytic Functions of Several Complex Variables*. Englewood Cliffs, N.J.: Prentice-Hall, 1965.

KAPLAN, W., *Functions of Several Complex Variables* (lecture notes prepared by Glen D. Anderson). Ann Arbor: Ann Arbor Publishers, 1964.

KNESER, H., *Funktionentheorie*. Goettingen: Vandenhoeck and Ruprecht, 1958.

OSGOOD, W. F., *Lehrbuch der Funktionentheorie*, Vol. 2, Part 1, 3rd ed. Leipzig: B. G. Teubner, 1929.

*Index*

# Index

ABCDE69876